D1026470

OIL TRADERS' WORDS

A dictionary of oil trading jargon

Stefan van Woenzel

First published in July 2010

Second edition published in August 2012

This third revised and expanded edition of the book was created
in Stavanger, Norway and published February 2016

Copyright © Stefan van Woenzel

The moral right of this author has been asserted.

All rights reserved.

No part of this publication may be reproduced, stored in a retrieval system, or transmitted, in any
form or by any means, without the prior permission in writing of the publisher, nor be otherwise
circulated in any form of binding or cover other than that in which it is published and without
a similar condition including this condition being imposed on the subsequent purchaser.

Typeset in Minion Pro

Design, editing, typesetting and publishing by UK Book Publishing

UK Book Publishing is a trading name of Consilience Media

www.ukbookpublishing.com

ISBN: 978-1-910223-62-8

Disclaimer

This book is written based on the author's 28 years of experience in the oil market.

The book is meant to be used as a guide or dictionary in oil trading language. It is the author's best efforts to help explain and convey the oil traders' business talk to the people working in the oil industry and people with an interest in the oil business.

The words are explained in the most practical way according to the author's interpretation. Readers may have a different opinion regarding the way the author has explained a definition or about the advice from the author related to a particular word.

The author does not have a masters degree in oil trading and therefore the content is based on the author's interpretation of oil talk and the author's dedication to oil trading and logistics. Therefore, any commercial risk resulting from the use of this book is to the reader or user of this book.

The author cannot be held legally and/or financially responsible for any consequences of claims resulting from decisions based on the words' explanations of this book.

It is the reader's and user's own responsibility to read or not to read this disclaimer before using or reading this book.

Contents

"Ahh...that's what it means!"

In the oil business, we express ourselves by the use of oil business jargon. This book explains the meaning of this jargon in a practical way. A first step in the right direction.

This book is about practical explanations with a touch of real experience from the workfloor.

It contains tips, advice and humour that make this book something you just must have on your desk.

This is a good useful book rather than a reading book if your day-to-day routine is related to activity in the oil business.

It is a good reference book or reading book when you have an interest in the oil business and especially if you really want to know what oil people are talking about. Throughout the book I have used the pronoun 'he' to refer to traders and other oil workers, for simplicity, but please read it as encompassing female workers as well. The book was already long enough without lots of 'he or she', 'his or her' etc.

The book demystifies the secrets of commercial oil jargon. Everybody should be able to understand the discussion.

Practical and straight forward.

When you find a definition and read the explanation, I hope you will say: "Ahh…that's what it means!" My goal is that the explanations make sense to you. Of course, you can go deeper into each subject, but then this book would be an encyclopaedia. Practicality is the aim of this book.

I am convinced that I have achieved that.

Stefan van Woenzel

Prologue

The Oil Trader's Words are always important to listen to and to understand fully.

The oil trader, as I describe it, is a person who is actively trading physical oil cargoes. That trader is responsible for buying oil cargoes, selling oil cargoes and hedging his position with a target to secure a certain income for the company he is working for. In my view, that is the trader's core business. However, the experience and knowledge to create that business requires much more than the trade only. There is so much activity in trading going on. It is about refining, blending, logistic optimisation and much more. A trader has to know his market and that means that he needs a lot of information and a good network. Such a network is not easily built when he is sitting watching a screen. Travelling, participation in conferences or workshops, wining and dining, and business meetings are part of the job. It is important that the trader can move away from his desk when needed. A colleague trader has to be able to cover the market, guarding the open positions in the meantime. The trader is part of the market and therefore he has to be visible and present himself as a representative for the company he is working for. New market information might lead to further growth, new business, confirmation of a market view or a complete change of opinion. In the meantime, the major companies come up with more and more rules related to trading, risk management, credit handling, counterparty checks, HSE and all kinds of different company requirements. With the current economic circumstances in our world, those rules make a lot of sense. Money, HSE and reputation is at risk all the time. Reputation and the way, related to ethical behaviour, a company makes money is important. The activity of the trader in a major oil company can easily create more than a billion Dollars' cashflow per year per trader. As a trader is able and has the mandate to deal with that much money (sum of all traded cargoes) every person working in an oil trading environment just has to understand what the trader is talking about, as you may be connected to that amount of money.

If you work in the oil business then the main question you need to ask yourself is 'Do I understand traders' jargon?'. Many people starting in oil trading, working in risk departments and in back-office positions hear the trader talking about their business activity and positions. When you hear all those discussions where traders' jargon is used then you will get used to the words even without knowing what those words mean. You forget to ask questions like 'what do you mean' and maybe some think you may look dumb asking too many questions. So because of that you will just agree with the trader, as that is the easy way out. Therefore, the most common way to act is to listen to the oil trader's decision and agree, because he probably knows best. However, I am sure that most people know what their responsibility is. I believe that many people work on autopilot. Understanding the job is what makes a day at work an exciting day. Success always starts with good communication. However, communication works only when business is clear and understood. Try to ask your children when they read a book about the meaning of certain words. There are many words that children can read but do not understand. It works in the same way for adults. Ask your colleagues if they understand the words 'structure, forward market, backwardation or contango'. These examples are basic words in the oil business but still difficult for many people to understand. Nevertheless, many people use the words without knowing how business works.

When I started my career in oil logistics, I did not know anything about the oil business. I could speak English and German, and apparently I was a nice person because I got a job in oil logistics at Van Ommeren, or after I left called Vopak. My first job was to nominate a barge to load naphtha from a tank at a terminal with Germany as destination. It was easy to say 'yes' and then enter an order in the computer and send a fax to a loading master at the storage terminal, as that was the job I had to do. I wanted to know more about the business. What is naphtha? What is a tank and what is a barge? I started to learn the logistics and finally I got good at it. Ship documents landed on my desk and I always went through them, curious as I was and still am.

Then after 10 years in storage I got offered a job with Statoil in Norway. I started in operations but very soon after that I started trading gasoline. Due to my logistic background I had at least something to lean on, but soon I found out that trading knowledge is substantially different from operations. I heard other traders talk about their activity and I agreed all the time. If I had a problem I asked the experienced traders. They replied to me in a way that I did not understand. So again, I had to learn and pick up the trading terms and again I got good at it, because I am always curious and interested to keep learning.

In 2012 after more than 25 years in the oil business I called myself reasonably experienced and I used an awful lot of trading jargon. I used a language that is rich in all types of popular trading terms. Experienced traders know what they are talking about and everybody always agrees with the big trader. Sometimes I get a question and then I give an answer that is loaded with trading terms and after the discussions I assume that I have answered in a clear way. It made me think and I remembered the way in which I started out. I remembered also that there were no complete glossaries around with oil trading terms. So, therefore, I started to collect each oil-trading-related word I heard and wrote it down. Then I got to the point where not many other new words got added to my list. So it became time to put them in an alphabetic order. It was a hell of a job – close to 1000 trading terms is what I collected in a word-file. Due to the amount of pages, I had the idea to share my collection in a book. The first book was published in July 2010 and since then more and more words kept being added to my file. I have also been looking around on websites of different companies and by using LinkedIn I got even more words and expressions that I could add to my book. The book content has doubled since 2010 and it became a real complete overview of oil business related words. The second edition of the book contained close to 2000 different definitions.

However, time moved on and we are now in 2016. Markets have changed and so did my career. I moved to crude origination, was involved in some North Sea projects, and was very active in creating the Russian business. Again, market circumstances changed and therefore I moved to oil logistics in crude oil. Logistics I have seen before, but this time I look at all logistics related to North Sea crude production, cargo and shipping operations.

The market changes and the changes in my career path were a source and reason for revising and expanding my book to 2016 standards. The last three years I have collected another 400 definitions. When I look back at the way words came into my file then it is interesting to see that oil-trading jargon is a collection of definitions from different groups and departments. There is a jargon for each commodity and for each commodity there is a jargon for each department. Oil trading jargon, oil logistics jargon, contract department jargon, oil administration jargon, oil risk department jargon, oil surveyor jargon, oil business service providers jargon; they are in a certain way different from each other. Nevertheless, all various oil departments talk to each other and have to understand each other's group jargon. It makes understandable communication complicated. That makes this book suddenly more interesting. It is, in my view, complete and can therefore function as a bridge between many departments and groups. Competence levels need to be increased when working in the same activity with fewer people. I am sure this book will be a valuable book for many people in the oil business.

Although I am more than 28 years in the oil business, I have no Masters degree in trading or oil logistics. I only made this a book based on experience from my side. A book meant for practical use. This book is not meant to be used as a scientific piece of work in connection with any commercial or operational decisions related to oil trading activity. It is meant as a guide for every person working in oil related companies. The commercial and operational risk in the oil trading activity belongs to the user or reader of this book, not to the author giving his interpretation of the meaning of words.

I believe that my book is the only published oil trading related glossary, as a printed book and as an e-book. It should be a book or file which just has to be on each desk or electronic device at any oil related company. Back office, mid office, refineries, marketers, inspectors, shipping agents, tank storage companies, bankers, brokers and many more oil-interested people should have this book on their desk. It contains my list of words with my interpretation of the meaning of the words that each trader could possibly meet in the business when trading oil. It includes some oilpaper terms, logistic terms and shipping terms as well. As an oil trader, you just need to know a lot. Not only oil traders must have this knowledge base, however. In addition, those people working closely with the traders or who have a job that can influences oil logistics and the cost of oil or the trader's P&L. Understanding the terms is a good basis for perfect communication. And good communication can be a basis for success in the business but certainly for someone's career path.

So next time, after reading and understanding a lot of terms from this book, you should be able to see how knowledge is required for survival in the oil business. I sincerely hope you can fully understand every oil discussion, through using this book, when you listen to the **"Oil Traders' Words"**.

So please spread the word and show the book to others.

Stefan van Woenzel

What can you find in this glossary?

I haven't listed each word with a page number. That type of content would be overdone in a glossary. Instead of that I have made a little overview of seven trading areas under which my terms can be grouped. Those are general trading terms, paper trading terms, risk terms, logistic terms, refinery and product terms, documentation terms, and of course HSE. At the back of this book, I have also included some words of wisdom, phrases of oil traders that I have picked up in the market. It contains wisdom and a little sense of humour. For calculation purposes, there is also a chapter with conversion calculations.

General trading terms: Many terms in this book are related to pure general oil trading terms. Without understanding those there is no point starting oil trading. Terms like contango and backwardation are maybe the most used words in oil trading. Time is money, so if you understand time value you understand physical trading behaviour. The other principle 'buy low, sell high' sounds easy but it is the simple basis of trading. Also, understanding how fundamentals can affect market prices is of great importance. Due to good market knowledge the trader will make up his mind and will position himself accordingly.

Paper trading terms: The physical oil trader buys, sells and takes physical oil positions. Those positions need to be hedged in order to lock in a contango result, to minimize risk or for locking in a margin. To be able to do that, traders must know what kind of paper tools are available, where they can buy or sell paper contracts and how to utilize that. Furthermore paper prices like futures for crude oil are registered on the screen. Understanding of the screen as well as knowledge about technical trading and its terms must be part of the senior trader's competence. Pure paper traders would most often follow the technical trading signals in the market more than the fundamentals of the market. The physical oil trader would look at both.

Risk terms: A trader not understanding risk is a dangerous man on the floor. Without control trading can turn out into huge positive and negative financial result effects. Traders are monitoring their risk on a daily basis and then every minute of the day. A trader who is attending a long lasting meeting, while he is having a huge risk position in the P&L, may get into big problems. He will have no control or cannot monitor the market prices during the meeting, and the market is volatile. A trader holding a big position should stay behind his screen. Understanding of value at risk, outright position and spread is a must. Each trader has a certain mandate and has to be able to respond in case he is in breach of his mandate. The trader has to know what action to take in order to change his trading position when he is out of mandate. He needs to get back within mandate. Therefore the rules and the understanding to manage risk are again of great importance to the oil trader.

Logistic terms: When trading physical oil, the understanding of the logistics is of great importance. Next to time value and making money on margins, the oil trader has the opportunity to add Dollars into his P&L by logistic optimisation, such as freight optimisation. Furthermore, logistics are very important when it comes to blending activity, arbitrage activity or activity such as break of bulk business or refinery supplies. Luckily, the trader gets good help from his operators. A good operator gets involved and involves himself with the trade. Only then, an operator can assist in logistic optimisation and will certainly add extra Dollars into the trader's P&L. So a good operator can turn a bad deal into a good deal and a bad operator can turn a good deal into a bad deal. Here communication and good understanding are important as both traders and operators have to be on good speaking terms. Only dedicated people in the oil business can create success. That includes often hard working and long working days.

Refinery terms: When you trade physical oil it would be good to understand that the product being traded originally comes from a refinery process and that crude is a feedstock to be delivered to the refinery. Therefore, I think it is good to have some refinery understanding. Sometimes one can read in the news from the screen that certain refineries have a shutdown, sometimes planned and sometimes unplanned. Then it can be useful to understand the link between the refinery unit, which has been shut down, and the product to be traded. Some products will be refined less which can cause product shorts in the market, or a refinery can have quality issues in their refined products. And if you understand refinery margins you might understand why a refinery cuts runs when margins are low. Refinery margins or product cracks may also affect crude oil prices. So traders must have knowledge of this. Furthermore, in refineries a lot of blending activity is on-going and on some occasions the refinery needs a certain feedstock. Therefore it is important that product knowledge and specification requirements are part of a trader's and operator's competence.

Documentation terms: Documentation is something more for operators' knowledge. Nevertheless, a trader must know what a B/L or an L/C is. Also customs documentation and customs status of the product is something a trader needs to be aware of. Is the product free of import duties or not? A trader who makes the mistake of selling an import duty free product when that is not possible has the risk of paying up to 5 or 6% import duties over the product value. But also certain oil grades from certain locations in the world can be imported duty free as there are preference certificates like a Form-A document available in certain countries. The operator should know that as well, but as an oil trader you take the first commercial decision, then it is nice to be aware of the possibility to get benefits based on such documentation. Last but not least VAT regulations must also be understood when importing and exporting oil. Customs need to know what comes in and what goes out. Terminal and logistics people have the overview and the obligation to inform the authorities. Missing out something can become a cost which often will be booked in the trader's P&L. Does every trader or operator know this, or is it not your "bread and butter"?

Health, Safety and Environment (HSE): Oil trading is connected to operations with products that are bad for environment. Oil is dangerous, flammable and sometimes explosive. We do not want to harm the environment, we have to be careful with the world we live in and safety to the people who work with oil is something to keep in mind. Always work with quality vessels vetted and approved according to the requirements of the companies and counterparties you work with, including your own company's requirements. Product information like an MSDS has to be available on request when one is asking for it. Any other information one would have about an oil operation should be brought up. From oil trader to field operator, we all are responsible for working in a safe, healthy and environment-friendly way. We stick to the company rules and ethics. This relates also to vetting of vessels. Various companies have their own set of rules and requirements when it concerns clearing of vessels. The business has to respects all various requirements of each other. Vessel owners are aware of the requirements. They will make sure that their vessel is safe for every company. If not, then their vessel would be out of business.

Oil Traders' Words of wisdom: Typical phrases of oil traders, picked up in the market. Some are to think about and some are for fun.

Conversions: Some calculation skills are needed in the oil business. Some calculations are needed for logistic reasons and some calculations are there to calculate costs, cracks and blending value and also shipping related cargo calculations are available. Some small conversion tables can be found on the last pages of the book.

As you can see, the physical oil trader is involved in many aspects of business. But please understand that an oil trader is not successful because he is a walking dictionary. Trading is much more than only knowing terms. Each trader has a different background, and different moral or ethical standards and values. Personality is a big thing. Are you a good talker, can you socialise, can you approach people you have never met before, do you have a market view and can you act accordingly, how is the risk appetite, how much business can a trader handle, are you a disciplined trader, are you creative, how fast can you anticipate market changes, are you dedicated to your job, can you sleep at night, is your private life fine... and many more traders' personal issues could be mentioned. Next to that the trader is dependent on the company he works for when it concerns the size of a trading book, location of the company, mandates given to trade, at what level is a trader controlled, the quality of trading and top management and trading results achieved so far. And last but not least to mention, even though a trader takes the trading decisions, he is part of a team with operators, risk controllers, accounting personnel, contract specialists, claims specialists and many more. The communication in such a team has to be understood by each individual. This guide to the terms of the oil business might help when you, as part of a team, listen to **The Oil Traders' Words.**

OIL
TRADERS'
WORDS
A-Z

A

AA (Always Afloat)

Floating on water (AA) is a shipping clause in the charter party to prevent a vessel from orders to arrive at a berth where the vessel may touch ground before discharging or during loading. This is an always safely afloat clause. HSE related. See also 'UKC – under keel clearance'.

AAA

American Arbitration Association. Based in New York. An organisation that takes care of arranging arbitration processes. Many oil contracts include an arbitration clause which refers to the 'AAA'. So here binding decisions are to be taken in case two companies are not able to agree on different matters related to the agreement they have. The AAA itself does not arbitrate.

AAD (Customs document used within EU)

This document has been replaced by an electronic version, the 'EAD', but hereunder you can read some background information related to customs documentation in the EU. Administrative accompanying document (AAD). The transport of non-excised excisable products takes place with an administrative accompanying document (AAD). The sender of an AAD is always an EGP-holder. The receiver can also be an EGP-holder, or a 'registered company'. A registered company is allowed to receive non-excised goods and pays the excise duties on these. A registered company is, therefore, not allowed to have any non-excised goods in storage. An AAD consists of several copies. The first copy is for the company that issued the AAD. The second, third and fourth copy must accompany the goods. The second copy is for the company to which the goods are destined. The third copy must be signed for receipt and has to be returned to the seller. This proves that the goods are received by another EGP-holder and included in his EGP, or that the excise duties are paid. The fourth copy is for the treasury. If the third copy is not returned within the timeframe set by customs' rules, the sender of the product may get into trouble. A new exemplar (copy AAD) can be issued again and will be sent to the receiver of the product so it can be signed off. If that document does not come back or if the receiver does not know the delivery then it is possible that something illegal has happened. The seller of the product will be seen as the responsible owner of the product and is therefore risking paying all excise duties of the cargo. Excise duties are roughly 5 to 6 times the value of the product. Late eighties, early nineties, when an AAD was called a 'T2 document', lots of barge loadings with destination Germany never arrived at the assumed place of destination. Claims of up to 20 million Dollars had to be paid by different trading companies for barge-loads of 2000 tons of heating oil. So in connection with this customs documentation, companies selling oil in barges run the risk of not getting their customs documentation cleared. Nowadays it would still be unthinkable that a barge with oil disappears that easily. It is not easy to hide a barge and besides that most barges can be tracked by GPS. Nevertheless, getting AAD documents cleared is a high priority for the companies issuing those.

AAR
Association of American Railroads. The AAR committee consists of AAR, railcar owners, manufacturers, and rail hazmat customers, with active participation from the U.S. DOT, Transport Canada and the National Transportation Safety Board (NTSB). They develop technical standards for how tank cars, including those used to move hazmat, are designed and constructed. It is all getting more and more sophisticated and oil producers have their own set of HSE requirements. AAR responsibility includes safety standards, maintenance, operations, service and repair, care hire, mileage rates and car service rules.

ABC (Technical Trading)
Elliott wave terminology for a three-wave countertrend price movement. Wave A is the first price wave against the trend of the market. Wave B is a corrective wave to wave A. Wave C is the final price move to complete the

countertrend price move. Elliott wave followers study A and C waves for price ratios based on numbers from the Fibonacci sequence. It is important for a trader to find out at what stage is the movement of the price. A trader must be upfront and will use more technical indicators to find out in what direction the price will move. The ABC theory in itself is not enough to determine how price fluctuation goes. See also 'Fibonacci'.

Absolute Bottom Sample

Sample from a tank taken from the bottom. This sample is taken by the use of a special sample tool which can be opened from the bottom. The oil from that sample might contain water, sediments, slurry or, if you are lucky, good oil. When using a tank for a long time it is good to know what substances are lying on the bottom of the tank. The substances on the bottom may affect the quality of the oil in the tank, but also when one needs to empty a tank he might supply some slurry to his customer. That would make a cargo off-spec. Have a look at 'sampling'.

ACAOP

Nomination quantity of a cargo: As Close As Operationally Possible. So here, quantity can depend on production, availability, draft level or other factors that may have influence on quantity. There seems to be no restriction on the maximum or minimum quantity. So the one ordering it must have a certain level of experience and expectation for this cargo to be loaded.

Accelerated Payment

See 'early payment'. Payment earlier than standard payment terms. Can be possible if the receiver of the money pays for the financing cost or gives a discount to the buyer. In the oil business this payment can only be done after the Bill of Lading and relevant shipping documents are received. A pre-payment would be done before commencement of loading a cargo and is related to avoidance of credit risk.

Accept

When a trader says 'deal done' he accepts the commercial part of the contract. After having accepted that part of the deal a contract has to be sent which contains all other terms & conditions. Traders at the desk rarely go that deep into details when they negotiate a deal. As the contract arrives sometimes up to a week after the conclusion there is a lot of work to be done in contract departments. They have to finalise the contract and dot the 'i's. Most physical oil trading contracts are standardised in the oil business. A challenging issue is that different companies prefer to describe their GT&C in their own way as advised by their lawyers and contract departments. When all terms, the commercial and the other GT&C, are agreed between both counterparties, then everything is final and binding. When discussions are related to longer term contracts then a trader might not be able to accept immediately because most traders have only a mandate for spot cargoes or a limited time in future. In that case it is very natural to accept subject to manager's approval. Normally the trader has the backing from the manager, but still then the manager wants to have the final word. If all is in place and internally approved the trader will call his counterparty in order to lift subject. All that is left in that case is putting a signature under a contract if required. A good reason to raise another glass has been created, time for a signing ceremony.

Acceptance

Acceptance constitutes an unconditional obligation on the part of the accepting party to pay the draft at maturity. A draft accepted by a bank is called a 'banker's acceptance' whereas one accepted by a company is called a 'trade acceptance'.

Accepted Cargo

When a vessel arrives at the jetty and starts discharging the oil, then the cargo is legally accepted by the receiver. When afterwards it becomes clear that the cargo was off-spec then the buyer has to bear the consequences. Therefore before discharging it is important for the buyer to be sure about the quality on arrival. An inspector is to be used to check quantity and quality. The same counts for a tanker picking up oil on a FOB basis. In case the oil is pumped on board the vessel then also here the buyer accepts the cargo; besides that, as soon as the oil is on board the vessel title goes over from seller to buyer. Monitoring quality is very important as the cost related to off-spec product can be high. In case the oil is found off-spec before loading or discharging, the buyer is allowed to refuse the cargo. Often a discount is negotiated before the cargo can be loaded or discharged. In my opinion that is the cheapest solution and acceptance by both parties shows a good relationship. Refusal of cargoes often leads to frustration between companies and traders. Costs will arise as the vessel owner starts charging demurrage when a vessel gets into overtime as result of refusal to take the off-spec cargo onshore. Only when the cargo is not allowed to discharge alternatives have to be found and claims departments will be busy. In the case of FOB cargoes the quality as it is reported in tank at loadport is the accepted quality. There is a little risk of contamination in the pipeline especially with smaller cargoes like in the ARA barge market when loading on FOB basis. The receiver of the oil is often the one who has to bear the consequences. In some cases also here a commercial solution may be found based on a good relationship between both counterparties.

Accommodation Trading

Competitive trading entered into by a trader, usually to assist another with illegal trades. Committing a barge trade during the Platts or Argus window and then buying it back from the same counterparty or even cancelling the deal could be seen as such. Borderline business, Platts or Argus might suspend (boxing) such a company from window trades and neglect all prices and activity for a certain period of time. Also the business as such can be reckless and refuse future trades with such companies, which in my opinion is the correct approach.

Account

An arrangement by which an organisation accepts a customer's financial assets and holds them on behalf of the customer at his or her discretion. A statement summarising the record of transactions in the form of credits, debits, accruals and adjustments that have occurred and have an effect on an asset, equity, liability or past, present or future revenue. Basically just like a bank account related to exchange activity and here meant for futures and other derivatives. Such an account may also apply for 'Clearport'. It is important that an account is able to financially cover the trading position. If such a position starts to lose money the owner of the account would get a margin call. He can either add money on the account or unwind some positions.

Account Party

Party for whom a Letter of Credit is opened. 'Account party' and 'applicant' are the same, but sometimes one party will agree with the issuing bank to make all payments under a Letter of Credit showing the name of another party (as in the case of affiliated companies). Banks may refer to one of these parties as the applicant and the other as the account party.

Accuracy

The ability of a measuring instrument to indicate values closely approximating the true value of the quantity measured. In order to guarantee good accuracy measurement equipment has to be checked and maintained on a regular basis, calibrated equipment. Quality has value and analysed specification in loadport should be close to the same as in disport.

Acid Corrosion

Due to a high acid content in the oil (TAN) refinery equipment is 'eaten' away. Acids may be hydrochloric acids or sulphuric acids.

Acid Number

The quantity of base, expressed in milligrams of potassium hydroxide, which is required to neutralise the acidic constituents in 1g of sample. Most refineries do have restrictions based on the acid number, but there are refineries able to cope with high TAN crude (TAN is Total Acid Number). High TAN crudes are discounted in price and that makes it an interesting feedstock for some refineries.

Acid Rain

Rain containing acids such as sulphur dioxide and nitrogen oxides which have been exhausted into the atmosphere due to industrial activity. Forests, lakes and nature can be heavily damaged as a result of acid rain. Rules and laws have been set up in order to reduce air pollution and further destruction of nature. An example from the past is UK industry exhaust which was an important cause of the acid rain in Norway.

Acid Trains

Separate reactor session or processing units that can handle acid oil and gases in a refinery. Acid crudes are price discounted; the refinery can process relatively cheaper crude. Often high acid feedstock can be associated with the heavier crude qualities.

Acid Treating

The process in a refinery where the bad smell of crude is removed. The bad smell is often caused by the contents of acid gas like H_2S and mercaptans.

Acidity

Also called acid number or acid value. Acidity is often measured in crude. But also in bio-diesel acidity is a point to focus on. Acid causes corrosion. See 'TAN' or 'acid number'.

Act of God

An event resulting from an unforeseeable natural phenomenon, i.e. an earthquake, tsunami, lightning, hurricane, etc. Force Majeure, in contrast, refers also to impossibility of contractual performance by reason of human interference, i.e. the action of a sovereign state in prohibiting exports or even a strike. An Act of God is generally recognised as valid grounds for non-performance. In that case no money- or damage claim would be awarded. In 2011 an earthquake at sea close to Japan caused a huge tsunami which had a big impact on the Japanese economy. It can be considered as an Act of God with huge consequences.

Actual

An actual is a physical commodity which is delivered at the completion of a contract, as opposed to a futures contract on that commodity. A futures contract will specify the number of units/lots (1 lot of crude on the futures exchange, ICE or Nymex, is 1,000 barrels and 1 gasoil lot is 100 tons or 42,000 gallons) of the cash commodity that must be delivered, and also the specific features of the cash commodity.

Accumulation

A situation in which the market is dominated by buyers, who increase the trading activity by keeping on buying futures. Probably caused by a bullish sentiment and certainly bullish when a couple of accumulations days follow each other. More buyers may follow until one or more traders start profit taking. First a trend is created and after profit taking it may happen that the trend is broken.

Additive Level

The total percentage of all additives in oil. (Expressed in % of mass [weight] or % of volume.) Additives could be flow improvers etc. Too much additives in oil may cause an opposite effect. I have seen cold properties going in the opposite direction when too much additives were blended. Therefore it is important to know the additive level of a product before further treatment is done.

Address Commission

A payment made by vessel owners to charterers. It is stated in the charter party as a fixed price or percentage of the amount paid in freight. Address commission does not require any particular services on the part of the charterers, and amounts therefore to a slight reduction in the freight rate. A charter made without provision for address commission is said to be free of address. Address commission may vary between 1 and 4 cents per barrel. Normally this commission is not forwarded in trades, it is the charterer's benefit.

Addressee

The recipient of communication/notices sent under an agreement. In the Bill of Lading, in the box 'consignee', the name of the addressee is to be entered.

ADP (Alternate Delivery Procedures)

An allowance/provision of many energy futures contracts which makes it possible to make or take deliveries of the underlying products in a different way to what is described in the terms of the futures contract. ADPs always occur following the expiration of contracts for the spot month, after deliveries have been matched. However, in energy most futures contracts which are open and matched after expiry date are balanced through cash settlement.

Ad Valorem

According to value. Base for calculation of import duties, other taxes and in some cases for insurance purposes.

Advanced Notice of Arrival (ANOA)

96 hours before a vessel, arriving from foreign ports, enters US water, she is required to give her ANOA. It is a requirement from the US Coast Guards for vessels that are planning to enter US waters. The meaning is to control traffic, eventually deny vessels that are suspicious because they are considered as unsafe and/or as a potential terrorist threat, but also to be prepared in case of accidents happening such as oil spills.

Advance Payment or Pre-payment

Advance payment is a trading method in which the buyer pays for the goods before they are sent out. This method is used when the buyer is of unknown credit worthiness or cannot present an L/C. In the oil business prepayment is done from time to time for smaller volumes of oil products. It is applicable in international and domestic trade. Often the buyer would require a slightly better price as the seller would get a credit advantage when receiving the money earlier compared with a normal contract. In crude trading agreements the standard payment term is 30 days after B/L and in product trading agreements the payment is to be done 5 days after B/L date or 3 days after notice of readiness at disport, whichever day comes first.

Advising Bank

Bank that receives a Letter of Credit from the issuing bank for authentication and delivery to the beneficiary, the seller of the oil. The advising bank is usually a correspondent of the issuing bank located in the same country as the beneficiary. The advising bank informs or gives notification to the seller that a Letter of Credit has been opened by the buyer. The seller will check the L/C first on each word, number, dot and comma. Thereafter he will advise if the L/C is approved or not.

Adverse weather

Important for offshore loading. Adverse weather is a weather condition whereby the 10-minute mean wind is 40 knots or more and with its associated sea state. The challenge for offshore vessels is wind and waves. At waves over 4.5 metres, loading will not be possible. When the weather does not improve, the storage at the offshore oil field may run full, getting towards tank top situation. Production may have to stop. Adverse weather is a big problem in wintertime or during hurricane season in the Gulf. Offshore fields prefer to have their storage as empty as possible in order to handle the situation. See also 'tank top'.

ADU

Atmospheric Distillation Unit. Primary distillation, the first process in the refinery to produce oil products.

Affiliate

In the oil business we see lots of major companies using lots of entities. You trade with a company with a good name but the address and counterparty name on the contract is different from the headquarters address and name. If the 'mother company' controls more than 50% of the daughter company then you could call them an affiliate. Some companies working with open credit would need a parent company guarantee to secure credit. A lot of hassle sometimes, but there are good enough legal reasons to be organised as such. So if you trade with a company then ask who the counterparty on the contract is as it happens from time to time that such a company is indeed an affiliate but a PCG is lacking or that affiliate is not even registered in your company. Without a PCG, giving open credit would be a risk. If the mother company closes a money losing affiliate or gets rid of it, you might get into a situation where you do not get your invoices paid or where it becomes a hassle to get your money. Also called 'subsidiary'.

Afra

Average freight rate assessments. See also 'aframax'. These freight assessments for 80kt cargoes are to be found back in quotation reports in Imarex, Argus or Platts and others under dirty tankers. Such quotations may be used in pricing formulas to netback to a FOB price. A CIF oil price quotation minus the freight quotation. Freight quotations are reported in worldscale, not in Dollars. Worldscale multiplied with the flat price is the total freight price excluding additional cost such as ice dues, port cost, etc. See also 'worldscale'.

Aframax

A tanker with a standard capacity of 80kt being registered as such under worldscale quotations (generally, tankers 80,000-110,000 DWT). This size is typically used for dirty oil. Crude and fueloil.

After-Hours Trading

After-hours trading (AHT) refers to the buying and selling of securities on major exchanges outside of specified regular trading hours. Often these deals are done in the OTC market, frequently with the interference of a broker. See also 'OTC'.

AG

Arabian Gulf. See also 'Arab Gulf' for further explanation.

AGA

American Gas Association founded in 1918 in order to represent companies related to natural gas supplies or manufacturing. The goal of AGA is to secure supplies and those supplies have to be at reasonable prices.

Against Actuals

A transaction generally used by two hedgers who want to exchange futures for cash positions. Also referred to as against actuals or versus cash. See also 'exchange for physical'.

Agency Fee

A fee charged to the ship by the ship's agent, representing payment for services while the ship was in port. Agents provide service to the vessel. They arrange documentation, they are the contact with the pilot station and the terminal for where to load or discharge and they may arrange bunkers and food supplies and much more. Agencies can be a great source to provide an overview of harbour activity. Sometimes called 'attendance fee'.

Agents and Brokers

Persons or organisations that act as a representative for others in negotiating contracts, purchases, or sales. Agents and brokers typically earn a commission or fee for their services and do not take possession of, or title to the traded commodity. Basically the risk level for brokers and agents is extremely low as long as they commit their business according to the rules. In 2009 a paper broker in London started to trade without orders from any customer. As a result of that activity the Brent prices moved close to a Dollar up which had its effects in the market. The broker company lost a lot of money and the person involved got into problems. In this case the rule was broken and the broker unfortunately had a negative result.

Aggregate Risk

The total amount of exposure a customer has to the movement of spot contracts and forward contracts. The exposure and position of all trades together are reported in the P&L. See also 'P&L'.

Aggregation

The policy under which all paper and physical oil positions owned or controlled by one trader or a group of traders are combined to determine reportable positions and speculative limits. The way that the P&L is set together and is reported. The P&L is an important tool for the trader to start the day. It shows his position and result on that day. The trader will need to take the decision in the morning if hedging or position taking is required.

Aggressor

Someone who trades with an aggressive mode. Can be because one wants to enter a new market, or one would like to set higher or lower Platts or Argus quotations because of a paper position or one or more cargoes are pricing in or out. An aggressor may move markets up or down.

AGO

Atmospheric GasOil. Gasoil produced from first distillation at a refinery. This gasoil will in most cases be further processed to make it ready for consumption in different markets. Gasoil is then known as heating oil and diesel.

AGW

Noticed when I got the ETA of a Vessel: ETA 05.08.15 10:30 WP AGW. Means expected time of arrival fifth of August 2015 at 10:30 weather permitting and (AGW) all going well. An ETA from the master of the vessel who is sure he will make that timing based on current circumstances. AGW provided that nothing happens which can affect the current planning. Weather could change or technical issues may arise but one would not expect that.

AHTS

Anchor Handling Tug/Supply vessel.

Air Draft

The distance from the vessel's water line to the uppermost point on the vessel, usually the top of a mast or radar tower. When a vessel has to transit areas where there may be overhead obstructions (bridges, power lines, cranes, loading arms, etc.) it is vital to know what its air draft will be at the time of transit. The air draft of a vessel will vary depending upon the draft of the vessel and its trim. Most important is to know the air draft based on being empty – after discharging the cargo the vessel lies higher in the water. Problems may be solved by taking in extra ballast water to get to a draft level which is required to leave a port after discharging.

Air Pollution

Toxic or radioactive gas or particulate matter introduced into the atmosphere, usually as a result of human activity. Acid rain can be a consequence, but also a bad smell due to oil containing sulphur or mercaptans will make people complain to the authorities. When vessels are loading or discharging product with high mercaptans content, problems may arise. Some refineries are situated close to the cities or villages that would suffer and complain about the activity of the oil terminal. Most oil terminals set limitations on mercaptans and/or H_2S levels. Also vapour recovery units are good solutions to avoid emissions. Other solutions are cargo treatment on board the vessel, where additives are blended on board, before discharging on arrival at the berth, in order to 'sweeten' the cargo.

ALARP

Volume nomination, As Low As Reasonably Practicable. Looking for the minimum, which is operationally or contractually, possible. Below contractual volume is not allowed unless deadfreight is paid.

Alcohol and Alcohol Blends

Family name of a group of organic chemical compounds composed of carbon, hydrogen and oxygen. Examples are methanol, ethanol and tertiary butyl alcohol. Alcohol and alcohol blends are added to gasoline in order to make it burn cleaner. In some places/countries there are extra fences around the ethanol tanks, as it is obvious that there are more ways to consume alcohol than just burning it in a car. Nevertheless too many accidents happen as polluted ethanol or methanol come into the wrong hands and wrong bottles into drinks. Binds easily with water and can cause issues to oil qualities such as octane.

Alkylate

A gasoline blending component composed of iso-butane and propylene or butylene. The properties are good on octane, density and aromatics. It is often higher priced than gasoline. Interesting here is that MON and RON differ just 3 to 5 points. In addition it is clean and can be used to correct most off-spec gasoline. Can be rather expensive, a gasoline factor of above 1. See also 'gasoline factor.'

Alkylation

A process in a refinery which uses iso-butane as the main feedstock in presence of a strong acid catalyst. This combination causes a kind of chemical reaction in the unit. The temperature in the unit is between 0°C and 35°C (32°F and 95°F). The product coming out is called alkylate and is a high value blending component for gasoline due to the good octane numbers and other properties. Alkylate helps improve the environmental qualities of gasoline as a result of low vapour pressure, no sulphur content, no olefin content, no aromatics and no benzene.

Allowances

The discounts or premiums allowed for grades or locations of a commodity lower or higher than the par (or basis) grade or location specified in the futures contract. Grades that are better than the grade as defined in the futures contract would be valued at a small premium over the contract price. However, the buyer bought the spec as according to the futures contract which means that the seller would supply oil with 'giveaway'. The seller is not allowed to supply a specification that is worse than the futures spec. The seller would get real problems with the exchange if that happens.

Allowed Laytime

The number of hours allowed for loading and discharging a cargo as stipulated in a charter party. Often there are standard hours available for different vessel sizes. An aframax often gets 36 hours laytime for discharging and loading a full cargo. When a vessel is using more than the allowed laytime, a demurrage claim may follow. The time used for sailing from pilot station to the berth till being at status 'mooring completed' does not count as the time used. Six hours after NOR is tendered at the pilot station the clock starts ticking. Those 6 hours or part thereof are only available as waiting time at the pilot station.

Alternative Energy

Also called green energy. Energy that is more and more popularly used. It is well known as solar, hydropower or wind energy. Alternative energy is often subsidised to end-consumers as it is more expensive than fossil energy. See also 'renewables'.

Alternative Fuel
Other fuel than the traditional fuels as we are used to, such as gasoline and diesel for transportation applications, include the following:

· Methanol.
· Ethanol and other alcohols.
· Fuel mixtures containing 85 percent or more by volume of methanol, denatured ethanol and other alcohols with gasoline or other fuels (E85).
· Natural gas.
· Liquefied petroleum gas (propane).
· Hydrogen (is it safe?).
· Coal-derived liquid fuels.
· Fuels (other than alcohol) derived from biological materials (biofuels such as soy diesel fuel); in this sector there is still a lot to explore.
· Electricity (including electricity from solar energy). The electric cars are gaining in popularity. We see more parking places where those cars can be charged.

Ambient Temperature
Temperature of the area/surroundings where the cargo is present. Call it room temperature if you like. Red wine to be poured at ambient temperature.

American Option
An option that may be exercised on any day ahead of expiry. Provides a greater degree of flexibility than a European option, and therefore generally will have a higher premium. American options trade on the futures exchanges (Nymex).

Andrew's Pitchfork (Technical Trading)
Three parallel trend lines are drawn linking a major low or high, with a point either side of this marking an intermediate high or low. The lines are extended to generate support/ resistance levels. The lines look a bit like the prongs of a pitchfork, hence the indicator's name.

Anhydrous
Free of water. A cargo of oil without water content or traces of water.

Anode Grade Coke
Coke, low in metals suitable for calcination and use in the aluminium industry. See also 'needle coke' and 'sponge coke'. 'Shot coke' would be an off-spec anode coke.

Anonymous Trading
Bids and offers are seen in the market but it is unknown who the buyer or seller is. In oil business it is difficult as all physical cargo trading is done on OTC basis. In paper trading it is easy to be invisible though as that can go through Clearport or by the exchange, the system where the buyers and sellers are unknown.

Anti-Corruption Clause
Clause in an oil-contract in which companies describe and require correct and good ethical behaviour of the counterparty. Each company has their own rules and description which may lead to discussions between the lawyers of different companies. At the end of the day they want the same. Stay correct and behave – common sense.

Anti-Knocks Index
(MON+RON)/2. Normal gasoline 85/95 would have antiknocks 90. In most occasions gasoline has a maximum antiknocks index. Because of blending the supplied gasoline could have MON 85 and RON 97.5; as a result of that the antiknocks is higher because of the difference between MON and RON. This big difference could cause problems with the receiver of the oil and can create potential problems in car engines, also, when the RON is far too high. See also 'PON'.

Anti-Oxidants
Anti-oxidants can reduce deterioration of gasoil and gasoline. Anti-oxidants in gasoil/gasoline can cause acids and gum-forming (polymers). These insoluble gums cause engine problems, because of poor combustion and even fuel filter plugging. A good anti-oxidant can delay the oxidation process significantly, which makes prolonged storage possible. Gasoline has, for example, a gum specification. Look at 'gum'.

Anticipating
Looking and thinking forward in time to operational or commercial activity.

If an operator anticipates any changes in loading programmes or blending activity, he can take action immediately to avoid problems to come. The same goes for the trader who has to try to look into the future and be prepared for changes in the market situation. In order to anticipate any changes an operator needs to know what is going on logistically and a trader has to be in the market 24/7. To be able to anticipate any market changes one has to be dedicated to his job and have full control. Money and HSE matters are paramount in the oil business. Be ready to take action before potential problems arise, be pro-active.

APEC

Asia-Pacific Economic Cooperation. Each year in Singapore (September or October) there is an APEC-week and an APEC conference where the global oil market comes together at different events. Companies meet each other for business and social gatherings. A good opportunity to network and to play golf. As the Asian market keeps growing this event is becoming more important. See also 'NPRA' and 'IP week'.

API

American Petroleum Institute, founded in 1919, was the first oil trade association to include all branches of the petroleum industry. They represent the oil and gas industry in the USA and their mission is as described on their website: "API's mission is to influence public policy in support of a strong, viable U.S. oil and natural gas industry essential to meet the energy needs of consumers in an efficient, environmentally responsible manner".

API Gravity

An arbitrary scale expressing the gravity or density of liquid petroleum products devised jointly by the American Petroleum Institute and the National Bureau of Standards. The measuring scale is calibrated in terms of degrees API. Oil with the least specific gravity has the highest API gravity. The formula for determining API gravity is as follows: Degrees API Gravity = (141.5/Specific Gravity at 60 Deg. F) - 131.5. In crude oil business densities are discussed in API gravity. In Europe products' densities are talked in kilos per litre at 15°Celsius, while in USA products are reported in API gravity. Oil with a high API gravity is light oil and vice versa. Light crudes generally exceed 38 API and heavy crudes have an API of 22 or lower. Intermediate crudes fall in the range of 28 API to 38 API gravity, like Brent and WTI.

API Inventory Figures
The most widely watched body of data in the petroleum industry. This report compiles changes in domestic petroleum production, imports, refining capacity and product movements into and out of primary storage. Traders use this information to access supply and demand on a week-to-week basis. These figures are usually released Wednesday afternoons (in Europe) or the third working day of the week. The release of these reports is often a catalyst for movement on the futures market. Most oil traders are seated behind the screen waiting for the moment that the figures are presented as they need to respond by taking or leaving trading positions, in case the oil prices are moving up or down as a result of unexpected storage numbers.

Apparent Consumption
Total consumption of energy in a country calculated by the International Energy Agency as production of fuels + inputs from other sources + imports - exports - international marine bunkers + stock changes. It includes coal, crude oil, natural gas liquids, refinery feedstocks, additives, petroleum products, gases, combustible renewables and waste, electricity and heat. In countries like China and India where the economy is growing at high speed we see an increased apparent consumption. This says that these countries are increasingly becoming a more important market for oil supplies. It will have an effect on oil prices in the future. The daily consumption of oil in the world will become or is already bigger than new oil discoveries in the world.

Apparent Loss
Quantity differences after discharging which cannot be related to a physical loss. These losses can be caused by errors in measuring and should be corrected. These errors may be caused by wrong equipment, wrong procedures at a terminal, wrong temperature observation, tank calibration problems or other mistakes which can become expensive if an error is not admitted. Good terminal procedures, inspections and clear discharge instructions may take most errors away. See also 'physical loss' and 'voyage loss'. One has to realise that oil is not cheap anymore. Every loss will have a big financial impact on the trader's P&L. Just calculate and think about the difference between 500 barrels' loss at an oil price of 10 Dollars and the same loss at an oil price of 100 Dollars per barrel.

Applicant
Party requesting a bank for a Letter of Credit to be opened. The buyer of the oil cargo will need to apply to his bank to issue the Letter of Credit to the beneficiary who is the seller of the cargo.

Appreciation
An increase in the value of an asset over time. The increase can occur for a number of reasons including increased demand or weakening supply, or as a result of changes in inflation or interest rates. This is the opposite of depreciation, which is a decrease over time.

Approved Delivery Facility
Any loading location that is authorised by an exchange for the delivery of commodities tendered on futures contracts. In non-exchange related business oil companies commit on a regular basis to inspections at different facilities where they may have plans for long term commitments such as storage activity. Such a facility is then to be approved by the company's vetting department.

ARA
Amsterdam, Rotterdam, Antwerp (including Flushing or in Dutch 'Vlissingen'). Trading hub in The Netherlands where prices are set in the market by trading barges in lots of 1-2kt per trade at fixed prices being shown and reported in the market during the Platts or Argus window sessions. In case of cargo markets, Platts and Argus are referring to prices Basis NWE Rotterdam. Typical cargo sizes are 10-30 kt for gasoline and low sulphur fueloil, or 100kt REBCO. This hub is very important in Europe due to its location where oil is supplied over the rivers and pipeline systems to Germany and where 5 big refineries in Rotterdam plus 3 or 4 refineries in Antwerp are processing crude oil, producing products. Storage capacity and blending activity in Rotterdam, Amsterdam and Antwerp is big. In addition, due to the heavy shipping traffic in the area the bunkers' business brings benefits. This makes ARA the most important and most liquid price setting market in Europe.

Arab Gulf
This phrase and its abbreviation 'AG' are current in some sectors of the oil industry, especially the tanker world, as a designator for the Persian Gulf, which is the correct name in international law for the body of water bordered

by the UAE, Saudi Arabia, Qatar, Kuwait, Iraq and Iran. Note that there is a Gulf of Arabia which is not the same piece of sea-area as the Persian Gulf.

Arab Oil Embargo of 1973-74

During the Arab-Israeli conflict in October 1973, Arab oil producers cut off shipments to the United States and The Netherlands in retaliation for their support of Israel. At the same time, they cut down production. The shortage was felt by all oil-importing nations, with world prices moving sharply higher. It introduced the idea of holding a 'car-free Sunday', a day of protest by avoiding fuel consumption, saving energy. I remember people cycling and roller-skating on the highways in The Netherlands on that car-free Sunday. A lovely quiet day. As consequence the USA introduced a law that prohibited export of crude from the USA. This would secure the USA of enough oil in storage if such an embargo would happen again. Since the increased production of shale oil in the USA the situation has changed. As from December 2015 the USA law changed and exports are allowed. MV Sea Queen arrived in January 2016 in Rotterdam with the first exported crude oil from the USA. Due to overproduction crude prices have come down to approx. 27 USD per barrel.

Arbitrage (Arb)

Difference in prices between various price-quoted geographic areas. As an example, the difference between ARA quotations and the USGC quotations. World economies and prices are changing all the time. With open arbitrage conditions cargoes will be moving Trans-Atlantic until prices change as a result of oversupply. Traders are always looking at the opportunity to export and lock in (hedge) the arb and move oil in order to take profits. With closed arbs the activity slows down rapidly. Shipping prices go down due to lack of transport demand, which could cause another open arb possibility. Arbitrage trading is most often seen as an opportunistic trade. However, some flows will never stop due to long term obligations. Also called 'location spread'.

Arbitrage Channel

The range of prices within which there will be no possibility to arbitrage between the cash and futures market.

Arbitration

The process of settling disputes between parties by submitting their differences to the judgment of an impartial person or group appointed by mutual consent or statutory provision. See also 'AAA' and 'LCIA'.

ARCO
ARctic Crude Oil. Trade name for crude oil produced from the Arctic. The name was introduced by GazpromNeft when they supplied their first cargo of Arctic crude from the Prirazlomnoye field in April 2014 to Rotterdam, arrival first of May 2014. Four cargoes were loaded in 2014. The low oil price is, in my view, not making this field profitable as production costs in this difficult and challenging area are extremely high. The Russian government had to give tax breaks for this field to make production possible. It is sometimes possible in Russia to get tax breaks for oil production projects when the oil is very difficult to produce. Without state subsidies, it may be a financial challenge to produce this. The costs for fields with huge challenges, wherever in the world, are tremendously high. Low crude prices may slow down field development and production, especially for low value oil qualities.

Argus
Argus is a leading provider of price assessments, business intelligence and market data for the global crude oil, petroleum products, gas, LPG, coal, electricity, biofuels, biomass, emissions, fertilizer and transportation industries. As described on the Argus website.

Arm's Length Price
The price a buyer achieves by selling 'the concerned cargo' to a third party buyer. It is the traded price for a certain cargo, which relates to the market value. When a contractual used quotation as part of the pricing mechanism is not available or taken out of the quotations reports then the buyer and seller can agree to use an arm's length price as an alternative until they agree on a new quotation. A reasonable solution between buyer and seller when price data is missing. Based on trust and good relationship. The price related to this definition must always be reasonable and market related, else it would be a rip off.

Aromatic Crude Oil
Crude oil containing less than 50% saturated hydrocarbons and over 50% aromatics. A crude oil which, due to its viscosity, requires heating during

transportation or COW at discharge. These types of crude oil generally have a high viscosity and may also be called high viscosity crude oil.

Aromatics

Hydrocarbons with a distinctive, (un-)pleasant smell, hence the name, characterised by having at least one benzene ring in their molecule. Present in the various fractions obtained from the primary distillation of crude oil and, more notably, in products deriving from some improvement process including catalytic reforming of virgin naphtha, which is mainly used to increase the low level of octane. Commercial petroleum aromatics include benzene, toluene and xylene (BTX). Best property of aromatics is the high octane value. Otherwise there is a strong limitation on aromatics content in the standard specification of gasoline. Aromatics are round molecules, flows easily. Paraffins are long chained molecules and can be very sticky. Aromatic oil spills are easier to clean, but spills should be avoided in any case – just meant to create a picture.

Arrival Range

The period in which it is allowed to deliver/take re-delivery of product into/from the storage tanks or refinery. The arrival range shall be a period of an agreed number of days. In most traded oil cargoes this is a 3 or 5 day period and this period is better known as delivery dates, loading range or loading dates. Vessels are most often chartered on a 3 days arrival time at loadport.

Arrival Temperature

Temperature of a cargo arriving at disport. Important to know as the receiving terminals have restrictions on oil temperatures for handling. Firstly because of HSE regulation, people have to work with it. Secondly, hot oil contains more volume than what is stated on the Bill of Lading. The Bill of Lading shows oil quantities at 15°C/60°F. The oil has to fit in the tank and I have seen traders making this mistake and having a problem fitting the last 100 to 200 Cbm in tank. See also 'hot oil'.

Ascending Triangles (Technical Trading)

A price-chart pattern that indicates that a market is consolidating and is about to break out to either the upside or downside. Ascending triangles are identified by charting the closing prices of a stock, futures contract or other financial instrument in a technique called 'technical analysis'.

ASCI (Argus Sour Crude Index)

Daily value of sour crude oil in USGC based on physical spot deals done on a particular day. The ASCI refers to a basket of volume weighted average of 3 grades of crude: Poseidon, Southern Green Canyon and Mars (in 2012). The ASCI may be used as a benchmark for other grades. In Europe sour crude is traded with Brent crude as a benchmark and in Asia it could be Brent, Dubai or Oman crude as the price reference.

ASEAN

Association of South-East Asian Nations. Member countries are Brunei Darussalam, Cambodia, Indonesia, Lao PDR, Malaysia, Myanmar, Philippines, Singapore, Thailand and Vietnam.

Ash

Impurities consisting of silica, iron, alumina, and other non-combustible matter that are contained in coal. Ash increases the weight of coal, adds to the cost of handling and can affect its burning characteristics. Ash content is measured as a percent by weight of coal on an 'as received' or a 'dry' (moisture-free, usually part of a laboratory analysis) basis. Ash is also measured in heavy fueloil. High ash content is not wanted. At high burning temperatures ash can cause corrosion of metal surfaces. Removal of high ash contents is too expensive, therefore most traders pay a lower price for off-spec fueloil on ash and blend it with fueloil containing low ash.

Asian Option

An option that is exercised against an average value of the underlier over a certain period of time during the life of the option. Also known as an 'average option'.

As-is

A contractual expression in the oil trade, usually referring to density. The intention is to avoid (de) escalation of the price of the oil based on the density being different from the quality standard. Next to density 'as-is' can also mean that the buyer accepts the quality as it is loaded. Some trust, experience, good relations and a good price can convince the buyer to accept such a deal. It means also that the receiver who buys and accepts a contract where the quality of oil is described as 'as-is' does not have any right to claim when the product is off-spec. In most cases the quality would not differ that much from the specs that were indicated during the negotiations. A few times I have had a quality in which one of the parameters was far off from the negotiated spec that was indicated. Even though I had no right to claim I always found a commercial solution. It all depends on your relationship with your counterparty and the business understanding between companies.

Ask

The price visible on the screen at which a seller will sell a futures contract, e.g.. Brent 'ask' on the IPE or WTI 'ask' on Nymex. Between ask and bid the spread is often 1 to 3 cents. Each time the 'ask and bid' price hit each other a transaction is committed. See also 'tick'.

Ask Price

The minimum price acceptable for a seller to execute a trade. Also known as the offer price. In the Platts or Argus window oil traders place their offers, the ask price. When a bidder hits the offer the deal is done and confirmed; the seller cannot flake. On the exchange, as on the screen, transactions are automatically done when the 'ask' and 'bid' price are equal. Buyers and sellers will be matched at the end of the day by the exchange. Statements of what has been bought and sold at a certain agreed price and volume are reported on the accounts. One cannot see the counterparties of the deals. Trades are done directly with the exchange which is not an OTC market.

Ask Size

The number of futures or cargo size offered for sale at the ask price. Futures are traded in small batches. One lot of crude oil equals 1,000 barrels and a crude oil cargo consists of 0.6 up to 2 million barrels. In the case that one would bid 1,000 lots in one order at the futures exchange the market would significantly move up. The purchase would become expensive. To avoid moving the market price too much, those volumes are purchased in smaller lots. Often the brokers are regulating that activity on behalf of their customer as they have to fulfil the orders at the price as ordered by the buyer or seller. Also a broker has to perform.

Asphalt

Asphalt from refinery production is also known as bitumen or tar. A very sticky and viscous product and only floating at extremely hot temperatures. Further processing in a refinery is basically not done. Asphalt will be of use for road construction. Such road construction is often subsidised by governments and done in summertime as in cold winters the asphalt would cool down too fast to build roads. Therefore the production of asphalt or bitumen is more profitable in summertime, sometimes also called 'bitumen season'.

Asphaltenes

Aromatic substance in crude oil. Insoluble heavy formation which can be found back in heavy fueloil after distillation. Asphaltenes may form sludge left behind in diesel engines, fuel systems, oil recovery, oil-carrying pipelines, and refinery operations. Crude oil with a high asphaltene-content is most often found in heavy crude and tar sand. This crude is priced at a discount versus the benchmark crude ASCI, Brent or WTI. Most heavy crude can be processed in coker units and flexi-cokers, two examples of refinery units which are complex but 'eat' everything. Some say: 'These units are even able to make gasoline out of shoes.'

Assay

A laboratory assessment of the characteristics of a crude oil, i.e. Yield, which helps determine its market value and refining capabilities. Assays of some kind are usually required as part of all crude oil sales. Most marketers/ producers of crude oil publish the assays on their website. See also 'yield'. The making of an assay of crude is not cheap and once an assay of a certain crude grade is made it will become the standard for the grade for a long time until major changes in the specification occurs. The buyer of the crude will use the assay to set the technical value for his refinery and buy when the price works, assuming that the refinery can handle the crude.

Assessment (Platts)

A Platts-assessment is the product of a market survey and the application of strict methodological rules to determine the repeatable tradable price range for a commodity during the assessed period. Assessment typically aims to zero in on these typical transactable levels by discarding unrepresentative market information (out-of-market bids, offers and transactions), and the process differs in this respect from indexation, which is an inclusive process, averaging all available market information. Platts produces indexes in highly liquid markets, for example North American natural gas, and assessments in illiquid markets, such as those for physical oil. Platts-assessments are typically published at a low-high range for each instrument. Sourced from

Platts-website. Argus, the other reporter quoting prices, has its own system and methodology.

Assessment

The methodology used by Argus, Platts or any other price reporter in making their quotations. There are many roads leading to Rome. Each price reporter takes a certain approach to setting a price in the market and what rules are to be followed in accepting market prices as input to the quotation. Platts and Argus have a different way of reporting and calculating the market price. Their quoted prices are not always the same but are often close to each other; they work in the same market but have their own approach. Traders do also have a view on pricing, especially when they are bidding and selling in the trading windows that set the market prices. The discussion between price reporters and traders is always on-going as each trader has a different position and a different approach depending on their activity. Most traders are advising the reporters following their wish to get a higher or lower quotation depending on their trading position. The communication between these agents and the market is very important. Platts and Argus must know the market very well and have to listen to what goes on in the oil environment. Markets are changing, some crude production might disappear and new crude comes into the market. Also oil product qualities are changing as a result of environmental requirements. Even new gasoline and diesel are adopted in the market as a result of new environmental requirements. Those new products are to be adopted in the price quotations when they are well enough traded. Liquidity is important and specifications as well. The reporters must keep creating figures which represent a liquid and honest market. In the meantime there are many opinions in the market as to how these quotations should work related to qualities, locations, cargo size, loading or delivery window and bid/offer windows. Platts and Argus are independent organisations and take their own final decisions how to quote oil values based on their own view and opinion as to how a market should be represented in a fair way.

Asset

An economic resource or item owned by a business that is expected to benefit its future operations. When credit rating a company, it is interesting to see what assets are in the books. Based on a healthy financial balance and asset-owning open credit could be considered. Most trading companies do not have assets; they buy and sell and maybe create long term contracts to trade around, using L/Cs.

Associated Gas

Gas which appears during crude oil production and cannot be avoided as such. It is also known as flare gas. The gas is burned off on the production field. Associated gas could be combined with natural gas and on some occasions with gas-condensate. Associated gas is a petroleum gas and consists mainly of C1 through to C4, methane, ethane, propane and butane.

Associated Person (AP)

An individual who solicits orders, customers or customer funds on behalf of a futures commission merchant, an introducing broker, a commodity trading advisor or a commodity pool operator and who is registered with the commodity futures trading commission.

AST

Aboveground Storage Tank, a land tank made of steel. Project people call it an 'ast'. Caverns are underground storage facilities; call those manmade caves, often in rock formation. See also 'ust'.

ASTM

American Society for Testing and Materials. ASTM is giving a description for testing methods of crude and petroleum products. Some specifications have a certain minimum or maximum requirement (i.e. Max sulphur). The test may be done according to ASTM standard. Often different companies have different requirements regarding how to test a product and how to report it. Sometimes some methods are preferred for testing because of a lack of the required testing equipment at a certain lab. When deviation from the standard testing method is wanted, the seller may ask for a waiver to the buyer. Such a request does not happen a lot and in most cases the waiver is granted. Each method has a number and they may be found in the ASTM book. Results observed through most of the various methods are often the same, but when it comes to a claim situation then the testing method may become a big issue. So be sure that the buyer and seller agree on using a method that is acceptable to both parties. There are no friends in court.

ASTM Table uses for calculation

• For Crude Oil

API
 · Table 6 (to convert GOV to GSV)
 · T11 (to convert GSV to Long Ton)
 · T13 (to convert GSV to Metric Ton)
 · Temperature in F, Quantity or volume in Barrels (Bbls)

Density
 · Table 54 (to convert GOV to GSV)
 · T56 (to convert GSV to Metric Ton)
 · T57 (to convert GSV to Long Ton)
 · Temperature in C, Quantity or volume in Cubic Metre (M3)

• For Product Oil

API
 · Table 6B (to convert GOV to GSV)
 · T11 (to convert GSV to Long Ton)
 · T13 (to convert GSV to Metric Ton)
 · Temperature in F, Quantity or volume in Barrels (Bbls)

Density
 · Table 54B (to convert GOV to GSV)
 · T56 (to convert GSV to Metric Ton)
 · T57 (to convert GSV to Long Ton)
 · Temperature in C, Quantity or volume in Cubic Meter (M3)

ASWP

'Any Safe World Port.' This could appear in a CIF, CFR or DAP delivery offer, but in reality such flexibility is not offered in the real oil market. If a seller has unsold oil in stock and he has not chartered a vessel then he could offer ASWP and charter the vessel after the trade. It means that the seller must be aware of the freight cost to many places. The seller will make his decision based on the netback calculation. He sells on best value and probably uses the FOB netback for that. See also 'netback'.

At Best

An instruction to a broker or dealer to get the best price or rate that he is able to get at that time. Basically you can be 100% sure that your order will be executed when you place it 'at best'. It does not mean that you will be happy with the execution price – often you buy too expensive or you sell at too low a price. 'At best' means basically acceptance of bid or ask without any attempt to negotiate.

ATB

Atmospheric Tower Bottoms. Another fancy name for straight run fueloil or residue coming from atmospheric distillation.

ATC

Automatic Temperature Compensation. Volume changes with temperature. Oil pumped through long pipeline will heat up a bit due to friction in the pipe. With calculations of quantities correction, conversion tables are used to report the numbers in a correct and precise matter.

ATDNSHINC

Any Time Day or Night Sundays or Holidays Included. Time counting and used when a vessel is on charter and is at work. Very important for demurrage calculations. The oil business is a 24/7 business and that counts for shipping logistics as well. Such kind of abbreviations may be found in charter parties.

ATK

Aviation Turbine Fuel (kerosene). Another way of naming jet fuel.

Atlantic Basin

In oil trading discussions are about markets, about production and refining. The Atlantic Basin is here meant as a trading area where different continents are connected by the Atlantic Ocean. Europe, East Coast USA and Latin America plus West Africa. It is therefore interesting to follow the flows of oil linked to the trading activity around the Atlantic Basin. But let's not forget the oil cargoes that are going from the Atlantic Basin to Asia. Cargo tracking is important to follow the flow.

Atm

Abbreviation for 'at the moment'. Sometimes this kind of abbreviation is used when they are not needed. I saw this one a couple of times and had to ask what it meant. Took some time to find out. Just a sentence: "Terminal atm. indicates earliest berthing 25th/noon, but will constantly monitor weather." Atm: The situation under current circumstances and with current knowledge of any possible change and other expectation.

Atmosphere

The air on this globe which we need for the existence of all flora and fauna. So atmospheric distillation is the separation of crude oil to products in a column which is not under much pressure. We call it simple refining or primary distillation.

Atmospheric Crude Oil Distillation

The refining process of separating crude oil to petroleum products at atmospheric pressure by heating or boiling the crude in the column at temperatures up to roughly 350 to 380° Celsius or 660 to 700° Fahrenheit. It is also called the primary phase of refining. The crude will evaporate in the columns and by condensing of the fractions, by cooling, the gas, the light, middle light and heavy components of the oil are pumped into separate tanks. These products are called straight run products or virgin products. Further treating (cracking etc.) is required to extract maximum value in refining. A refinery will always aim to produce the oil products that give maximum value. That is a matter of refining the perfect crude which can produce the products in the best economic way. Crude yield is important. See also 'yield'. Condensing occurs at the dishes in the distillation column. The placing of the dishes in the column and the configuration of the refinery determines the favourite crude to run in a refinery. Of course, the price of this favourite crude quality is important as well.

Atmospheric Distillation Unit (ADU)

First distillation process in a refinery separating crude into gas, naphtha, kerosene, gasoil and residue. The majority of these products are to be processed further till final oil products for consumption-, trading-, or further processing purposes. Read more at 'atmospheric crude oil distillation'.

Atmospheric Pressure

Normal pressure, as in the situation we live in. Atmospheric distillation is therefore a way to distillate by just cooking oil and catching light and heavy elements on different levels within the column.

Atomic Energy

Energy released in nuclear reactions. It is a relatively cheap producible type of energy and a good alternative for fossil energy. Problem is the bad image of nuclear energy as a result of the disaster in Chernobyl, Russia 1986 and after the earthquake in Japan 2011. More countries are now considering phasing out that activity in densely populated areas. The risk is too big when accidents happen. The release of radiation would be a serious threat for human health and nature.

At or Better

A type of security or commodity order that specifies that the transaction occurs only at the specified price or better. Here you often give a minimum or maximum level in your order for a certain number of futures to buy. Basically you prefer to take the benefit from peaks or dips during a trading day.

Atres

Atmospheric residue. Another abbreviation of a word that is the same as straight run fueloil.

At-the-Money

A condition in which the strike price of an option is equal to (or nearly equal to) the market price of the underlying security. A trader would rather see a position in-the-money, as then he starts making a profit.

Auctioning

Selling a cargo to the best bidder after a bidding competition. In the case of high demand for a certain cargo in a market with a minimum number of offers a trader can decide to challenge his buyers and let them compete until the best bid comes out. It is not always seen as a popular way of doing business in oil trading. In the long term buyers may turn their back on the seller. This happens in the OTC market. Soon different bidders know who they are competing with. Even though sometimes a trading company may buy the cargo and sell it on at a better margin to an end-user. This can be the case as not every market participant prefers this way of trading. If such a cargo is sold at a very high price a new level for this oil is soon set for future cargoes. Most buyers prefer to avoid that; buying low is also a strategy. In a tender process all buyers or sellers offer one price only. The counterparty with the best price bid or offer wins the tender and gets the contract. Having said that, it happens that after bidding or offering for the first time on a tender a few companies (top 3 or 5 participants) may be re-invited to bid or offer for a second time. The seller wants to stretch the prices a bit further. In my view not the way a tender should work as that gives a smell called 'auctioning.' Often this way of tendering might be explained in the tender invitation. Then you try to be at least at a level to get re-invited again for the real bid of offer.

Automatic Sampler

A device used to extract a representative sample from the liquid flowing in a pipe. The automatic sampler generally consists of a probe, sample extractor, flow meter, controller, and sample receiver. The sample from this system represents the average sample of a loaded cargo and is generally accepted in the oil market. At some refineries at loading by inline blending some qualities of this sample can be checked all the time during loading. In the case of one of the spec requirements going wrong, adjustments can be made during loading by changing the inline blending ratio.

Avails

Availabilities. When a trader asks for avails he would like to know what the seller can offer. What oil and what qualities are available or are on offer in the market?

Average Price

Average of the quoted prices within a certain timeframe, e.g. a month, a 5 day quotation range or average pricing of a certain number of days around Bill of Lading date. The average price can also be the average of two different products or from one product but then the average over two different quotations. See for example at 'mean of the mean' and 'floating price'.

Aviation Gasoline

The shorter version is called 'avgas', which used to be leaded gasoline for aviation purposes, small pleasure planes. In Europe only one refinery still produces it. Avgas is a special grade of gasoline for use in aviation reciprocating engines. A complex mixture of relatively volatile hydrocarbons with or without small quantities of additives, blended to form a fuel suitable for use in aviation reciprocating engines. Small private 'sport planes' (not the jets) still consume some avgas. It will be phased out in the short term.

Aviation Gasoline Blending Components

Naphthas which will be used for blending or compounding into finished aviation gasoline (i.e. Straight-run gasoline, alkylate, reformate, benzene, toluene, and xylenes). Excludes oxygenates (alcohols, ethers), butanes and pentanes. Oxygenates are reported as other hydrocarbons, hydrogen and oxygenates. Just note that components do not have a standard quality. RVP, octane, density, aromatic are changing in components all the time. That makes blending complicated and exciting all the time.

B

B5

Diesel fuel containing up to 5 percent biomass-based diesel by volume. Even with only 5% biomass content, we call it bio-diesel.

B6-20

Diesel fuel containing from 6 to 20 percent biomass-based diesel by volume. The more bio content in the diesel the more challenging it will be. It has to meet a specification that is usable for a car, but at the same time, the diesel should not damage the engine. Acidity can be a challenge in bio-diesel. It does depend on the components that are used to make this oil.

B20

A mixture of 20% bio-diesel and 80% petroleum diesel based on volume.

B100

Biomass-based diesel fuel, 100 stands for 100%, pure bio-diesel. Tests have been done with city buses in some places with this type of oil. Good for a company trying to promote an environmentally friendly image. I think it is not economic; it can have worse environmental effects on places where the feedstock is produced. However, it is a start of thinking in the right direction, still to be further developed – that never stops.

BB/DD

Abbreviation used when a trader refers to the spread of the crude quotation between Dubai and Brent. Arbs from different pricing areas may be open or closed based on this differential. However Brent and Dubai crude are benchmarks and depending on qualities and market circumstances, crude is priced at benchmark with a discount or premium. This makes calculating an arbitrage possibility and taking the decision to supply a cargo from one trading area to another trading area very challenging.

B/L
See 'Bill of Lading' and read about of Bill of Lading types.

B/L Day
The B/L Day is the day that a vessel is ready from loading her cargo. To be precise it should be the moment as stated in the vessel's timesheet: 'hoses disconnected'. Not 'loading completed' as many would think. As long as hoses are connected oil can still go in or out of the vessel.

B/L Figure
Quantity as stated on the Bill of Lading. Quantities are most often stated in metric tons, litres at 15°C/60°F for products in Europe. On the Bills of Lading for crude oil it is obvious that those are stated in barrels as well. One can request the adding of long tons or other volume indicators on the B/L as well. The Bill of Lading figure is important and has to be correct as the commercial invoice is related to that number. The operator in the oil company has to enter these numbers into the trading or operational system which is connected to the traders' P&L. The quantity may be more or less volume, compared with the quantity that the trader had entered into his P&L in the first place. The change in quantity is a result of the loading tolerance as stated in the contract. The change of volumes has a small resulting effect and the trader might need to adjust his hedge. The Bill of Lading figure is compared with the final discharge figure and in most cases there is a loss in quantity, which can be considered as an operational loss as long as it stays within reasonable limits (0.1%). If the loss is much bigger then something is wrong at the receiving terminal, or something went wrong on board the vessel, or at loadport the Bill of Lading figures were overstated. As the Bill of Lading figure is the commercial invoice quantity it is wise to make use of a good and reliable inspector to see to it that volume and quality are as they should be. One thousand barrels' loss of oil on a crude cargo is only 0.1% but

that has a value of 100kUsd. Enough reason to really focus on getting correct B/L figures.

B/L Pricing

Agreed pricing period around the Bill of Lading. B/L +/- 2 means: '2 quotations before the B/L date, the quotation on the B/L date and the 2 quotations after the B/L date'. Pricing can also be after B/L, 3 or 5 days after. This is a floating price and the dates are not always easy to hedge as the B/L day may shift one or more days due to operational issues. To avoid sudden changes the buyer and the seller may agree to create an assumed and fixed B/L day before pricing starts, also called 'deemed B/L day'.

Babysitting

A trader is babysitting his position for some time means that he was holding a losing trade for too long a time, desperately hoping for the price to go up again so he can leave the position at breakeven. This trader did not cut his losses in time.

Back

To withdraw from a position. Pulling back an offer or a bid. Not a problem if a trader does it before the market shows real interest and mentions prices. If such backing off happens after the market shows their interest, it will frustrate the traders and the market. When a trader starts bidding on a certain cargo then he shows his position as being short of cargo in the market. Other market participants might see that and may benefit from the situation where one is backing. The trader backing off in such circumstance is quickly called a flaker. See also 'flaking'.

Back End

'Back end' is a term used in the barge market during the Platts or Argus trading window. It means that the loading window in the offer or bid is based on the last 5 delivery days as set during the window session of that trading day. During the window it is abbreviated to the offer or bid price which includes 'b/e', e.g. Company X bids 550USD b/e for 2000 ton of high sulphur fueloil barges fob Rotterdam. See also 'front window' and 'full window'.

Backhaul

Backhaul voyages occur when a cargo is moved on the return leg of a journey.

As charter rates incorporate the return ballast leg of a journey, backhaul opportunities represent an opportunity for supplementary income for tanker owners. For example, a vessel could load in West Africa and head East on its return from a laden voyage from the Arabian Gulf to Europe or the US. See also 'freight optimisation'. A popular route is gasoline supply ex NWE to USA and backhaul distillates to NWE.

Back Loading

Taking oil back on board after discharging. Can be a new cargo for a backhaul, but can also be some cutterstock (LCO) for crude oil washing purposes after discharging heavy crude. After the crude oil wash (COW) the vessel pumps the oil into the receiver's shore tank. The receiver hopes to get all oil from his original cargo and avoid oil losses. See 'oil loss' and 'voyage loss'.

Back Office

Administration and support personnel in an oil company. They carry out functions like contract sending, claim settlements, clearances, record maintenance, regulatory compliance, HSE control, controlling and accounting. When the order processing goes too slow due to high volume of trades, it is commonly referred to as 'back office crunch'. Customers may not be happy with the service. Companies want to grow all the time, but costs have to stay low as well. It may happen that the business grows faster than expected which may result in such a back office crunch.

Back Testing

The process of testing a trading strategy on prior time periods. Instead of applying a strategy for the time period forward, which could take years, a trader can do a simulation of his trading strategy on relevant past data in order to gauge its effectiveness. Most technical-analysis strategies are tested with this approach. But even then I would say: "Good results from the past are not a guarantee for the future."

Back to Back

Transaction where all the obligations and liabilities in one transaction are mirrored in a second transaction. Most often all terms and conditions in the sale and purchase are exactly the same. The only difference should be the price where the sales price is a bit higher than the purchase price. That difference is called the 'margin'. With a 100% back-to-back-deal even the price is the same and no results are added to the P&L; it would be the same as a 'wash-out'.

Back Trading

Taking a trading decision based on pricing quotations that are already known. Afterwards telling how a trade should have been done based on information which you know after the trade is done. Back trading is not a popular thing to do. It is often seen as cheating. But in some cases this opportunity is available in the market. Look therefore at 'look back opportunity'.

Back Up

A position you can refer to in case business does not go as planned. When a trader buys or sells a cargo with the plan to sell or buy it back later with profit, it would limit risk when having an alternative place to discharge or source the cargo. When the cargo cannot be sold, the cargo can always land in storage. Such a back up option may cost something but one has to consider that as a kind of insurance. Instead of being squeezed by the market the back-up is a cheaper solution and in some cases a trader can still take a decision to sell a cargo as long as the back-up opportunity is not used. Creating a back-up option is important for a trader. It helps people trade as the back-up option is available as a kind of insurance when business does not go as expected in the first place.

Backwardation

Situation where the market expects that the forward paper market would be lower priced than the prompt market. Prices are highest in the nearest data periods and are lower on forward delivery dates. Buyers will try to delay their purchase as much as possible while the seller wants to sell as early as possible. Storage will be empty or minimum used. In normal circumstances backwardation indicates a strong market in the front; there may be shorts in products. As a result of that prompt short situation refinery margins should be good and attractive. Traders would struggle to make money and refiners should be happy. In 2011 we saw a backwardated market and low refinery margins. A combination of crude shorts created by Middle East troubles on one side and on the other side the big financial or economic crisis in Europe.

Bacteria in Oil

Yes, living things in oil. Bacteria survive at the interface between oil and water and they like a warm temperature. Normally one would not notice these bacteria in the oil, but the situation can be bad. A black slimy emulsion can be obtained and the oil cannot be sold without treatment. Some ppms of additives such as biocides are to be added into the oil. One of the elements – 'oil', 'water' or 'temperature' – which bacteria need to survive, must be removed. As you cannot remove heat and you do not want to get rid of the oil, it is obvious that water in oil must be avoided. Bacteria are most often prevalent in gasoil. It is therefore important that refineries and terminals remove water from gasoil tanks on a regular basis. Water in oil can come from vessels and rainwater. The water-housekeeping at a storage terminal is a very important task in order to avoid any problems with bacteria in oil.

Balance of Trade

The difference in value between the total exports and total imports of a trading unit during a specific period of time; a balance of payments.

Ballast

Seawater taken into a vessel's tanks. Ballast can be taken into cargo tanks, double bottoms, fore and aft peak tanks and/or segregated ballast tanks (SBT). Taking in ballast water is meant to increase draft so that the propeller is fully immersed, stability and trim are maintained and stresses minimised. When a vessel gets a good backhaul possibility, she would avoid taking in ballast water on her trip back – a great cost saving. Types of ballast are departure ballast, clean ballast, dirty ballast, segregated ballast and heavy water ballast. Have a look at those as well.

Ballast Speed

Speed of the vessel without cargo on board on her way to next loadport. Standard speed can be arranged in the charter party. If more speed is required the charterer can ask for maximum laden speed, but that will cost extra bunkers. If a vessel has plenty of time before the agreed loading window then the vessel gets a lower laden speed or 'eco-speed'. Saving bunkers and money. However, when an operator tries to arrange allowance to load a day earlier it could save a day of idle time when the end receiver accepts the earlier arrival day in disport as a consequence. Sometimes when earlier loading there is a rule that the time gained at loadport can be given back at disport. Then the owner hopes that the vessel can discharge on arrival, then his vessel becomes available earlier for the next voyage. A buyer can also request a faster laden speed, but then the extra bunkers consumed will be for the buyer's account.

Ballast Tank

A tank intended to be filled with seawater to keep floating equipment stable.

Ballast Type

- **Departure ballast**

  Ballast taken on board prior to departure. If loaded into tanks that have previously contained cargo it may contain traces of oil and be termed dirty ballast.

- **Clean ballast**

  Ballast contained in cargo tanks that have been COW'd and thoroughly water washed. It may be discharged to sea when it meets MARPOL requirements.

- **Segregated ballast**

  Ballast that is contained in dedicated ballast tanks serviced by dedicated ballast pumps and lines with no permanent connection to the cargo system.

- **Heavy weather ballast**

  Additional ballast loaded into cargo tanks to enable the vessel to maintain a safe sea-going condition under extreme weather conditions.

Bal. Month

Balance month. When a trader sells paper tools like a swap or CFD which represents the actual month then the pricing is meant to be all quotations from this day until the end of the month. So a May gasoline swap sold on the 5th May is pricing 5-31 May (1-4 May quotations are known and back trading is not allowed). It happens as well that prompt physical cargoes are sold based on balance of the month pricing. In logistics balance of the month can be related to the available time for loading or delivery. A sale on the 10th August with loading dates 'balance of the month' means that the buyer can load on any date between 10 and 31 August. In most contracts there is a nomination clause indicating that the loading order or nomination has to be received 3 days before arrival of a barge or 7 days before arrival of a vessel.

B

Baltimax

Tanker designed for loading cargoes being bigger than a suezmax but still having a maximum draft of 15 metres. Parcel size would be typically between 150 kt and 200 kt (1.1-1.5 million barrels). So far this vessel size has never become a success. The cargo size is too big for refineries and trades. Crude oil loaded in Russia goes in lots of 725kb (100kt) and fuel oil may go in lots of maximum 140 kt.

Bank Holiday

A bank holiday is a public holiday in both the United Kingdom and Ireland. There is some automatic right to time off on these days, although the majority of the population not employed in essential services (e.g. Utilities, fire, ambulance, police, health-care workers, London Underground) receive them as holidays. Those employed in essential services usually receive extra pay for working on these days. Bank holidays are often assumed to be so called because they are days upon which banks are shut, but this is not in fact the case. Some of the assumed bank holidays are days on which the banks are shut but are not, in fact, a bank holiday (e.g. Good Friday and Christmas Day). Legislation does not allow certain payments to be deferred to the working day. On bank holidays the oil market in London is closed while in USA business continues. Also oil operations never stand still. The oil trader and most other people working in the oil industry are always on call if something happens. Oil business is a 24-7 non-stop business. On bank holidays the European futures market is closed and therefore a day to relax for many traders in Europe when the UK is closed.

Bar

Pressure expression. 1 bar is equal to 100 kPa, kilopascal. 1 kPa is a pressure of 10.2 gram per square cm. Reid Vapour pressure is sometimes reported in bar, but most of the time in kPa. See also 'kPa'. RVP is measured at 37.8° C/100° F.

Bar Chart (Technical Trading)

A chart that graphs the high, low, and settlement prices for a specific trading session over a given period of time. Also called 'candle stick'.

Bare Boat Charter

A charter in which the bare ship is chartered without the crew. The charterer,

41

rather than the owner, appoints the crew and pays for all operating expenses. The charterer has full control and responsibility. They make the rules for the vessel, which include HSE standards and requirements towards personnel. The owner of the vessel is more or less an investor or financer, willing to take risk and aiming for cash.

Barge

USA related: Small tanker vessel carrying oil for bunkering, containing anywhere between 8,000 to 75,000 bbl (1,000 to 15,000 metric tons). Barges are often used for lightering at places where tankers may not be able to arrive due to draft restrictions.

European related: Barges are flat-bottomed boats used to carry small cargoes on inland waterways. They are often used to transfer cargoes from larger vessels to terminals only accessible to smaller boats (look at 'lightering'). In ARA barges are used to transport the refined oil to Germany over the rivers. The barges are also linked to the Rotterdam barge market as quoted in Platts and Argus. See also 'Vletten'. Barges are very much dependent on the water level in the rivers into Germany. During a dry summer barges may only load half cargoes due to draft constraints in the river on the way to discharge port. In such a period freight prices may be high as more barges are needed to bring the same volumes of oil to Germany. In the case of extremely high water levels it may be that the authorities do not allow heavy traffic on parts of the river. Oil has to be transported by rail or truck when such a situation does not change for some time. See also 'barge trading'.

Barge Broker

A person who sells freight orders for barge owners in exchange for a commission. A lot of barges are owned by private people who are not that familiar with the oil market, meaning these are private companies which would be the potential customer for the barge brokers. Therefore barge owners may use a barge broker to arrange the next cargo order to load at a terminal which fits best in the logical plan of the barge. Often owners prefer longer term contracts with barge agencies. The barge broker may be able to guarantee a fixed price and by that the barge broker takes the risk of freight levels in the barge market.

Barge Cargo Spread

The difference between the FOB barge market quotations and the CIF cargo quotations in Europe. Normally traders would like to see that the Rotterdam barge quotations plus the European freight prices are equal to the CIF North West Europe quotations. Due to that a trader could buy a few barges to have the barge quotations priced on a higher level. By that action he wants the CIF quotation to go up as well. The reason for that barge buying activity could be that the trader has sold some cargoes which are pricing out his customer. So by buying 5 barges (5kt) he might price a 30kt cargo at a higher level. But it can happen that the reporters just see a barge peak which will not affect the cargo market quotations. I have seen Rotterdam FOB market prices being higher priced than the CIF market, a result of imbalances in the European market or too heavily played barge market.

Barge Market

Also called the cash market. In ARA barges are loaded and traded on a daily basis. A very busy activity. Barges are sold to Germany and The Netherlands or other countries connected to the rivers (Rhine and Maas). But also many barges are collected in tank to make bulk for export purposes. For blending and trading barges are going from terminal to terminal. Connected to that activity there is also a paper market for products, a swap market. This entire activity makes the barge market THE price setting market for oil products in Europe. See also 'ARA', 'break bulk', 'make bulk', 'cash market' and 'leverage game'.

Barge Trading

The Rotterdam barge market, or better said the 'ARA market', is a very important market which basically sets the prices for petroleum products in Europe. The barge trading activity is also called the cash market for petroleum products. Barge deals of 1,000 to 2,000 tons are heavily traded during the Platts or Argus window, the last 30 minutes before the market closes. This is a very liquid market and traded over the counter. All deals are done at fixed prices. The price reporters have, with this barge trading activity, a good tool to set their assessments. The Rotterdam barge market's fixtures are the basis for setting the values in Europe. This includes the cargo market on CIF and FOB basis. Companies in Rotterdam being active in the barge market may be the local refineries, blenders, traders and wholesalers. To be active in the barge market, it is often important to have a logistic system in place; tank rental and barge charter contracts are therefore often required. Back office functions may be loaded with work as the number of transactions is very high. Ten barge deals equal the same volume as one cargo deal in products trading. Barge trading is also used for the leverage game play. See also 'leverage game'. As a result of that we sometimes see a barge market overpriced, but a trader can also sell down a market which results in an under-priced market. All a result of supply and demand based on paper trading strategies plus availabilities and needs for physical oil.

Barrel (Bbls)

Bbls, blue barrels, a volumetric unit of measure for crude oil and petroleum products. A unit of volume equal to 42 U.S. gallons; 158.978295 litres. Crude oil is priced per barrel in lots of 1000 barrels. Just note that a barrel is reported at 60°F. The standard in Europe is volume at 15°C vac. 60°F is equal to 15.5°C so to convert from barrels to litres one has to divide the barrels by factor 6.293. European M3@15°C times 6.293 is US Barrel@60°F. Just for the sake of good order, some people link barrels to API gravity. Just be aware that this conversion factor is used based on European standards of volume reporting at 15°C. In the USA volume density is reported at 60°F, so no corrected conversion factor in that case. Since API gravity is measured in air some may think that barrels are reported at 60°F in air. This is wrong; volume is volume and is neither reported in air nor in vac. Only weight is reported in air or vac. There are roughly 7.33 bbls of crude oil to a ton (1,000 kilos), but the precise conversion obviously depends on the specific gravity or density of the oil. Have a look at the conversion calculations in the back of this book.

Barrel of Oil Equivalent or BOE

One barrel of crude oil or one barrel of natural gas liquid (NGL) or eight thousand (8,000) standard cubic feet (SCF) of natural gas. So a source producing a certain number of oil equivalents is able to produce a certain sum of crude and gas as mentioned above. One cubic foot is 28.3168466 litres and 1 barrel is 5.61458 cubic feet. The total production of oil and gas combined from one production field only.

Barrels per Calendar Day

The maximum quantity that a refinery can process per day, 24 hours. It is also called the maximum refinery capacity. Here one assumes that there are no hiccups in the refinery which may slow down production. Slowdown of production may be caused by different reasons. I can mention technical reasons such as maintenance programmes, or logistic reasons such as lack of feedstock, and economic reasons such as bad refinery margins. Also an unplanned shutdown caused by a technical problem or accident would reduce the barrels processed per day. Discussions between traders and refiners often start with the information related to refinery capacity. Small refineries take 20-50 kb of crude oil or less per day in and the biggest refineries can process more than 300kb. It indicates the potential of business with certain counterparties. Barrels per day are reported as 'bpd', 'b/d' or 'bbl/d'. Sometimes it is also called 'barrels per stream day'. In yearly overviews refineries report the average barrel per day which represents the real processed number of barrels at the refinery. Here all types of slowdown are included as well. The average will therefore always be less than 100% of the max capacity. KBD, kilo barrels per days, is often the more popular way to talk. Then kbd is very much related to the production capacity of a crude oil field.

Barrels Per Stream Day

The maximum number of barrels of input that a distillation facility can process within a 24-hour period when running at full capacity under optimal crude and product slate conditions with no allowance for downtime. Planners always try to let a refinery run as optimally as possible. It depends on the market if that is possible. Refinery supplies have to be well planned at the right purchase price and qualities of feedstock must be perfect. The production has to be on-spec and be sold at the right price with the right timing. The perfect stream day depends on the circumstances of the market and the logistics. It indicates the potential of the refinery.

Barter

Trade in which goods or merchandise are exchanged directly for other import or export without use of money. A barter deal is often done for logistic reasons or can be done to enter a new market – e.g. I give some products from equity/production and get something back in a market which I am eager to enter. Time and location do have value and sometimes a barter deal can include a little premium or discount. A trader could sell a certain crude oil to a customer, but would require a cargo back in another trading area, also location swap.

Base Price

A base price is the price of the cost of a new car without getting any other options, just standard options. Nothing optional or anything like that. Think base price of an oil-grade, the standard specification like Brent or WTI. Some specifications of crude cargoes have a better quality than the benchmark oil. That results in a premium on top of a base price. If some specifications of crude oil cargoes are worse than the standard, then this results in a discount versus the base price. So the base price is the price of the commodity which is used as benchmark in a certain deal, Brent or WTI dated. This can also be a certain grade of crude oil, standard gasoil or gasoline as according to Platts or Argus quotations. In case the oil cargo was sold on the exchange, expiry of a futures contract, then it is not allowed to supply a quality that is worse than the minimum specification as described at the exchange. There will also not be a premium calculated on top of the futures price when the spec is better than the basis grade. The buyer would then receive oil with 'give-away'. See 'basis grade'.

Basis

The difference between the price of a spot commodity and a forward commodity or the difference between the price of a commodity at one location and another location. Those differentials can be the basis for the next trading decision.

Basis Grade

The minimum specification of the oil grade as described according to a futures contract. Any spec which is better quality than the basis grade would be considered as give-away. Give-away of blending value. Traders prefer to supply their product as close to the basis specification as possible. Borderline blending. Oil supplies with a specification worse than the basis grade are not allowed when it relates to the exchange grades, the futures grade. Not even at a small discount. Most often the physical crude oil cargoes are not traded by the use of futures contracts as there are so many different qualities of crude oil around which deviate a lot from the basis grade. Heating oil, for example, in ARA area in Europe can be traded by the use of futures, although it is not that high a quantity and often part of a small trading strategy which can only be fulfilled by the bigger trading companies and producers. Sometimes it can be a barge trading game. Often it gives more stress to the operations department than to the trader. Loading schedule is extremely tight; being off schedule results in lots of re-arrangements with the exchange. At physical delivery, fulfilment of the futures contract, the exchange will mention the counterparty so that the logistics can be arranged. A balance quantity which cannot be loaded on a barge will need a cash settlement, EFP.

Basis Risk

Price exposure based on the relation between the physical position of the traded commodity and its hedging tool. Crude is hedged with futures, and gasoline is hedged with gasoline swaps in Europe or Rbob futures in USA. And so naphtha, fueloil, and more oil products have their own hedging tools. Paper hedges are always forward in time and not always exactly equal to the quantity of the physical trade. So the perfect hedge does not exist – there is always a basis risk. These risks may be associated with location, product specifications and time variations.

Basis Swap

Basis swaps are used to hedge exposure to basis risks, such as location risk or time exposure risk. See also 'swap'.

Basket Offer

An offer for supply of different crude oil grades or different petroleum products' grades in one contract to a receiver. A wholesaler could be interested in a basket of gasoline, diesel, jet, etc. Or a refinery would buy a basket of different grades of crude which could be processed in the refinery. In this case the basket is the variation of different type of cargoes and grades. Each grade has its own price in the supply contract. Each price per grade is negotiated separately. A basket price is something different. See also 'flexi-short'.

Basket Price

The average price of a group of nominated crude oils. OPEC calculates an average price for their production. They aim for a certain value per barrel for their oil production. In case the price gets too high then the OPEC would try to control the price and produce more oil in order to lower the oil price to their desired basket price. The ASCI quotation from Argus is also a basket of different sour crudes. Brent is a basket as well, an average of BFOE. Or based on qualities, a basket of crude oil grades with differing gravities, sulphur content, sweet and sour. The basket of different crudes together has one basis price only. See 'basket offer'. A basket price or basket crude may then also become a benchmark like the sour crude quotation from Argus called 'ASCI'.

Batch
A measured amount of crude oil or refined product in a pipeline or storage tank. 100kt of oil could be pumped over in two batches of 50kt. Working with batches is done for logistic reasons.

Bbl/d
Barrels per day. Often this relates to oil production. Also in oil trading offices, they prefer to calculate their sales quantity in barrels per day or rather in 'kbd', kilo barrels per day.

BBQ
A composite of Bonny, Brass River and Qua Ibo crude from Nigeria.

BCF (Billion Cubic Feet)
The cubic foot is a standard unit of measure for gas at atmospheric pressure. 1 BCF is equal to 0.178107 barrel or 1 barrel is equal to 5.64 BCF.

Beam
The width of a ship. Also called its breadth. If a jetty is located in a canal then there could be berth restrictions based on beam allowances.

Bear Market (Bear/Bearish)
When prices are declining, the market is said to be a 'bear market'. Individuals who anticipate lower prices are 'bears'. A trader who expects falling prices is said to be 'bearish'. This is based on the outright prices. A backwardated market has a curve that goes downwards, which is often caused by a strong prompt market. The forward curve looks bearish but the outright price might still go up due to the tightness in the front. If the front market gets bearish and the outright price goes down then it could mean that the forward market gets flat and might even flip into contango. Furthermore one can be bearish based on fundamental or technical indicators. Opposite is 'bull market'.

Bearish
You are bearish when you believe that the outright market prices are going down. In the oil business 'believe' must be based on the market view of the

trader. The trader will position his book accordingly in case it is his strong market view.

Beat

Beat a number, giving a better bid or offer in order to get a trade done. A trader may invite you for a last look on a potential deal. Are you able and willing to beat the number? If yes, then you have a deal. However, keep in mind there are traders using your number again to let another trader beat your number. In that case, that trader is auctioning a cargo, which is not really the best way to conduct a good business relationship. When you want to beat a number, make sure that your counterparty is firm and will accept the deal. No calling back option, do not accept "I call you back in a minute".

Benchmark

A basis commodity used to compare or to indicate an overall trend and set prices towards other types of commodities linked to this particular basis commodity. Brent, Dubai and WTI are the common benchmarks for crude oil pricing. In products it could be the qualities as quoted on the daily reports from Platts or Argus. One can also create a certain benchmark for a certain type of oil for a certain location. The trader would use an attractive firm offer or bid and compare it with other offers and bids in the market. He tries to get the best deal possible by benchmarking his position. As a trader, would you be giving firm offers or bids for spot cargoes and give the counterparty lots of time to think about that? I would love to get firm offers and bids in such a way.

Benchmark Crude

A crude oil that is traded so regularly in the spot market that its price quotes are relied upon by sellers of other crude oil as a reference point for setting term or spot prices. Brent, West Texas Intermediate and Dubai are all benchmark crude oil. The ASCI quotation from Argus is a basket of crude and is often used as basis to price sour crude.

Benchmarking

A systematic procedure of comparing a company's practices against the best practice and modifying actual knowledge to achieve superior performance. Traders might be in the market checking offers in order to use the received market numbers to evaluate before committing to a good deal with another party. That party could potentially lose the business if a better offer is given. So if something is on offer the trader would try to limit thinking time to avoid too much shopping around by the counterparty.

Beneficiary

A term often used by banks to identify the 'beneficiary' to the credit, the one who receives the right to receive or claim or can execute pay out of financials.

Benzene

An aromatic hydrocarbon present in small proportion in some crude oils and made commercially from petroleum by the catalytic reforming of naphthenes in petroleum naphtha. Also made from coal in the manufacture of coke. Used as a solvent, in manufacturing detergents, synthetic fibres, and petrochemicals and as a component of high-octane gasoline. Benzene can cause cancer and is therefore limited as a gasoline component. Before the year 2000 there was an allowance of about 5% of benzene in gasoline. Today it is max 1%. Gasoline blenders and refineries are very good at handling this maximum level. Benzene has not disappeared of course. Chemical factories may prefer it as feedstock for their processes.

Berth

The mooring, dock, anchorage, wharf, submarine line, single point or single buoy or single berth mooring facility, offshore location, offshore facility, alongside barges, lighters or any other mooring facility nominated by the relevant party. The time used for sailing from pilot station until arrival at berth does not count as used part of the laytime. Berth is same as jetty. The place where the loading arm will be connected to the ship manifold in order to discharge or load the vessel. Different berths in different locations may have restrictions such as draft, length, beam, etc. The receiving terminal must have approved the vessel beforehand, else problems may arise. So one has to deal with the port restrictions before chartering a vessel.

Berth Restriction

Maximum technical abilities at a terminal which would enable a vessel to berth at a jetty. Can be based on draft, LOA or beam and vessel connection points. This is not the same as port restrictions as a port may have more terminals with different requirements. In Rotterdam there are terminals (Europoort and Maasvlakte) which can handle the draft of a VLCC while other terminals (Botlek and Pernis) are not able to handle more than a draft of 38 feet. Berth restriction is the same as jetty restriction.

Berthing Prospects
Information required for the arrival of a tanker at its final destination. It involves timing, berth availability and berth number, pilot services, even how a pilot would come on board the tanker and at which position on sea. All items in order to arrange for the safest arrival at the berth. For the logistics, this information is important to have. A ship owner needs the information to be able to plan the next voyage for the vessel. If the berth prospects do not show a berthing on arrival than demurrage will be the consequence. For the owner of the vessel it may cause logistic challenges as he may have planned the vessel for the next trip. He needs to find an alternative vessel in this case. Re-scheduling of the fleet could be one of the consequences. Delay in disport is not only costly but creates a lot of work for ship-schedulers and cargo operations. Re-scheduling requires new vetting processes and re-issue doc instructions and all other types of orders connected to it. Awareness of berthing prospects is just an important way of anticipating any problems that might arise in case waiting time is expected.

Best International Petroleum Industry Practices
Standard way/behaviour of acting/performing in the oil industry. Acting in a way that is generally accepted in the international petroleum industry related to safety, economics, environment, efficiency, development, production, processing and transportation of crude oil and oil products. Common sense is leading, the industry has a standard way of working and that is what different companies can expect from each other. In case of claims and discrepancies between 2 companies one could check by arbitrage, using one or more third parties, if business standards have been used. Those standards may be different between the trading areas in this world. It can be complicated as those standards are not described in a contract – it is possibly the big 'gentlemen's agreement' in the industry based on behaviour and business relations.

Bid
An expression of willingness to buy a cargo of oil or a paper contract like a swap at a given price. Or the price at which a product can be bought

immediately without dispute or negotiation. See also 'bid price'. The opposite of bid is 'offer' or 'ask'.

Bid-Ask

The amount by which the ask price exceeds the bid price. Prices offered to buy and sell respectively, on spot market deals. An interested party can sell at the bid and buy at the asked price. Spot prices are not reported as a straight number, but rather, in terms of bid and ask. The bid-ask spread is low in markets with high liquidity like the crude oil futures market.

Bid/Offer Spread

The bid/offer spread (also known as bid/ask or buy/sell spread) for securities (such as swaps, futures contracts or options) is the difference between the price quoted by a market maker for an immediate sale (bid) and an immediate purchase (ask). The size of the bid/offer spread in a given commodity is a measure of the liquidity of the market. The bid/offer spread in physical oil trading can be rather big. It depends on the market situation. Differences of 10 Dollars per ton in products cargo trading are possible. It can be related to special qualities, market tightness and many other reasons. Even though the bid/offer spread looks unreasonably big a lot of business will get committed. That is just a matter of negotiations and bridging the gap.

Bid Price

The price that a dealer is prepared to pay for an oil cargo or derivative. When you make a bid you participate in the market. In the OTC market everybody can see your bid and is allowed to make a counter. When one hits your bid, then you are booked and you have a commitment. You are allowed to withdraw your bid before you get hit. You may do that because you change your mind or you found a silent seller who prefers to hide his business, which is a bit naive in an OTC market. Nevertheless, withdrawing a cargo during negotiations is not something that makes a trader popular in the market. See also 'bid', 'back' and 'flaking'.

Big Belt

The Great Belt is a strait between the main Danish islands of Zealand and Funen. The draft restriction there is 15 metres. As a result of that VLCCs would not be able to leave Russia to open sea when fully loaded. (Draft of a loaded VLCC is app. 22 metres). An oil supplier needs to keep this 15 metres draft in mind in case something has to be loaded or discharged in that area. Due to the restriction of the big belt a lot of ship-to-ship activity is done at the Skagerrak (Skår or Skaw), north of Denmark. Also the storage terminals in Rotterdam benefit from this restriction.

Big Figure

Refers normally to the first three digits of an exchange rate that dealers treat as understood in quoting. For example a quote of '30/40' on Euro/Dollar mark could indicate a price of 1.3130/40. The 1.31 is the part which was understood and the main focus is on the 30/40 which fluctuates during a trading day.

Big Swinging Dick

A trader who buys and sells big cargoes on a global basis and gets lots of attention from the market for it, especially when he is seen as a successful trader. Big cargoes with the size of an Aframax, Suezmax or VLCC going from one continent to another continent, like a full VLCC of cracked fueloil M100 from Europe to Singapore.

Bilateral Agreement

A written statement signed by two parties that specifies the terms for exchanging energy, e.g. Governments which have exchange agreements related to holding compulsory (strategic) stock in different countries. See also 'compulsory stock ticket'.

Bill of Lading (B/L)

A B/L is the basic document between a shipper and a carrier and between a shipper and a consignee. It represents the contract of carriage and defines the terms and conditions of carriage. It is the final receipt from the carrier for the goods shown on it and for the condition of the goods. It describes the nature, quantity and weight of the cargo carried. It is also the document of title of the goods shown. In the oil business we see most often that a set of B/Ls consist of three original stamped and signed documents. The B/L rarely goes on board the vessel to its final destination. All original documents including many copies related to the oil cargo are sent by courier from the office of the seller who will endorse them to the buyer. The vessel will get copies on board.

Bill of Lading Type

B/Ls are issued or ordered as in the following different types:

- **Amended B/L**

  B/L which has been updated in a way that does not affect its financial value. Quantity remains unchanged. It is more a text issue which has been changed. It cannot be called a corrected B/L.

- **Clean B/L**

  A B/L which represents oil on board the vessel which has not been damaged or contaminated during loading and has that same status on board the vessel. The oil on board is received by the carrier as 'apparent good order and condition'. Sometimes 'clean and bright'.

- **Consolidated B/L**

  B/L combined or consolidated from two or more B/Ls. When vessels are involved in STS operations then the sum of the B/Ls from all vessels discharged into the receiving vessel (most often a VLCC) will become the new consolidated quantity to be issued on the B/L of that big vessel.

- **Corrected B/L**

  B/L whose update results in a change of value. Often a correction of loading figures such as a change in density which also affects the weight of the cargo has financial consequences. Discussions of differences between ship figures and shore figures may be a reason to issue a corrected B/L. A new B/L will be issued, whilst at the same time the originals can be destroyed to avoid having double sets which is not wanted. A ship agent may sign and stamp the B/L on behalf of the captain or owner of the vessel.

- **Duplicate B/L**

  Another original Bill of Lading set may be issued in case the first set is lost. Also known as re-issued B/L.

- **Negotiable B/L**

  Transferrable B/L from consignee to a third party. The B/L will be endorsed or assigned to the other party, the buyers. The B/L is written 'to order' of the first consignee. Basically this B/L can be transferred between a chain of buyers and sellers. Thus, a shipper's order (negotiable) B/L can be bought, sold, or traded while goods are in transit and is commonly used for Letter of Credit transactions. The buyer must submit the original B/L to the carrier in order to take possession of the goods.

- **Non Negotiable B/L**

  A copy of a B/L, often recognised by the stamp on the B/L stating 'copy non-negotiable'.

- **Original B/L**

  The part of the B/L set that has value, especially when negotiable. Rest of the set are only informative file copies. Often a set of B/Ls consists of 3 original B/Ls with a certain number of copies. The original B/L gets a stamp with 'original' on it. Copies often get a stamp 'copy non negotiable'. In most cases the vessel receives copies on board the vessel. The original documents are sent by post (courier) from loading terminal or agent to the seller. And from the seller to the buyer.

- **Split B/L**

  When one oil cargo is planned to discharge at more than one disport or to more than one receiver, the total cargo on board the vessel can be represented by more than one B/L. Each split B/L represents each delivery. Call it the opposite of a consolidated B/L. It may happen that the decision by the trader to sell the cargo to more than one receiver is taken when the vessel has already left the loadport where one B/L was issued. In that case the B/L needs to be re-issued and split according to discharged quantities. To be able to do that the operator might wait till the vessel has discharged and discharges figures are known. In that case a split B/L is issued with correct quantities; eventual losses versus the B/L figures are shared pro rata between the different B/Ls. The total quantity (sum) of all split B/Ls must be equal to the quantity of the original B/L that was issued in the first place.

B/L Related Pricing

Floating pricing system. The price of a cargo is related to the quotation days before, around or after the Bill of Lading date. Traders prefer to hedge their cargoes. B/L dates can change from one day to another depending on the vessel arrival and performance of the loading terminal or offshore field. Therefore a few days before loading the traders prefer to agree with each other on a fixed B/L day, also called 'deemed B/L'.

B/L's Status

The status informing in which administration phase the B/L is kept at a certain moment. Phases can be input, cancelled, rated, reconciled, printed, endorsed or released to the customer.

BIMCO

Baltic and International Maritime Council (BIMCO) is an independent international shipping trade association which represents ship-owners. See also 'ice clause'.

Bio Diesel

Diesel containing a minimum required percentage (often 5%) of environmentally friendly components such as rapeseed oil, palm oil etc. An 'environmentally friendly' biodegradable transportation fuel for use in diesel engines that is produced through the transesterification of organically derived oil or fats. It may be used either as a replacement for or as a component of diesel fuel.

Biofuels

Biofuels are liquid fuels, such as ethanol or bio-diesel, made from biomass. Biofuels can be used to run cars, trucks, and hopefully in the future, ships and aircrafts. It is seen as the future oil and should be more environmentally friendly. As well as the consumption the production of biofuels should be done in an environmentally friendly way, not only in Europe but also in other parts of the world. Food prices may be affected by the increase of biofuel production.

Biomass

Organic waste which through simple processing can be used for energy production. Types of biomass are wood and agricultural products, garbage, wasted food, not plastics etc. Biomass is a renewable energy source.

Biomass-Based Diesel Fuel

Bio-diesel and other renewable diesel fuel or diesel fuel blending components derived from biomass, but excluding renewable diesel fuel co-processed with petroleum feedstock.

Bitumen

Extremely heavy semi-solid product of oil refining made up of heavy hydrocarbons. It is used for road-building and roofing. Bitumen season is most often during warmer weather periods (March – October). In that period demand and the use of bitumen is best. The bitumen related business is purchasing its needs in that period. In some countries it can be a well subsidised business when linked to road construction. Bitumen is produced at the so called bitumen-refineries.

Bitumen Refinery

This is a refinery set up which is able to process the most heavy and difficult crude oil. They also produce gasoline and other petroleum products. Heavy crude oil is well discounted versus the standard grades, which may make it economically possible to run such a refinery in a profitable way. Often these refineries have a fluid cat-cracker unit and coker units such as a 'delayed coker' or 'flexi-coker'.

Black Oil

Crude oil or heavy fueloil from the bottom of the refining process as opposed to 'white' oil. Also called 'dirty oil'.

Black Out

The emergency loss of the source of electricity serving an area caused by failure of the generation, transmission, or distribution system. From time to time a refinery can have a black out. It causes big problems in a refinery when the failure is not solved soon enough. If a black out turns into a shutdown then traders have to take action and re-position their trading book and start thinking of solutions related to term supply obligations. For FOB sales the refinery could declare force majeure. As result of a black out some products may become off-spec. Creative solutions are required from all people involved in order to reduce financial losses – e.g. it can be a solution to re-blend the oil at a refinery or maybe for off-spec products a discount can be given for a few spot cargoes. It is obvious that information about a black-out should not be announced in the market. It might come out when the black-out turns into a serious disruption of the production process at the refinery. The market would see the traders of that company being very busy covering shorts or offering feedstock into the market.

Blank Endorsed

A negotiable Bill of Lading in which the title to the merchandise is passed on to another party by means of an endorsement. The holder of the 'blank endorsed' Bill of Lading is entitled to take possession of the merchandise.

BLCO

Bonny Light Crude Oil. African sweet crude oil. This is crude produced in Nigeria. Two majors are the two main producers together with the Nigerian National Petroleum Company. Unfortunately many people who claim to be a trader are offering BLCO, so be careful with unknown suppliers, and look also at 'idd'.

Blender (In Tank)

A device for mixing two or more oil components to achieve a homogeneous end product. A blender in storage can be a propeller in a tank or a system where oil is pumped out of a tank in a pipeline which returns the oil back in another entry of the tank. Pumping around or homogenization.

Blender

Company that buys components and is specialized in blending those together to the required finished product. The company will make money based on blending margins. Also for a blender time is money. Blending in a contango market would generate easy money. See also 'easy money'.

Blending

Refiners can often boost the quality of straight-run refinery production, re-use 'off-spec' material and upgrade lower-quality imports by adding components. Blending occurs for all major products except liquefied petroleum gas, but is most common in gasoline as refiners seek to meet more stringent and often niche market standards. Blending is also done as part of a pure trading strategy in storage places. Traders might have access to different oil components which may be blended to create a certain specification of gasoline, diesel or fueloil. The target is to make a blending margin. It is important that the traders know the specifications of the products very well and can set value to the different parameters of the specific product to blend, i.e. Octane value, RVP value in gasoline, cold properties, flash point in gasoil or sulphur and viscosity in heavy fueloil. Also crude oil blending is possible. Tailor made blends can be created as refinery feedstock. Often the refiner likes to know what blend he gets. Blending crude in the USA is more accepted than in Europe. In Europe traders prefer to buy unblended cargoes and let the refineries capture the blending values.

Blending Economics

The potential blending margins that can be created in the market. It does also include the time value related to blending, the purchase price of components and sales price of finished products. Blending related costs such as storage rental, homogenization, inspection and financing cost are part of the blending strategy. It all fits into the big picture of blending activity. In a contango market the blending economics are generally better than in a backwardated market. However, as described earlier, it all depends on the price of the available blending components and the price at which the finished product can be sold. In bad markets traders complain about the bad blending economics. In good markets traders prefer not to tell others.

Blending Margin

Profit which is made by buying unfinished products or products with quality give-aways. By upgrading or downgrading, profit can be made if the required components are bought at the right value. The blender buys components at a price which would match economically in his blend. A gasoline with an octane specification which is much higher than the market requirements can be blended with lower octane components that are cheaper than the basis price of gasoline.

Blending Order

When blending petroleum products, it is very important to pump the different components in the right order into the tank. Most tanks are filled up from the bottom. To create a blend that is easy to make homogeneous it is important to start with the components that are most heavy in density. Lighter blending components pumped into heavy oil components commingles (blends) immediately up in the blend and becomes easily homogeneous. If you would start with light oil and add heavy oil last you would create a layered tank. Blending in the wrong order will make it more difficult to get a blend in tank homogeneous. Circulation of the oil in tank may have to be done for more than 24 hours and then again time is money. A tank is declared homogeneous when the differential in density between top and bottom is less than 11 points. A density differential of 0.0011.

Blending Plant

A facility which has no refining capability but is either capable of producing finished motor gasoline through mechanical blending or blends oxygenates with motor gasoline. A storage terminal being a specialist in blending activity, with easy access to components in the nearby markets.

Blendstock

An oil grade or component to be combined (blended) with other oil to produce a finished refined product. Often stored in smaller tanks as the final blend is done in the biggest tanks.

Bleve

Boiling liquid expanding vapour explosion. When liquid pressured gas turns into gas and starts boiling, a storage tank or transport unit might explode. In some cases gas may explode without any ignition. Consequences of a gas (LPG) explosion can have huge consequences, e.g. in 1978 a 'bleve' occurred in a truck close to a camping place in Spain. Many lives were lost. Storage and transport of gas requires quality equipment. Bleve must be avoided in the future. That is why, related to HSE, it makes the vetting of means of transport and storage units very important.

Block

Geographic area (local) in which oil exploration can be done and where licence for production of oil can be given. Countries divide the land or sea areas into small parts. Each small part may have a potential for oil or gas findings. The small part is called a block. Once oil or gas is found plans are made to produce oil. Then the block is producing under a licence number, but most often, it gets a crude or field name. Depending on quality or quantity on a block field development can easily take up to 20 years. Good capacity and valuable quality is prioritised. Field development must be worth the investment. When the price of oil is low the development of most fields is delayed. A company wants to be sure that the investment is worth the money. In volatile markets, it is therefore difficult to do a proper planning of personnel. When crude prices are lower than foreseen, projects may be delayed or even be stopped. It has a huge effect on job requirements. In addition, orders related to field projects and development are minimised. Low oil prices may be good for the economy, but for those working in the oil industry it would be a serious threat. Much more could be written about block and bidding rounds, but then we deviate too much to upstream jargon.

Block Train

All train tank cars together in one transport. Each tank car has her own loading ticket. The main ticket is the sum of all wagons together. In my days doing train operations in Europe each wagon had to be cleared at the customs. Mistakes in docs would cause big delays at the border. For inland transport like in the USA this would be easier. Train operations, especially related to documentation, can be a lot of work. It is important to get the block safe from A to B. Train systems go through civilized areas; accidents can have big consequences. Safety must take the highest priority when it concerns oil by rail transport.

BLS

Bow Loading System. Typical for shuttle tankers loading offshore crude oil. The vessels receive the oil through hoses at the front of the vessel. However, when discharging, it will pump through the manifold mid-ship like normal conventional vessels.

BO

Buyer's option. A quantity is bid or offered with a certain loading tolerance but it is in buyer's option related to the quantity (within the tolerance agreed) to load on board a vessel. FOB cargoes are assumed in seller's option as in that case the buyer is fixing the freight and logistics. However, some FOB sales may be based on seller's option, e.g. Russian crude oil supplies which are offered on FOB basis in seller's option (so).

BOEPD

See 'barrels of oil equivalent per day'.

Boiling Point

The temperature at which a substance boils, or is converted into vapour by bubbles forming within the liquid. It varies with pressure. See also 'distillation curve'. Water at 100°C / 212°F.

Boiling Range

Range which reports different percentages of oil being evaporated at certain temperatures. First drop evaporated and condensed is called initial boiling point (IBP) and the last drop of oil condensed in that list is called final boiling point FBP). See also 'distillation curve' and also 'customs classification for mineral oil'.

Refined prod.	Carb. atoms	Boil. Points	Density	Boil. Points	API
LPG/gas	C1- C4	<40°C	<0.6500	<104°F	> 86
Naphtha	C5 – C12	30°C – 200°C	0.6500 – 0.7100	86°F – 392°F	86 - 68
Light naphtha	C5 – C6	30°C – 90°C	0.6500 – 0.6700	86°F – 194°F	86 - 80
Heavy napthta	C6 – C12	90°C – 200°C	0.6700 – 0.7100	194°F – 392°F	80 - 68
Petrol/gasoline	blend	40°C – 240°C	0.7100 – 0.7800	104°F – 464°F	68 - 50
Jet	C6 – C16	150°C – 205°C	0.7750 – 0.8400	302°F – 401°F	51 - 37
Kerosene	C6 – C20	200°C – 275°C	0.8000 – 0.8600	392°F – 527°F	45 - 33
Heating	C14 – C20	200°C – 290°C	0.8000 – 0.8800	392°F – 554°F	45 - 29
Diesel/LCO	C16 – C30	200°C – 350°C	0.8000 – 0.9000	392°F – 662°F	45 - 26
Heavy fueloil	C30 – C100	>300°C	0.9000 – 1.1000	>572°F	26 - -/-3
Rest/bitumen	>C100	>350°C	>0.1100	>662°F	< -/-3

Bollinger Bands (Technical Trading)

Because standard deviation is a measure of volatility, bollinger bands adjust themselves to the market conditions. When the markets become more volatile, the bands widen (move further away from the average), and during less volatile periods, the bands move closer to the average. The tightening of the bands is often used by technical traders as an early indication that the volatility is about to increase sharply.

Bonded Petroleum Imports

Petroleum imported and entered into customs bonded storage. These imports are not included in the import statistics until they are: (1) withdrawn from storage free of duty for use as fuel for vessels and aircraft engaged in international trade; or (2) withdrawn from storage with duty paid for domestic use. It is for many people a hassle to understand the import duty system. Especially to EU and NON-EU qualified oil. I see many doc instructions with requests for certain customs documentation, which is impossible. I see people asking for EU documentation for crude when supplying into the EU. Just to explain: crude is a refinery feedstock and undergoes a process in a refinery.

Therefore, no import duties are due for crude oil when entering the EU. It is the same for naphtha used as feedstock in naphtha crackers, or straight run fueloil to a refinery. This can all be non-EU in Europe. Fueloil to a utility must be imported and have EU-qualification since that fueloil does not undergo a process. That oil is consumed by the utility in order to generate heat for steel production. In a bonded storage the customs status of the oil is well controlled and reported to the customs. What goes in must go out. Oil should not disappear without a reason. The customs will find out and fines can be severe.

Bonded Warehouses

Warehouses that are authorized by the customs for storage or manufacturing of goods on which payment of duties is deferred until the goods are removed into customs territory. These goods are not subject to duties if re-shipped to foreign points. Most storage companies have those arrangements and keep administration of the oil imports and exports. They often also arrange the customs documentation. When nominating a barge or vessel with a bonded storage terminal as destination, an excise number or EGP number must be provided in the order. In Europe transport between bonded storage places can be executed without payment of excise duties; the oil stays under control of the customs. See also 'AAD' and 'EAD'.

BO

Buyer's option. A quantity is bid or offered with a certain loading tolerance and it is in the buyer's option to nominate what quantity (within the tolerance agreed) to load on board a vessel. FOB cargoes are assumed in buyer's option as in that case the buyer is fixing the freight and logistics.

Book

The total of all forward positions held by a trader or company. Traders talk about the gasoline book, the fueloil book or the crude oil book. Also called 'trading book' or 'P&L'.

Booked

The recording of a transaction. The deal is done. "You're booked, you'd better not flake."

Book Transfer, Book Out

The transfer of title of a cash commodity to the buyer without a corresponding physical movement. Also called 'wash out'. Something which is often seen in the barge market in ARA. It even happens that a barge is sold through a chain of buyers and sellers and ends up with the first seller again. Would become a series of book outs. Related to a 'chain', see also 'daisy chain'.

Booster Station

A petrol station used to increase the pressure of oil received through a main pipeline to transmit it to the next station or terminal. It will therefore increase the pumping speed. If oil is pumped into a tank from an import line and directly pumped further through an export line to its final destination then such a tank is used as the booster station or also called a 'booster tank'.

BOPD

Abbreviation for Barrels of Oil Per Day. Can be related to crude production or refining capacity.

Bottom of the Barrel

Refers to the heavy molecule content of crude, heavy fueloil, cokes, asphalt and bitumen after cracking and coking. In some cases one would refer to the yield of the crude oil as being the bottom of the barrel.

Bottom wash

Crude oil washing operation restricted to the lower parts of the tank bulkheads, internal structures and bottom of tanks. This can only be carried out by vessels equipped with programmable tank washing machines. Crude oil washing is done to avoid crude being left on board after discharging. The operational loss must be minimised. 1,000 barrels loss on a cargo is just a small percentage and normally such small losses are generally accepted after discharging. However, the operator has the task of keeping such losses at a minimum. At 50 USD per barrel a loss of 1,000 barrels is an expensive loss and the trader will notice it in his results. A crude tanker may prepare for a COW during transport. Some crude oil is pumped into the slops tank and will be heated. The hot oil will flush the vessel tank bottoms or spray the walls. ROB, remains on board, will be zero.

Bottoms

The liquid which collects at the bottom of a vessel (tower bottoms, tank bottoms), either during a fractionating process or while in storage. Bottoms most often contain sludge and have to be seen as operational loss (not always a small financial loss). Dirty or waxy bottoms may be cleaned by flushing the tanks with gasoil. Sometimes called 'de-waxing'. When you are emptying a tank you will get the tank bottoms in the cargo – you might risk receiving sludge, water or other contaminated oil. Normally with clean oil such a problem would not arise as water contents would be drained from the tank before the start of any operation. Bottoms in crude oil vessels may be cleaned by a crude oil wash (COW). It is important that vessels do not leave too much bottoms behind. Oil losses in tank may become very expensive; oil is no longer cheap.

Bottom Wash

Crude oil washing operations restricted to the lower parts of the tank bulkheads, internal structures and bottom of tanks. This can only be carried out by vessels equipped with programmable tank washing machines. After carrying heavy or aromatic crude, lots of sludge and sediments would sink to the bottom. The vessel needs to present her clean for the next voyage. And the receiver of the oil cargoes wants all his oil if possible, as operational losses are costly.

Boutique Crude

Crude oil with special properties which are very different compared to the market standards. This type of oil could have extremely good cold properties, an extremely good yield, etc. But can also be extremely bad oil. Very heavy, very high sulphur, very high TAN and terrible yield. Either this crude is worth the benchmark plus a huge premium – but who would pay that? – or the crude is extremely bad and the question would be how much discount and who could process this? Often a matter of finding niche markets and they do exist. When a trader talks about his oil then he might call it boutique crude; it is a bit special.

Boxed

Someone who flakes on a window deal can get boxed by Platts or Argus for a certain period of time. That means that Platts or Argus would not take any deal done by the boxed company into consideration when assessments are done. A boxed company has, temporarily, no role in price setting the market. Even though each company is part of the market and you cannot rule them out for the full 100%.

BPS

Baltic Pipeline System, Transneft pipeline in Russia. There are lines to Primorsk, Ust Luga, Murmansk, Novorossiysk, Yuzhniy, Tuapse, Odessa and ESPO to Kozmino. See also 'pipeline systems'.

BPS2

The pipeline to Ust Luga is a Russian pipeline which became operational in 2012 and is called the 'BPS2'. As a result of the use of this new pipeline the pressure on Primorsk has eased a little as Primorsk's activities were already on their maximum capacity. Furthermore, supplies to the Gdansk terminal are planned to be cancelled and may have to be delivered waterborne based. Due to the new pipeline including the ESPO pipeline you could say that there is some overcapacity in Russia on the pipeline, which should give Russia some commercial advantage in logistic optimisation. See also 'pipeline systems'.

Brackish Water

Sweet-Salt water. Where river water meets salt seawater. Brackish comes from the Dutch word 'brak' (pool). When the Dutch made land, they built dikes towards the sea creating a pool ('Polder'). That water was called 'brak-water' and pumped out to the sea again. This is also why The Netherlands is called the 'Lowlands', land below sea level. Density of brackish water seems to be 1,012. See also 'BWAD, brackish water arrival draft'.

Branded

Product that is sold under a trademark owned by a refiner (or reseller in some instances) and usually affiliated with integrated or major oil firms. Branded product often carries a premium to unbranded product, since it can be sold under a branded 'flag'. Branded gasoline can be sold as unbranded product, but the reverse is not possible. Most gasoline and diesel at petrol stations is supplied based on location exchanges. Therefore the gasoline or diesel is not really branded as such. It may be called branded due to the additives in the petrol when available at the petrol station. Often only that makes a 'difference' per company as the basis specification is equal to all sellers.

Break (Technical Trading)

A swift downward move in price, breaking through technical values. Often the price would move up again to the point where the technical value was set, testing the price. If the price would come off again, the market would become bearish, prices may fall further and a new trend, a downtrend, is starting. Even though trading is not that easy as markets are more volatile than they were in the past, the rule of trading discipline needs always to be followed. See also 'discipline'.

Break-Bulk

The practice of breaking large imported cargoes into smaller, easier to handle lots. To discharge a big cargo and supply it in smaller lots to local destinations. In Rotterdam big cargoes of naphtha are discharged in storage tanks and from there it is transported by barges over the river (Rhine) to Germany. Opposite of 'make-bulk'.

Break-Even Point Analysis

Analysis of the level of sales at which a project would make zero profit and zero loss. Often when starting new oil business in new markets break-even deals are done as part of the strategy to enter a new market. By doing business more information will come in. Break-even oil trades are not that bad as long as they have the purpose of gathering market activity information and it helps as a start for development of new business aiming for profits later.

Break Out (Technical Trading)

Technical analysis term used to describe price action rising above resistance or dropping below support. Break outs may come through the continuation of an exciting natural trend, or after new bullish or bearish information has been made available to the market. After the first break out prices might go back to the support or resistance line testing the market. After testing the price level would go back to the earlier trend, then there was a false break out, or the market will find new levels and a new trend possibly after a volatile new start.

Breakwaters

Some time sheets show 'passing breakwaters' with date and time. It is the synonym for COSP, commencement of seaport, or EOSP, end of seaport. If you can picture the sea and the place where the port starts, you may see dykes or stone walls stretching out into the sea, the entrance of the port. The walls function as breakwaters, minimising strong side streams of water or sand/sludge from the sea bottom that affects draft in harbours. Saving on dredging work in harbours.

Brent

Benchmark crude oil with a standard quality, API 37.5-39 and sulphur 0.35-0.40%, which is traded in the European crude oil market (physical and paper). Qualities coming from other places in the European market can be of better quality than the Brent spec and are therefore priced at Brent plus a premium. Other qualities can be worse than Brent and will be traded at the Brent price minus a discount. Brent is a waterborne cargo market while in USA WTI is a mid-continent pipeline market. Keep in mind that the Brent price is an average of a basket of crude, a Brent blend,(BFOE).

Brent Blend

The most commonly traded North Sea crude oil. Brent has an API of about 37.5-39 and sulphur 0.35-0.40%. The blend is technically a mix of crude from the Shell UK-operated Brent field and the BP-operated Ninian field. The blend is, however, commonly referred to simply as Brent. See also 'BFOE'.

Brent B-Wave Pricing

A weighted average of Brent futures prices. This new 'B-wave' pricing formula was first adopted by Saudi Arabia in July 2000 (followed by Kuwait and, six months later, by Iran) for oil pricing in its term contract sales to Europe. It replaced the traditional dated Brent benchmark.

Brent, Forties, Oseberg, Ekofisk (BFOE)

A pricing mechanism for the Brent crude market, which allows the delivery of Forties and Oseberg as alternative grades to Brent. The system was devised by pricing service Platts in 2002 to replace the traditional Brent price index and was intended to limit manipulation of the index as liquidity dropped. With North Sea production declining the assessment of the prices quotation will become more challenging. Too little trades would make the business less liquid. A wider trading range from 21 days to 25 days is one solution, but in the long term maybe other crude should be added to the basket.

Brent Name

The name 'Brent' comes from the naming policy of Shell UK Exploration and Production, operating on behalf of ExxonMobil and Royal Dutch Shell, which originally named all of its fields after birds, in this case the 'Brent goose'.

BRIC Country

Brazil, Russia, India, China. Countries seen in the market as countries being in the same stage based on economic development. Brazil and Russia are both huge oil producing countries while India and China are processing a huge trunk of crude oil per day. The economy in these countries is growing fast and oil consumption in China and India has a particularly high impact on the oil market.

Bridge or Bridging

When, during oil negotiations, the difference between ask price and bid price are getting close, both buyer and seller need to find a common solution to agree on the deal. Often the final deal price ends up somewhere in the middle between ask price and bid price. The buyer and seller are bridging the difference, narrowing the gap between each other related to price and terms in order to conclude the deal. Bridging the gap between ask and bid.

Bright and Clear

A visual test concerning the appearance of clean oil products. It is an impossible test for dirty oil. Should be as clear as clean water. See also 'hazy'. With gasoil it can be a hassle in winter as cold temperature may bind water molecules in the oil. Bounded water in oil makes a sample hazy. If you have a sample of gasoil in your hands and you can clearly see your fingers when you look through the sample then it is a bright and clear sample. When a sample is hazy you will not have a clear view through the sample. When the sample gets a bit warmer, the haziness might turn into a bright and clear view. Often, based on that change, a cargo will be accepted as bright and clear. A real winter challenge. In refineries production is often still warm. Therefore this challenge is often seen at storage terminals where the oil has been stored for a longer period as a result of a summer to winter contango.

Broker (Physical)

Person or company who brings buyer and seller together to make a trade possible. The brokers run limited risk and receive a fee for organising the business. Most often the seller pays 10-25 cents per ton or 1-4 cents per barrel. In some markets where the parcel sizes are very small we see both the buyer and the seller paying a commission or broker fee. Often those fees are higher priced. In paper business the traded volume is much higher than the physical volume. In that paper market the broker fees should be much less.

Brokerage (Futures Related)

The brokerage is the place that clears your transactions from trading. They are like the bank. They take your money and hold it on deposit. If you make money in a day they make a deposit. If you lose money then the brokerage takes money from your account and you in essence 'lose' that money. They charge transaction fees known as commission. They assist the trader with opening accounts, opening trading platform accounts and send regular statements based on activity ordered by the trader. You can receive these statements by mail or by e-mail. If you lose too much money and the calculated risk of your position does not cover the money on your account, then you get a margin call. Either you transfer more money on your account or you liquidate your position.

Brownfield

Oilfield which has been on full production and is getting closer to the end of its lifetime. New techniques of drilling are extending the lifetime so that production keeps flowing a bit longer. See also 'tail production'.

BS&W

Bottom, Sediment and Water, usually expressed as a percentage of weight. This analysis is important for crude oil and represents the difference between gross tons and net tons of a crude cargo. In the back of this book calculations related to BS&W and loss control are described. A standard test method is used along with solvent (typically toluene) and demulsifier chemical in a 100-millilitre sample cylinder and centrifuged for 15 minutes. BS&W is just part of crude oil production and is unavoidable. At a refinery the BS&W is removed before the oil enters the column for distillation purposes. BS&W can vary between zero and one percent. If higher than one per cent, one could call the crude oil off-spec and the buyer may get a discount for compensation. Disposal of the water can be costly especially when it contains a high content of H_2S. In my mind, all crude contains some water and sediments. So on a B/L gross and net can never be equal. NB: Crude and condensate are not the same. Condensate does not often contain BS&W because it such light material. Here BS&W sinks to the bottom of the storage tanks and should not come into a cargo.

BTOB

In traders' jargon this is the abbreviation for Back TO Back. Purchase and sale have exactly the same terms. See also 'wash out'.

BTX

Benzene, toluene and xylene. A mix of chemical products which is sometimes referred to as high aromatic reformate. Before the year 2000 there were no such restrictions on benzene and aromatic content in gasoline. In those days BTX was used as gasoline blendstock. A great octane booster in that time. After BTX was banned, MTBE became more popular instead. This MTBE will be replaced by biofuels such as ETBE and ethanol. BTX is now a chemical feedstock because of the high aromatic and benzene content.

Bucketing

Directly or indirectly taking the opposite side of a customer's order into the broker's own account or into an account in which the broker has an interest, without open and competitive execution of the order on an exchange.

Budget

Estimation of expenses for a certain project or trading activity. It can be for an activity as such but one can also make yearly budgets. In trading a trader could budget certain costs for operation of an activity. Building an arbitrage cargo may be expensive. Before a trader takes a decision he would calculate the expected costs for the operation. Such costs may consist of expected shipping costs, financing costs, ship to ship operations, inspection, demurrage etc. The total of those costs is the budget he would use to calculate if his planned arbitrage business will work or not. Of course purchase price, sales price and time value are part hereof. If the total sum works and turns out to be profitable the trader will take his decision. If all operations are going well then costs might be less than budgeted. Something earned by the operator, therefore a good operator is important.

Bulk Cargo
A homogeneous cargo stowed in bulk. Liquids are always shipped in bulk. In the past, a very long time ago, oil was shipped in wooden barrels.

Bulk Sales
Wholesale sales of gasoline in individual transactions which exceed the size of a truckload. Basically all oil sales waterborne and landlocked can be considered as bulk cargoes. It was a long time ago that oil was shipped in (wooden) barrels.

Bulk Station
A facility used primarily for the storage and/or marketing of petroleum products which has a total bulk storage capacity of under 50,000 barrels and receives its petroleum products by tank car or truck. A bulk terminal is nearly the same but relates to barges, vessels and pipelines.

Bullet Tanks
Horizontal pressure tanks that are the shape of a very fat bullet. I would rather call it a cylinder placed horizontal on a gas terminal. Bullet tanks are used to store normal butane, propane, and propylene. Other gas tanks have the shape of a ball. Gas tanks are therefore pressure tanks. Normally their maximum fill is up to 85%; the remaining 15% can be considered as vapour. A bullet-tank capacity can be as little as 2 tons and up to 40 tons.

Bulk Terminal
A facility used primarily for the storage and/or marketing of petroleum products which has a total bulk storage capacity of 50,000 barrels or more and/or receives petroleum products by tanker, barge, or pipeline. A bulk station is nearly the same but relates to tank cars and trucks.

Bullish
You are bullish when you believe that the market prices are going up. Or a way of describing the trend and sentiment driving a market in which prices are rising or expected to rise. This is based on the outright prices. A contango market has a curve that goes upwards, but a contango market is caused by a weak front market. Still then the whole complex can be bullish and the outright price goes up including the forward market. What also can happen is that the front prices are rising faster than the forward market. The first

month is bullish and then it could result in the forward market getting flat and the market might even flip into backwardation. Furthermore one can be bullish based on fundamentals or technical indicators. Opposite of 'bearish'.

Bull Market

A market where prices are increasing. Bull markets can happen as a result of an economic recovery, an economic boom, or technical trading related psychology. In 2008 crude oil went up from 80 Dollars to 147 Dollars per barrel. That was an extreme uptrend and following the technical trading pattern it was a perfect trend when using Fibonacci techniques. Next level after 147 US Dollars would be a little dip based on profit taking and then back up to 157 US Dollars. But new bearish news came in the market and instead of bouncing up after the profit taking levels the trend was broken which resulted in stop loss situations. Investors started to dump their futures and oil crashed down to maybe the real value of oil and even below that level. The market sentiment changed from bullish to bearish.

Bunker

A residual fuel used as fuel for vessels usually has a high sulphur content and high viscosity. International specs could have a sulphur content of maximum 3.5% but in the near future the sulphur allowance would come down further to 1 or 0.5% but that might be in 2025. In Europe the sulphur requirement for bunkers has been set to max 0.1% since 2015. In the first edition of this book (2010) I called it a first step in the shipping market for a cleaner world. See also 'SECA'. The impact of this change is huge as refiners are very much challenged to create that quality and to avoid production of high sulphur fueloil. Gasoil is to be used to meet the sulphur specs. More demand for distillates may be good for refinery margins if a solution is found for fueloil.

Bunker Survey

Inspection activity when bunkers are supplied to a vessel. It includes quantity and quality control.

Bunkering

This expression is used in Nigeria related to theft of crude oil from pipelines, e.g. In news items (2014/2015), it has been stated, that the theft concerns roughly 60 to 100kbd of crude oil. The crude oil ends up in vessels, barges or even illegal refineries. It gets a lot of attention from the local authorities, security agents. One can imagine that with current prices of crude oil this illegal business is about an awful lot of money. Criminals just take the risk and often they look away from any safety precautions. Criminals drill holes in pipelines and tap off the oil for making illegal money – an awful and dangerous business.

Buoyant
A market in which prices have a tendency to rise easily with a considerable show of strength.

Burner-Tip
The point at which natural gas is used as a fuel. Can be used to heat a furnace at a refinery or for power generation. But can also be transported by pipeline as part of normal gas production. At least a point that the gas has a usable and valuable function.

Business Day
For futures and options contracts, business days are trading days as determined by the exchange board prior to the start of the year. On those days the exchange is open and traders are actively buying and selling. See also 'bank holidays'.

Business Inventories
In this case it is oil related. All oil, components and other related liquid goods and materials in stock. It includes commercial stocks and operational stocks.

Butane C_4H_{10}
A hydrocarbon fraction at ordinary atmospheric conditions. Butane is a gas but it is easily liquefied by storing it under pressure or by cooling it down to roughly minus 17° Celsius/62.6° Fahrenheit. See also 'LPG'. Butane is a gas and is stored in bullet tanks. Typical density is 0.6000 kg/m^3. Butane may be used for gasoline blending during wintertime, for household cooking and heating, as petrochemical feedstock and it is used as fuel for cars. With car fuel, butane is often mixed with propane, e.g. 40% butane and 60% propane in the winter and 60% butane and 40% propane in summertime. These are rough indications. Driving on gas is very popular in The Netherlands. In summertime, the percentage of butane in gasoline is roughly 4 to 5 percent and in the winter it varies between 8 and 11 percent. The percentage of butane

use depends on the RVP of other components used in gasoline. Butane is cheaper than gasoline; therefore, a refinery or blender would always try to maximize the use of butane in gasoline. However, since more bio gasoline is sold, the use of butane is limited. Ethanol is the bio-component in gasoline. Ethanol has good octane properties but it has also a high vapour pressure. Five percent ethanol increases the RVP in gasoline by roughly 7 kPa. Gasoline in Europe has a winter spec of max 90/100 kPa and a summer spec of max 60/70 kPa.

Butanising

Blending butane into a gasoline blend. In the winter the gasoline specification requires a higher vapour pressure. When it is cold a car needs a more volatile gasoline to keep the engine running. To obtain higher vapour pressure butane can be blended into the gasoline. Some refineries may have an inline blending system but a lot of storage companies have another system which makes gasoline blending with butane possible. If you would just add 300m³ butane in a tank then you create a big gas bubble in the tank. The gas will escape out of the oil as the gasoline molecules cannot hold such a big amount of gas. Therefore the butane needs to be injected into the gasoline while it is being pumped around. If the pump-around-speed is 300m³ per hour, 30m³ of butane will be injected per hour into the gasoline stream (10% of the pumping speed). Now the gasoline is able to bind the gas and hold it. Butane has some advantages. It is cheaper than gasoline, the RVP is good for wintertime, it has good octane properties and it has a low density which gives value in escalation. In the summer time butane is blended on a limited basis. Gasoline contains roughly 4% of butane in the summer specification versus roughly 8% in the winter.

Butterfly Spread (Technical Trading)

Typically used as a low risk, limited reward options strategy that is built with 4 trades with one common expiration and three different strike prices. When done in the correct way, potential upside is greater than potential downside, e.g. Buy one Oct10 80 Call + one Oct10 90 call, while selling two Oct10 85 calls. Maximum profit is achieved if the underlying market is trading around the middle price at expiration of these options (mid-October 2010). Maximum loss is realised if the underlying is trading below the lowest strike or above the highest strike at expiration.

Butylenes (C_4H_8)
An olefinic hydrocarbon recovered from refinery processes. A product which is very much wanted in the chemical industry.

Buy Low Sell High
Typical saying in trading, showing how to make money in the easiest way. More of these are to be found in the back of this book. Take a look in the back of this book at 'words of wisdom'.

Buyer
The company that is willing to pay for a certain commodity and takes title and risk of the commodity at a certain moment in time. That moment of taking over risk and title is based on the delivery terms. The buyer will be long a commodity. The reason to buy may be because of consumption or obligations for supply at a certain stage. But also in a contango situation one can buy for storage in order to hedge and cash in the value of the forward market. The other reason to buy is just to take a position. In that case the commodity needs to be sold on again, an activity with a certain risk. See also 'seller'.

Buyer's Right of First Refusal
Negotiating situations where the seller of gas has the right to solicit third-party bids for his gas, a right of first refusal provision gives the buyer of the gas the option of meeting the third party bid price and continuing the contract on such terms.

Buyer's Market
A situation in the market where there are more sellers than buyers. There is too much oil in the market and the buyer can buy at a low price. The market will get weak and as a result of that the forward curve will show a contango market. The opposite is a 'seller's market'.

Buyer's Option
Look at 'BO'.

Buying Power
The mandate a trader is holding which allows him to take positions has a lot of influence on his buying power. With high oil prices the financing of

trading may get expensive and the ability for smaller companies to trade may shrink.

BWAD

Brackish Water Arrival Draft. Some disports have draft restrictions. A receiver would like to know what a vessel's draft is at different quantities on board a vessel, e.g. a receiver of a cargo would ask for draft at BW 600kb /650kb /700kb / 750kb /800kb. In such a case the vessel must also get the API or density of the oil as draft depends on tonnage of the cargo. The draft of a ship in brackish water is bigger than the draft of the same ship in seawater and less than the draft of the same ship in fresh water. Density of brackish water is between 1.005 and 1.012. Normal water is 1.0000. Salt seawater has a density of 1.025. So therefore, draft and type of water has an impact on cargo size. If one forgets to look at this then the consequences can be severe, from vessels not able or willing to enter a port up to grounded vessel. A very costly mistake.

By-pass

Pipeline system set up in such a way that it passes a pump, valve or other system. In this case a bypass at a terminal is done on purpose for efficiency improvements. But bypassing, skipping something, can also be done with people. In trading it could be that a broker is bypassed. The buyer and the seller talk directly with each other. In the case of a broker initiating the contact in the first place, it frequently happens that after a deal is agreed the broker will get his commission anyway. It would be common sense and normal behaviour in a market where buyers, sellers and brokers have good relations. Brokers may be needed to get market information – they capture the whole market.

C

°C

Degrees Celsius. Zero degrees Celsius is the freezing point of water and 100°C is the boiling point. One litre of water weights 1 kilogram at 4°C. Celsius is the European standard for temperatures. In the oil business densities are reported at 15°C. The USA standard is degrees Fahrenheit. Densities in the USA are measured at 60°F, which is not equal to 15°C. A small correction is always to be thought of when converting crude oil Barrels at 60°F to litres at 15°C. Yes, one barrel is 158.978295 litres at 60°F. People make mistakes with that, but now it has been explained to pay attention to the conversion factor. M3@15°C times factor 6,293 is bbls.

C + F

Cost and Freight, see 'CFR'.

C/gal

Cents per gallon, the pricing of heating oil and gasoline on the Nymex.

Calcined Coke

Green coke, from a coker unit, is to be processed to calcined cokes. See 'calcining'. Calcined coke is a product which is needed to produce anodes. Those anodes are used again in the aluminium and steel industry. So the refinery production of cokes finds its way to the steel and aluminium industry. See also 'needle coke', 'sponge coke' and 'bullet coke' – these say something about the quality of the calcined coke.

Calcining
Removal of volatile hydrocarbons from the green coke. Does not remove metal or sulphur.

Calendar Spread
The purchase of one delivery month of a given futures contract and simultaneous sale of another delivery month of the same commodity in the same market (same commodity). The purchase of either a call or put option and the simultaneous sale of the same type of option with typically the same strike price but with a different expiration month. Also called 'time spread'.

Calendar Year
A period of twelve (12) consecutive months commencing with the first day of January and ending on the last day of December, both dates being inclusive, according to the Gregorian calendar. Paper trades for a full year is possible. If you would buy a 10kt fueloil swap Cal17 then you get 12 swaps of 10kt for each month in 2017. The price for each month is the same and represents the agreed price for the year. In a contango market it would look like the first few months are bought at a price level over the market while the last few months are bought at a price level below market value.

Calibration
The process of adjusting, or of measuring the performance of a device. That can be calibration of an instrument to measure specifications of oil, or equipment to measure a tank in order to perform correct quantity measurements. When a brand new tank is built, it is important that the tank is standing stable on its underground. The tank is to be filled up with water to get the tank well settled, which takes one or more days. Then the tank will be calibrated and a calibration table of the tank will be produced so that one can calculate the quantity of the tank content by the level of product measured in millimetres. That measurement will be reported in litres at actual temperature and needs therefore to be converted to the standard quantity at 15°C (L/15) /60°F.

Calibration Table
Each terminal has a calibration table of their tanks. From that table one can read the litres per millimetre in tank. The level of oil in tank measured in millimetres multiplied by the calibrated measurement is the exact volume in tank. Do not forget to correct to the standard temperature of 15°C or 60°F.

Call Option

An option which gives the buyer the right, but not the obligation, to purchase ('go long') the underlying futures contract at the strike price on or before the expiration date.

Calm Weather

Calm weather is defined as a weather condition whereby the wind is less than 10 knots and the sea state is less than 1.0 metre. The challenge here could be that oilfields supplying gaseous products get into problems since the gas stays at the platform which can be dangerous. Some wind on open sea is always welcome.

Calorific Value

The energy content of a unit quantity of fuel. There are two calorific values: the gross (high) and the net (low) calorific value. The gross value is that which is obtained when all of the products of combustion are cooled to standard conditions, and the latent heat of the water vapour formed is reclaimed. The net value is the gross value minus the latent heat of vaporisation of the water. Caloric value tells you something about the burning value and is important in gas. Heavy density gas or oil has often a better caloric value. Dutch gas has a high caloric value and the consumption system is based on that. Dutch people heat their houses with gas and heat their furnace or oven in the kitchen with gas. Norwegian or Russian gas has a lower caloric value and cannot substitute for the gas from the Dutch consumption market. It would ruin the gas-burning equipment which Dutch people use in their houses. However, the industry can use the gas with a lower caloric value. There is a price difference between the two types of caloric values, but that is obvious. Caloric value also has significance when it concerns low sulphur fuel oil supplies to utilities. Also for bunkers caloric value is important. Fewer bunkers are consumed when caloric value is high. Get quality for money and know where you buy bunkers. Also known as 'net specific energy'.

Cancelling Date

A stated date after which, if a vessel is not ready to load, the intending charterers have the option of cancelling the charter. The passing of the cancelling date leaves the owner's obligation unimpaired unless the charterer releases. Most often the owners arrange for another vessel as soon as they see that the original vessel is not able to arrive in time. The charter is often vessel name 'X' or sub. It would become costly not to load at all. Therefore it does not often happen that a charter is cancelled because of late arrival. See also 'laycan'.

Cancellation Clause

A clause in a charter party whereby the charterer reserves the right to cancel the charter if the ship fails to arrive, ready to load, on a specified date at a named port of destination. Most often the oil must be supplied because of logistic reasons and the ship and the oil are needed. Only if the charter was expensive and the market came down a new price could be discussed, certainly when prompt alternative vessels are available. Cancellation clause is linked to the laycan.

Cancellation Fee

The price that has to be paid if one decides not to use a vessel that was already booked for a voyage. The cancellation fee is registered in the charter party. See also 'charter party'. When the oil price goes down or when you find a logistic alternative you may calculate if there is value in it to cancel a charter party. It does not happen a lot. Traders buy and sell oil for a reason and need the vessel to perform the trade.

Cancelling Order

An order that will delete or cancel a previous order placed by the client.

Candlestick Chart (Technical Trading)

A candlestick chart is a style of bar-chart used primarily to describe price movements of equity over time. It is a combination of a line-chart and a bar-chart, in that each bar represents the range of price movement over a given time interval. It is most often used in technical analysis of equity and currency price patterns.

Candlesticks (Technical Trading)

A Japanese charting system which maps the open- high-low-and close of periodic price movements. A box is drawn around the open and close, and painted white or green if the close is above the open and black or red if the close is below the open. The boxes and their little heads and tails look like candles and their wicks. Candlestick studies are full of exotic terms like 'morning star' and 'dark cloud cover' – these describe how the black or red and white or green candles look, and can be interpreted as buy or sell signals.

Capacity

The maximum volume of oil that is allowed to fill up a tank. See also 'max and work capacity'. But capacity is also related to processing rate at a refinery or other processing unit. Capacity is also related to pumping speed when the discussion is based on pumping capacity on a terminal or vessel. So it is the maximum throughput volume in a refinery, or maximum speed of a pump; it relates to the maximum ability of a unit measured in time or size.

Capex

Capital expenditure. Significant cost of investment which should pay off in future. See also 'opex'.

Capital Losses

Losses resulting from selling at a loss, often in significant amounts.

Capping

Routing a vessel around the Cape of Good Hope, South Africa. A VLCC loaded in Europe on her way to Asia has no other choice as she is too big for the Suez Canal. The good thing about capping compared with sailing through the Suez Canal is that there is a low chance of piracy. For smaller vessels the Northern sea route to ship a cargo to Asia could be considered too. It saves approximately 10 days of sailing plus less use of bunkers and it is therefore a cheaper solution than capping. See also 'Northern sea route'.

Captive Refinery MTBE Plants

MTBE (methyltertiary butyl ether) production facilities primarily located within refineries. These integrated refinery units produce MTBE from fluid cat cracker isobutylene with production dedicated to internal gasoline blending requirements. Most MTBE plants are based in chemical terminals. Due to the bio-fuel development most plants are converting their unit to ETBE (ethyl tertiary butyl ether) production.

CARB Diesel

CARB stand for 'California Air Resources Board'. It is a diesel which refers to the standard mandated specifications as set by this board. The challenges in this quality of diesel are the sulphur and very low aromatics. California is known as a heavy traffic area in the USA with smog challenges. These requirements are therefore very much needed. This CARB diesel is the cleanest one in the USA lowering the exhaust of sulphur dioxide, particular matter and oxides of nitrogen (NOx).

CARBOB
California reformulated blendstock for oxygenate blending. Not finished gasoline but it does not take much to blend this to consumer quality grade gasoline.

Carbon Dioxide (CO_2)
A naturally occurring greenhouse gas in the atmosphere, concentrations of CO_2 which have increased (from 280 parts per million in preindustrial times to over 350 parts per million today) as a result of humans burning coal, oil, natural gas and organic matter (e.g. wood and crop wastes). International programmes have been set up to reduce the exhaust of CO_2. A market trading in CO_2 tickets was formed. As a result of further economic growth in the world the concerns related to CO_2 are very serious. Cleaner fuel and efficient car engines are being continuously developed. See also 'CO_2 tickets'.

Cargo
Oil loaded into a ship. A crude cargo or gasoline cargo on board the vessel. A B/L represents a cargo on board the vessel. Physical oil traders buy and sell cargoes for local supplies and arbitrage opportunities. Cargo trading involves hedging activity on the paper market as well in order to minimise risk or locking in a profit.

Cargo Manifest
Document that lists in detail all the Bills of Lading issued by a carrier or its agent or master for a specific voyage. A detailed summary of the total cargo of a vessel. Used principally for customs purposes. See also 'LOI', letter of indemnity.

Cargo Plan
A plan giving the quantities and description of the various grades carried in the ship's cargo tanks. It is important for the captain of a vessel to know what he loads and in which order, but also where he has to discharge and which

parcel has to go out first. The charterer wants to maximise the use of the ullage when loading different grades on a vessel. From all that information the cargo plan is made and then it has to be agreed with the charterer.

Cargo Segregation

When more than one grade of oil is planned for loading on a vessel, the owner or the captain will show how his plans are on board the vessel to place the different qualities on board. Based on the different possibilities to load the different cargoes the charterer will choose the segregation that is the best way to optimise freight. The charterer prefers to utilise the capacity as best as possible in order to avoid deadfreight. The final decision on how to segregate the grades on board the vessel becomes the 'cargo plan'. As result of cargo segregating on board the vessel, the maximum capacity cannot always be 100% utilised. The transport of segregated cargoes is therefore a bit more expensive per ton or barrel.

Cargo Tracking

Following and registering of cargo flows in a certain market. For oil trading it is important to understand the flow of products in the market where they operate. Cargoes are followed from producer to trader and so on until the cargo reaches the refinery or other final destination. It gives a picture of the crude flow, it gives information about the market participants and in the short term one can see what the availability of oil is during the next few days or weeks to come. It shows if the market is tight or not. This information is important for price setting the market by the trader through offering and bidding on cargoes. Cargo tracking is mainly done in the crude market.

Carriage Temperature

Temperature of oil in cargo during transport. Important to know as heavy oil must be heated to stay liquid for pumping purposes. See also 'hot oil'.

Carrier

Any person who, in a contract of transportation, undertakes to perform, or to procure at his own responsibility the performance of transportation by rail, road, sea, air, inland waterway or by a combination of such modes.

Carrying Broker
A member of a futures exchange, usually a clearinghouse member. A broker who helps another broker and gets a fee for that.

Carryover
Commodities not consumed during the marketing year and remaining in storage at the end of a period. These stocks are 'carried over' into the next marketing year. Most oil companies prefer to limit the oil in stock at the year end. Oil is highly priced and it does not look good in the balance sheet of an oil company. As a result of that oil markets may be difficult to trade at year end. There will be good opportunities to buy cheap distressed cargoes from companies which prefer low stock at the year end.

Carry Trade
A trade that consists of borrowing and paying interest in order to finance the purchase of an investment that pays a greater interest or a dividend stream.

Cash and Carry
An arbitrage transaction involving the simultaneous purchase of a cash commodity with borrowed money and the sale of the appropriate futures contract.

Cash Commodity
The actual physical commodity as distinguished from the futures contract. Also referred to as 'actuals'.

Cash in Advance (CIA)
Payment for goods in which the price is paid in full before the shipment is made. This type of payment is usually only made for very small shipments. May be done by companies who prefer to avoid spending money on an L/C or if a company is not able to issue an L/C. Such payment must be done before change of title of the cargo. A payment is declared done and accepted when the bank of the receiver confirms receipt of the amount. A Statement from the bank of the buyer that the money is paid is more to be seen as information which helps tracking the money. Also referred to as 'pre-payment'.

Cash Market
A place where people buy and sell the actual oil products like at the ARA

85

barge market. Barges are traded in the prompt market up to 3 weeks in time. That is where the real price of petroleum products for today is set. The price quotations which are reported next morning by Platts and Argus are also used for setting the prices at the petrol stations. These prices are also the basis for setting the crack values, the refinery margins. For a lot of refiners it is therefore important to be a participant in the market. If it were not for the purpose of price setting, the activity of many refiners, wholesalers, blenders and traders to create a transparent and liquid market is of significant importance as well. But of course they are also involved to make money and to market their production or for the fulfilment of supply obligations to the market where the consumer is the final receiver of the oil.

Cash Settlement

A method of settling certain futures or options contracts whereby the market participants settle in cash (rather than delivery of the oil). Most futures positions are liquidated before the futures contract expires. In the case that you still have your futures contract after the expiry date you must take delivery or you must deliver. In case you are not able to do so, you need to cash settle the contract. If a real physical oil trader is involved in the cash settlement than the settlement might be at a cost as the oil company may have wanted or was able to supply the oil. So better avoid the trouble of cash settlements if you do not like the molecules, the physical cargo. Roll your futures position in time, well before the futures market expires. See 'rolling position'.

Catalyst

Substances in a unit which causes, on purpose, a chemical reaction of the feedstock in order to upgrade the oil. The catalyst – the substances itself – does not become part of the produced quality of oil. We see the catalyst back in the fluidic catalytic cracking process of residual fuel stocks. Particle size can range from sub-micron to greater than sixty (60) microns. These particles become more common in the higher viscosity marine bunker fuels.

Catalytic Cracking

Cracking using catalysts to break molecules and restructure hydrocarbons. Heavy oils are, by this process, converted to lighter products such as kerosene, gasoline, liquefied petroleum gas (LPG), heating oil and naphtha. As well as the use of the catalyst, heat and pressure are needed to break the heavy molecules into lighter fractions. Also called the 'cat cracker'. VGO or straight run fueloil can be the feedstocks. One of the products produced from this system is called 'full range cat cracked naphtha' which is one of the most important blendstocks for gasoline.

Catalyst Coke

In many catalytic operations (e.g. catalytic cracking) carbon is deposited on the catalyst, thus deactivating the catalyst. The catalyst is reactivated by burning off the carbon, which is used as a fuel in the refining process. This carbon or coke is not recoverable in a concentrated form. On average, once evert four years the cracker units need maintenance. I have been standing in a cracker unit during such maintenance once. The wall was covered in a layer of 3 to 4 centimetres of coke. It had to be hammered off. One can imagine then that such maintenance is needed to keep the refinery process in the most optimal way. A dirty catalyst will reduce the throughput of a refinery which can be very costly when refinery margins are good.

Catalytic Hydro-Cracking

A refining process that uses hydrogen and catalysts with relatively low temperatures and high pressures for converting middle boiling or residual material to high-octane gasoline, reformer charge stock, jet fuel, and/ or high grade fueloil. The process uses one or more catalysts, depending upon product output, and can handle high sulphur feedstock without prior desulphurisation.

Catalytic Hydro-Treating

A refining process for treating petroleum fractions from atmospheric or vacuum distillation units (e.g. naphthas, middle distillates, reformer feeds, residual fueloil, and heavy gasoil) and other petroleum (e.g. cat cracked naphtha, coker naphtha, gasoil, etc.) in the presence of catalysts and substantial quantities of hydrogen. Hydro treating includes desulphurisation, removal of substances (e.g. nitrogen compounds) that deactivate catalysts, conversion of olefins to paraffins to reduce gum formation in gasoline, and other processes to upgrade the quality of the fractions.

Catalytic Reforming

In this process, the main issue is to reform low octane naphthas into higher-octane naphthas, but also reformate is produced from the processing unit. Due to that process reformate may contain high contents of aromatics and benzene. The reformer is clearly linked to production of components for the gasoline pool. A refining process using controlled heat and pressure with catalysts to rearrange certain hydrocarbon molecules, thereby converting paraffinic and naphthenic type hydrocarbons (e.g. low-octane gasoline boiling range fractions) into petrochemical feedstock and higher-octane stocks suitable for blending into finished gasoline. Catalytic reforming is reported in two categories. They are:

- **Low Pressure**
  A processing unit operating at less than 225 pounds per square inch gauge (PSIG) measured at the outlet separator.

- **High Pressure**
  A processing unit operating at either equal to or greater than 225 pounds per square inch gauge (PSIG) measured at the outlet separator.

Cat Cracker
See 'catalytic cracking'.

Catfeed
Feedstock to a catalytic cracker, usually vacuum gasoil or straight run fueloil.

Cavern
Storage capacity under the surface in a rock underground. On the bottom of a cavern there is a water layer (waterbed). As oil is lighter than water it is impossible that oil would leak into the ground. If the water level in the cavern is too high then the water will have to be removed and cleaned. Caverns are most often much bigger than tanks. The size of a cavern can easily go up to 5 million barrels or more. Heating of oil in a cavern is done by the use of heat exchangers. Products such as crude oil, fueloil, gasoil, gasoline, kerosene and naphtha can be stored in a cavern. The gasoline in the cavern should in that case not contain oxygenates such as MTBE and/or ethanol, as the waterbed in the cavern would absorb oxygenates out of the gasoline, which affects the octane number of the gasoline. Also, water mixed with MTBE cannot be cleaned at low cost. You find caverns in Scandinavia where the coastline is very rocky. But also in other places, such as in USA and Asia, caverns would be available.

CBM/15

1,000 litres at a temperature of 15° Celsius/60° Fahrenheit. If products are getting warmer the volume becomes bigger. This can have an effect on logistics when a tank or vessel is meant to be pumped as full as possible. A cubic metre at 15° Celsius/60° Fahrenheit is, in the oil business, the standard for calculating cubic metres to metric tons.

CBA

Cost-Benefit Analysis.

CBG

Cleaner Burning Gasoline.

CBOB

Conventional Blendstock for Oxygenate Blending (gasoline production). Blendstock intended for blending with oxygenate; thereafter, when it meets all required specifications, it is conventional (normal) gasoline. Reformulated gasoline (RFG) burns cleaner than CBOB.

CCR

Cargo Control Room. Typically at a refinery or oil terminal, open 24 hours. People work in shifts. Lots of pumps and systems can be started and stopped in the control room. The control room is what most people call 'the heart of the terminal'. In addition to stop- and start-pumping the quality of oil can be monitored. Communication with planning departments and inspectors comes from here. Good ideas and logistic optimisation can also be generated at that place. Therefore, here work people that deserve attention – sometimes a trader needs a favour, especially related to late changes in planning. Be friends with the terminal people, as they are also involved in performing the contract from a trader.

CCR

Fueloil spec. Conradson Carbon Residue. This number indicates the effects in an engine as result of the forming of carbon deposits. A high CCR causes problems in the engine of a vessel in the long term. Carbon residue is the percentage of coked material remaining after a sample of fueloil has been exposed to high temperatures.

CDU
Crude Distillation Unit, also atmospheric distillation unit or primary distillation.

Celsius
Europeans' use of reporting the temperature. Physicist Anders Celsius developed a temperature reference that uses the freezing (zero) and boiling point of water (100°C) as references, 0°C - 100°C. USA uses Fahrenheit with 32°F as freezing point and212° F as boiling point.

Centigrade
Temperature based on 0°C for the temperature at which water freezes and 100°C for the temperature at which water boils. Europeans do not accept this term for Celsius. This term is accepted and used in North American chemical textbooks, so which term you use may depend on your location, but both are abbreviated with a degree symbol and capital C, so at least you now know what it means.

CEPS
Sourced from the CEPS website: Central Europe Pipeline System, a NATO pipeline used by the industry for jet supplies from refineries to airports. The CEPS pipeline network (with a total length of 5,100 kilometres) spreads across Belgium, The Netherlands, Luxembourg, Germany and France and connects, amongst others, six European deep sea ports (Antwerp, Ghent, Rotterdam, Le Havre, Dunkerque, and Fos) with military airports in Central Europe for the supply of kerosene. Furthermore, the airports Zaventem (Brussels), Bierset (Liège), Schiphol (Amsterdam), and those of Cologne and Frankfurt are connected to CEPS. The CEPS line is mainly used for the transportation of kerosene but certain sections of the network are also available for diesel, naphtha and gasoline shipments. See also 'NATO pipeline'.

Certificate of Origin
Certificate issued by the Chamber of Commerce in the country of origin. Often these documents may be used to get a discount on import duties in the country of destination. Once the product is mixed with another product the origin is lost. A certificate of origin is sometimes related to a Form-A or Eurl customs document.

Cetane

A paraffinic hydrocarbon used as an additive in diesel fuel.

Cetane Index

The cetane index is an indication of ignition quality in diesel. Regular diesel generally has a cetane number of 40-45, while most premium cetane has numbers of 45-50.

Cetane No. Improver

The cetane number of a gasoil gives an indication of the ignition quality. A relatively low cetane number can be a cause for incomplete combustion of the fuel, resulting in higher emissions and 'knocking' diesel engines. With the cetane no. improver a more steady combustion quality can be achieved.

CFD

Contracts For Differences, basically a crude paper swap based on short time periods, a week. Price is crude dated related. A tool to hedge crude and lock in a small timing difference. CFD timings are available as from 1 week after dated crude up to 6 weeks after dated crude. After those six weeks the market uses Brent futures for hedging purposes. With a CFD as hedging tool one can also hedge a couple of cents result when you buy on 5 days pricing window and sell on a 3 day pricing window in a backwardated market. So every cent counts in trading crude and again 'time is money'.

CFPP

Cold Filter Plugging Point measured in temperature. It is an important property for diesel meant to control the forming of ice crystals in diesel when the weather is cold outside. Diesel in an engine goes through a filter and ice crystals could block the filter so that a car engine would stop. During winter periods the requirement for CFPP can be minus 21° Celsius/5.8° Fahrenheit while in summer time the requirement can be minus 3° Celsius/26.6° Fahrenheit. Diesel winter and summer specifications are different based on so called 'cold properties'.

CFR

Cost of FReight included. The seller is chartering the transport at his account. Of course these costs are incorporated in the sales price. Even though the seller charters the vessel, it is the buyer who has title and risk of the cargo on board. B/L quantity is the invoiced quantity. If you buy on CFR basis you should not forget the insurance part of the job.

Change of Risk and Title

The moment when oil in transport changes ownership from seller to buyer. The moment of change of risk and title depends on the type of contract or agreed term of delivery. Some companies prefer to change risk and title as late as possible. In that way they reduce the risk of having their company name attached to any damage or potential accident or disaster like an oil spill. The one having the title on the products will be in the newspaper when things go wrong. See also 'INCO terms'.

Channel (Technical Trading)

A channel in which prices are moving. Parallel trend lines are drawn along the lows and highs of a price chart, forming a channel in which prices move. The trend lines form areas of support and resistance. Depending on the trend, the channel can be a down channel or an up channel.

Chapter

The bankruptcy code is organised into chapters. Except for chapter 12, the chapters of the present code are all odd-numbered. Chapters 1, 3, and 5 cover matters of general application. Chapter 7 is liquidation (business or non-business). Chapter 9 is municipality bankruptcy. Chapter 11 is reorganisation. Chapter 12 is family farm debt adjustment. Chapter 13 is wage-earner or personal (non-business) reorganisation. So now and then the oil business sees companies landing in chapter 11. Credit risk is significantly increased and actions are taken to reduce risk. Open credit might disappear and business may continue on an L/C related basis. Companies in chapter 11 have a chance of surviving after reorganisation in order to get a healthy balance sheet.

Characteristics

Some traders talk about the typicals of crudes and others about the characteristics of crude. They both mean the same. The quality, the yield or specification of crude and/or petroleum products.

Charge Capacity

The input (feed) capacity of the refinery processing facilities.

Charterer

The company or person given the use of the vessel for the transportation of a cargo for a specified time for a specified voyage.

Charter Disponent Owner

Charterer who has sublet the vessel and is acting as the owner as per the terms of the contract.

Charter Party

A document of contract, or agreement, by which a ship-owner agrees to lease, and a charterer agrees to hire, an entire ship, or all or part of the cargo space to carry a cargo for an agreed sum under certain conditions. In the charter party the commercial terms such as price, demurrage clauses, fees, laycan etc. are mentioned. In many companies, shipping departments negotiate the charter party. Would be good for a trader or operator to have read and understood a charter party.

Charter Party Differential

Price differential for sailing to another port than the basis destination to which the product has been sold, e.g. Gasoline sold based on delivery to Rotterdam, gets destination Antwerp. The extra cost for sailing to another port is fixed in the charter party or can be requested by the vessel owner. The differential becomes part of the commercial invoice to the buyer of the cargo. See also 'final price'.

Charter Rates

The market prices for chartering a vessel with a certain tonnage for a clean or dirty oil cargo. Traders like to be updated about those prices on a daily basis. Charter rates, given in worldscale, would be used to calculate netback prices and arbitrage opportunities. Rates may be available in terms of worldscale and prices per ton. That depends on the size of the cargo. I see in Europe more often a freight price in tons for products. Related to crude oil I see more often the use of worldscale. A freight price can also be offered as a lumpsum, one amount and all included.

Charter, To Fix a Charter

To reach final agreement on the terms of a charter party. When the trader indicates that he might need a vessel, the charterer, the oil company's shipping department, would first search for a cheap vessel and then take the vessel on subs. Thereafter the trader would know the available price and based on that he would commit to a trade. The vessel will be presented to the seller of the oil and this will start the approval process. If the vessel is not approved action needs to be taken. Is it a missing document or is it just not a good vessel? If the vessel is not approved an alternative vessel has to be found and the same process repeated until an acceptable vessel is found. When the vessel is approved the charterer can lift subs and the charter is fixed. A vessel approval depends on the vetting status at a company. In some cases a vetting approved vessel is refused as a result of technical reasons related to the receiving terminal or because of jetty restrictions such as draft.

Charter Types

• **Contract of Affreightment (COA)**
A service contract under which a ship owner agrees to transport a specified quantity of fuel products or specialty products, at a specified rate per ton between designated loading and discharge ports. This type of contract differs from a spot or consecutive voyage charter in that no particular vessel is specified. Rates are usually discounted below other forms of contracts. The vessel can be different from time to time. It is most often a vessel coming from the owner's fleet. You can have access to a number of performing vessels with a minimum required capacity. Some vessels may have overcapacity. This would make further freight optimization possible.

• **Period Charter**
Refers to consecutive voyage (C/V) exceeding four voyages, time charters (T/C) and bareboat charters. Often cheaper than 4 single spot freights.

• **Spot (Voyage) Charter**
A charter for a particular vessel to move a single cargo between specified loading port(s) and discharge port(s) in the immediate future. Contract rate (spot rate) covers total operating expenses such as port charges, bunkering, crew expenses, insurance, repairs, and canal tolls. The charterer will generally pay all cargo-related costs. Shipping departments in major companies fix the vessels. This freight market is a transparent market. In no time all competitors can see what cargo you might be planning to move.

- **Time Charter (T/C)**
  A charter for varying periods of time, usually between two and ten years, under which the owner hires out the vessel to the shipper fully manned, provisioned, stored and insured. The charterer is usually responsible for bunkers, port charges, canal tolls and any crew overtime connected with the cargo. The charter rate (hire) is quoted in terms of a cost per day or month per deadweight ton, excluding the use of bunkers and harbour dues etc. You control every movement of the vessel. Perfect for freight optimisation, but you have to be sure that there is enough work. In some cases, you can make your vessel available for third party voyages. It is to avoid having a vessel doing nothing or some additional income can be earned, due to high freight prices in the market.

Charting (Technical Trading)
The use of graphs and charts in the technical analyses of futures markets to plot price movements, volume, open interest or other statistical indicators of price movement. The most easy tool is to draw trend lines. However techniques such as Fibonacci, ABC theory, doji, morning stars etc. are very popular to look at in order to create an expectation for the next price movements.

Charts (Technical Trading)
Charts are used by 'chartists' to track market action. Chartists believe that prior action of the security's price as denoted on the chart gives useful clues as to the future price performance. Charts can be the 'ticker' or a longer term chart. Each technical trader is able to read something from his charts and take decisions which are not influenced by fundamentals. Maybe a technical trader thinks twice when huge events that affect the economy are happening. Important fundamental changes may change trends.

Cherry-Picking
Granting special treatment to large or desirable customers at the expense of small or undesirable customers. Can apply to any commercial activity in which product or service providers find it unprofitable to offer equal treatment for all customers.

Chlorides/Salt
Salt compound which may appear in crude oil and could cause troubles for refining. A refinery wants straight run material or 100% crude in their unit.

Salt is not wanted but cannot be avoided. Chloride in crude can cause severe corrosion in the refinery units. Often there is a maximum limit of chloride content that a refinery allows in the crude to be processed. In crude there are different types of chlorides or salts: sodium chloride, magnesium chloride and calcium chloride.

Choice of Law, Arbitrage Court
When trades are committed it is also important to agree on which law and court for arbitration the business is done. In Europe it is most common to use English law and arbitration in a London court. However, Russian producers require their own law and arbitrage in Moscow. It is important that both buyer and seller agree. Just make sure that your contracts department is able to handle your choice in case it is needed. Most companies do have guidelines for that. Arbitration in a less safe area, e.g. Lagos, Nigeria could cause problems.

Churning
Excessive trading that results in the broker deriving a profit from commissions while disregarding the best interest of the customers.

CIF
Cost, insurance and freight charges for shipping products. This INCO term refers to a sale in which the buyer agrees to pay a unit price that includes the free on board (FOB) value at the port of origin plus all costs of insurance and transportation. This type of transaction differs from a 'delivered' agreement in that it is generally ex-duty, and the buyer accepts the quantity and quality at the loading port rather than paying for quality and quantity as determined at the unloading port. Risk and title are transferred from the seller to the buyer at the loading port, although the seller is obliged to provide insurance in a transferable policy at the time of loading. If the quality on board the vessel is off-spec then the buyer has to realise that he has title on the product and so the quality on board is basically the buyer's problem, unless the supplier made the failure during loading. Therefore it is important to use an inspector during operations.

Circle-out
See 'wash out' or 'book transfer'.

Circulate, Oil

Making a tank homogeneous by pumping the oil out of tank through the low suction of the tank and pumping the oil back through the high suction of the tank. By pumping oil around it will be well blended. Most often this way of making a homogeneous blend is done with low flash oil, like gasoline. High flash oil may be homogenised by blowing air through the oil, like fueloil or gasoil. See also 'tank' and the tank drawing.

CIS Countries

Commonwealth of Independent States. Former Soviet Union. Countries are: Russia, Ukraine, Kazakhstan, Belarus, Azerbaijan, Uzbekistan, Latvia, Estonia, Georgia, Lithuania, Armenia, Tajikistan, Kyrgyzstan, Turkmenistan and Moldova. The CIS countries are organised and try to cooperate and agree on regulations. Their website is www.cos.minsk.by. The market would speak about FSU, Former Soviet Union, which will stay the jargon for now. However, the definition 'CIS countries' is getting better known in the market, more than 20 years since it was founded.

Claim

When you are in breach of the contract there may follow an official request or strong requirement for a financial compensation for suffered damage as a result of non-performance by the buyer or seller. Demurrage rates are often agreed in the contract, demurrage is not always a non-performance according to contract. A sinking vessel, consequences of late arrival, off-spec oil or contamination can be noticed as non-performance of a contract. Costs are made as a consequence of that and money will be claimed. If both parties disagree about the claim and no commercial solution can be found, then the case may become a court case; arbitration is also a solution. See also 'AAA' and 'LCIA'.

Clarifier

Machines used for a liquid-sludge separation in which the particles with a higher specific gravity are separated from the lower specific gravity of the liquid. Basically a water treatment system used on oil terminals.

Classification Crude (Density)

Crude oil is known as sweet and sour and valuated based on that. Also density is important. It indicates a yield expectation. Light crude often has a better value than heavy crude.

- **API <20** is extra heavy crude
- **API >20 - <28** is heavy crude
- **API >29 - <40** is medium crude
- **API > 40 - <50** is light crude
- **API > 50** is condensate

Classification of Petroleum and Crude Oil (Flash Point)

Classes A-C of petroleum are considered flammable and have a flash point of 80°F/28°C or below. Examples of these classes range from very light naphtha (Class A) to crude oil (Class C).

Class D cargoes such as kerosene and heavy crudes are considered combustible and have a flash point above 80°F / 28°C but below 150°F / 65°C.

Class E cargoes are gasoil (diesel and heating oil), heavier fueloil and lubricating oil and have a flash point above 150° F / 65° C.

In the past oil was classified as 'K1' flashpoint <28° C, 'K2' flashpoint >28°C <55° C, and 'K3' flashpoint >55°C. Even though k1/k2/k3 is a classification from the past, the market is still talking about these in relation to logistics. That is a result of the strength of business jargon.

Clean Ballast

Ballast contained in cargo tanks that got 'crude oil washing' treatment. The clean ballast water may be discharged into sea if it meets specific Marpol requirements. See also 'COW'.

Clean Bill of Lading

A receipt for goods issued by a carrier that indicates that the goods were received in apparently good order and without damage.

Clean Cargo

Refined products such as kerosene, gasoline, home heating oil, and jet fuel carried by tankers, barges, and tank cars. All refined products except bunker fuels, residual fueloil, asphalt, and coke. Opposite of dirty oil.

Clean Fuel

Fuels which have lower emissions than conventional gasoline and diesel. Refers to alternative fuels as well as to reformulated gasoline and diesel. Here clean is referring to 'environmental friendly'.

Clean Letter of Credit

Letter of Credit that calls for presentation of nothing more than a draft to trigger payment. This term is sometimes used incorrectly to mean a 'standby Letter of Credit with all documents presented correctly'.

Clean on Board

Oil delivered on a vessel without any contamination with other oil from the terminal where the vessel loads or from any clingage of the vessel itself. Good inspection during loading is required. Very much related to the clean Bill of Lading.

Clean Ship

Refers to tankers that have their cargo tanks free of traces of dark persistent oil that remains after carrying crude and heavy fueloil. A clean ship is either emptied from clean products or it has been cleaned properly. Some charterers and/or owners may have the requirement that the last three cargoes on board the vessel were clean cargoes.

Clearing a Trade

The process by which a clearing house clears all executed trades. In order to settle prices at the end of each trading day, the clearing house must match all buys to all sells. Once an executed buy is matched to an executed sell and the respective accounts are debited or credited, the transaction – the trade – is said to be 'cleared'.

Clearance Request (Vessel)

Request from a vessel charterer to receivers of the cargo to accept the vessel. The buyer of the cargo may ask his customer or the terminal for acceptance of the vessel. Each company has different HSE Standards and requirements at disport. If the vessel complies with all requirements then the vessel is cleared. A vessel is not only checked on an HSE basis, the vessel must also comply with the technical fit of the terminals where its loading or discharging. Attention is given to draft, air-draft, length overall and manifold placement, including how high or low the vessel is when full or empty. A request for clearance most often includes a Q88 of a vessel. When a vessel is not approved, the charterer may supply more related documentation in order to get it approved by a vetting department. In the case that a vessel is too old or does not technically fit in the discharge or loading port, then a new vessel has to be chartered or put on subs and cleared again. When a vessel is approved the charterer may lift subs and the vessel is booked. One cannot say afterwards that the vessel cannot be of use as in such a case a cancellation fee can be due. Sometimes an oil cargo is sold in a chain of many buyers and sellers. The final receiver has to send the clearance request through the whole chain until it reaches the supplier of the cargo. For the companies in the chain, they bought and sold on, the clearance is easy to do. They just have 'flash-title' of the cargo and will in most cases just accept the vessel. In some cases a company within the chain tries to contact the real supplier direct, but the supplier can only approve a vessel when he gets a vessel request from his direct counterparty. Many emails later and often lots of vessels are cleared for the cargo. A hectic situation in such special cases. It happens a lot with benchmark crudes like Fortis or Ekofisk which are traded because they are important for the dated Brent quotations. See also 'flash-title' and 'vetting'.

Clearing House

An agency or separate corporation of futures exchange that is responsible for settling trading accounts, collecting and maintaining margin monies, regulating delivery and reporting trade data. The clearing house becomes the buyer to each seller (and the seller to each buyer) and can assume responsibility for protecting buyers and sellers from financial loss by assuring performance on each contract. The good thing here is that you never run into credit risk, but you may get a margin call when your position starts losing too much money and your account does not cover such loss.

Clearing Margin

A margin posted by a member of a clearing house.

Clearing Member

A member of an exchange clearing house responsible for the financial commitments of its customers. All trades of a non-clearing member must be registered and eventually settled through a clearing member.

Clearport

In Europe lots of paper business is done by using Clearport, like diesel, gasoline and fueloil swaps. When using Clearport there is no need to worry about the credit terms. Flexible clearing services for the global OTC markets. CME Clearport is a comprehensive set of flexible solutions for decreasing counterparty risk in OTC trading. Launched in 2002 to provide centralised clearing services and decrease risk in the energy marketplace, today CME Clearport clears transactions across multiple asset classes around the world. With OTC clearing through CME Clearport, you can conduct business off-exchange, and gain the advantages of security, efficiency and confidence. (Source: CME Group website.)

Clingage

The residue that adheres to the inside surface of a ship's tank or shore tank, after it has been emptied. Often caused by thick and /or paraffinic oil. After too much clingage a vessel may have to be cleaned although the next trip with a light crude oil condensate may solve the sticky oil on the walls. Then that vessel will discharge a plus the B/L plus the dissolved oil in the ship. Clingage may cause oil losses when discharging a vessel – for sure when it is the vessel's maiden trip. ROB measurement is important for the supplier as well as for the receiving terminal, which is reporting oil in stock and often gets the blame for the oil loss.

Close, The

The period at the end of the trading session, officially designated by the exchange, during which all transactions are considered made 'at the close'. The close of the market is often also used as time bar for decision taking or performance requirement. A decision to be taken by COB, close of business. See also 'COB'.

Closed Gauging System

A method of obtaining measurements of the tank contents without opening the tank. This may be accomplished by using automatic tank gauges or by taking measurements through a pressure/vapour lock standpipe. This type of gauging is done extensively on vessels with inert gas systems. Measurements can be read from the screens in the control room of the terminals or vessels. Monthly measurement reporting is often done by taking a print out of the tank screens in the control room of a storage company. One cannot expect an inspector to climb up 20 or more tanks in one night at month end.

Closed Trades

Positions that have been either liquidated or offset. The result of that trade is then realised. In physical trading a trade may be considered closed after all final bills and claims are settled. The trade may be closed but the real final result will be known later. Claims and demurrage deductions from earlier reported results always come months later as a big surprise. A good operator has control over the logistics and may be able to find ways to avoid problems and demurrage.

Close Out

Finalising a transaction by making an equal and opposite trade to an open position. Often back to back with a price difference. After closing out the trade turns into a closed trade.

Closing Price

The last price paid for a futures contract on any trading day. Settlement prices are used to determine open trade equity, margin calls and invoice prices for deliveries. Also called 'settlement price'.

Closing Range

A range of prices at which futures transactions took place during the close of the market. The last differential between bid and ask at market on close.

Cloud Point

The temperature at which a fuel, when cooled, begins to congeal and take on a cloudy appearance due to bonding of paraffin. Cloud point is one of the cold properties in diesel. See also 'CFPP'.

Cloud-Point-Improvers

The cloud point of a gasoil is the temperature at which the first paraffin-precipitation can be observed. In order to lower the cloud point of a gasoil normally a blend with kerosene (containing no paraffin) is made to comply with the required characteristics. In the winter, one prefers to avoid diesel filters in cars being full with ice crystals. A car may stand still, a consequence of a filter being saturated. Therefore, the requirements for a low cloud point in winter are stronger than in summer. Cloud-point relates to CFPP, cold filter plugging point. Additives are used as cloud point improvers. A laboratory calculates how much additive is required to be blended in a tank with diesel. This advice is given in ppm: e.g. Add 300 ppm (vol.) Paraflow in tank 0301.

CNG
Compressed Natural Gas, an automotive fuel. Cleaner for environment compared with gasoline, diesel or LPG as it may be mixed with biogas.

CN Number
Customs Number. Product code that is linked to customs regulations for import duty calculation and excises. A Non-EU fueloil with customs code 27.10.19.64 has an import duty rate of 3.5%, while a Non-EU fueloil with customs code 27.10.19.51 is free of import duties. As an operator or trader you need to be aware of the various products you import into the European Union. See also 'nomenclature'. From time to time these codes are changed as that follows international market developement and changes of environmental requirements. E.g. Due to sulphur restrictions for fueloil and gasoil the codes for these commodities were changed based on sulphur levels.

COA
Contract Of Affreightment. A service contract under which a ship owner agrees to transport a specified quantity of fuel products or specialty products, at a specified rate per ton between designated loading and discharge ports. This type of contract differs from a spot or consecutive voyage charter in that no particular vessel is specified. Rates are usually discounted below other forms of contracts. However, the owner will offer a pool of performing vessels with a minimum required size. The owner could also present a vessel which is too big, but in that case the deadfreight is for the owner's account. If a vessel is presented which is bigger than the required size, there may be an opportunity to optimise the logistics and load a bigger cargo than originally planned. The owner and the charter can benefit from that optimisation.

Coal
A readily combustible black or brownish-black rock whose composition, including inherent moisture, consists of more than 50 percent by weight and more than 70 percent by volume of carbonaceous material. It is formed from plant remains that have been compacted, hardened, chemically altered,

and metamorphosed by heat and pressure over geologic time. Coal is one of the three energy sources for heating purposes at utilities. Natural gas and heavy fueloil are the other fuels used. The use depends on market price and capability of a utility. Environmental activists are against the use of coal because of the very heavy emissions. Compared with oil and gas, coal is the cheapest fossil source to generate electricity. Most utilities have more than one system to generate heat, often coal plus either gas or fuel oil. There is always a back-up plan in case of big price differentials or lack of one energy source at the terminal.

Coalescer

A small unit (bullet tank) used to separate and remove water from oil. See also 'demulsifier', which is an additive to speed up the separation. Water separation is done before crude is fed into the distillation unit at a refinery.

COB

Close Of Business. The end of the business day can be when the ICE or Nymex is closed. Most often COB is based on Platts/Argus window timing. The close of the market is often also used as time bar for decision taking or performance requirement. A decision to be taken by COB, close of business. Sometimes it means decisions to be taken before the trader is leaving the office. Even then a trader is still available on the mobile, surely, when the case is important to that trader.

CO_2

See 'carbon dioxide'.

CO_2 Ticket

Tickets which allows a company to pollute the air at a certain price. A company which is not able to reduce the CO_2 emissions has to pay for the air pollution being caused. He can do that by buying CO_2 tickets. Somehow the money paid for CO_2 tickets should be reinvested into nature. One can have some sceptical thoughts here. Trading around this is called 'emission trading'. A very clean company which is well within limits is allowed to sell tickets as a reward for their great performance and investment in an environmentally clean operation. Those companies show the world how clean they are and in the meantime they sell tickets allowing others to pollute the air. The allowance to sell those tickets should encourage companies to invest in cleaner machinery.

Co-Cracking

A petrochemical process related to light naphtha and C4/C5 mixtures. Cracking of two or more feedstocks in one unit. May also be called blended cracking. See also 'petrochemical feedstock'.

COD

Chemical Oxygen Demand. Related to free water drained from oil. The higher the test result the more expensive it is to process this water and make it clean again. In the past in Belgium (probably also other places) people were fishing and were throwing molasses in the water. The COD of molasses is very high. The molasses removes the oxygen from the water in the canal which results in fresh dead fishes at the surface of the water. It is no longer allowed to catch fish by the use of molasses. By this example I wanted to give an impression of what COD does and why costs increase when test results show a high outcome. A grade of potential pollution in water.

COD

Completion Of Discharge. This can be related to payment terms. When oil is bought on delivered basis and pricing based on delivery days, then payment in products can be related to that. Often the payment term is 3 days after COD or 5 days after NOR (notice of readiness). Payment due day is one of these two dates, whichever comes first. See also '3/5 payment term'. In case of a sale on DES or DAP terms, risk and title of the complete cargo goes over from seller to buyer at completion of discharge. However, lay-time of a vessel stops when hoses are disconnected.

Coiled

Heating system, most often on the bottom of tankers or land tanks. The coils can be heated by steam or hot water. Heating of oil is meant to keep the oil at a temperature that pumping or transhipment of oil is possible. Pipelines can be coiled as well (on the outside) – that is called 'traced' pipelines. See also 'traced line' and 'insulated tank'.

Coiled Ship

Refers to a tanker that is equipped with heating coils in the cargo tanks to permit the heating of the cargo if necessary. Coiled vessels are often required for fueloil or heavy crude oil cargoes. Heating is required in order to keep the cargo liquid enough to pump the oil out at disport. A too cold temperature might result in either unmovable oil or the risk of losses as a consequence of clingage. Bunker barges also have heating coils. Therefore see also 'dip'.

Coke
Solid carbons formed in the reactors of the unit which over time cause slowdown of production and therefore periodically need to be removed during maintenance programmes. Related to bunkers, oil coke does also refer to 'CCR' specification, where carbon residue may cause problems in ship engines.

Coker
An oil refining unit which processes heavy feedstocks such as straight run fueloil, VGO or heavy crude oil and is able to produce light products such as naphtha, heavy gasoil and petroleum coke or green coke. By use of heat the long hydrocarbon chain is cracked into smaller chains hence the production of lighter oils, while the residue from this unit is a solid product. See also 'green coke' and 'coking'.

Cokes
Product coming from the coker units also known as green coke. Green coke will be processed to calcined coke. Calcined coke qualities are well known as sponge coke, needle coke and bullet coke used for the production of anodes for the aluminium industry. There is also met-coke and pitch coke which is extracted by distillation from bituminous coal.

Coking
A refining process using heat to convert heavy residual (fueloil, VGO or heavy crude oil) into lighter products and petroleum coke. With heavy oil and fueloil at values below crude oil prices a coking unit creates much value to a refinery as the margins for a refinery are normally to be earned by sales of light products such as gasoline and diesel.

- **Delayed Coking**
  A process that uses heavy crude as feedstock which is cracked by heat and pressure. The products are a range of lighter oils and petroleum coke. The product may be used for further processing in other units in order to meet specifications of the final oil for export. The coke is a green coke. See 'green coke'.

- **Flexicoking**

  A cracking process using heat and processes feedstock as heavy crude oil, tar sands, bitumen, and distillation residues into light oils. This unit can handle extreme heavy feedstock even when the sulphur and metal content is very high.

- **Fluid Coking**

  A thermal cracking process utilising the fluidised-solids technique to remove carbon (coke) for continuous conversion of heavy, low-grade oils into lighter products.

Cold Properties

Requirement in certain specifications/qualities for diesel and gasoline with regards to temperatures, the weather conditions, which may affect the performance of the oil in the car engines. For gasoil it is related to 'CFPP' and 'cloud point'. For gasoline it is related to 'RVP'. See also 'winter spec' and 'summer spec'. Arctic diesel requires extreme low cold properties. Some call this diesel 'penguin quality'.

Collecting Bank

Any bank other than the remitting bank involved in the collection of a draft and/or documents.

Colonial Grade

Standard quality of oil product meant to be pumped through the Colonial Pipeline in the US product market. Because of standardisation of the quality, problems like contamination are avoided.

Colonial Pipeline

Organisation that delivers per day approx. 100 million gallons of clean oil products such as gasoline, kerosene, heating oil and diesel by pipeline into the consumers' market in USA. The pipeline network has a length of more than 5500 miles. The line goes through 13 states from the Gulf coast refineries up to the New York area and it is connected to more than 250 terminals selling on the products.

Column

Unit at a refinery. Distillation tower, crackers and other units at a refinery have the shape of a cylinder standing straight up. The trader and the refiner call such a unit a column, or rather 'the column'.

Combi-Cargo
Vessel carrying two or more qualities of oil. Combi-cargoes are most often loaded at refineries where different products are available for supplies to whole-sales or marketing systems. Combi cargo supplies often cause deadfreight. See also 'cargo segregation'.

Combination Hedging
A risk management strategy that uses a combination of hedges using different derivative instruments. For example straight run fueloil may be hedged by a certain combination of Brent futures and gasoil paper (futures or swaps).

Commercial Invoice
The invoice stating the value of the oil cargo. Often this invoice is not necessarily the final invoice but nevertheless it is good enough to be used as value declaration in order to calculate and charge import duties if needed. The final invoice is the payable invoice sent by the seller to the buyer.

Commercials
Oil trading companies but also banks and hedge funds, as opposed to speculators. Usually involved in a futures environment.

Commercial Risk
Risk that the buyer is not performing as expected where the consequences of undersupply may have a financial impact. IDD approval combined with business references with new relations is therefore very important.

Commercial Stock
The oil from the total inventory that can be loaded and sold from the terminal. The remaining oil in stock which cannot be removed is called the operational stock. See also 'business inventory'.

Commingling
Goods are said to be commingled when stored or shipped without physical separation. Commingling is done on purpose while contamination is often seen as an unwanted situation. Commingling may be possible when different

parcels to be loaded are the same product with the same qualities. In that case the ship capacity is better utilised. Another reason to comingle is to mix different qualities on board a vessel in order to supply one homogeneous product at the final destination. Commingling cargoes is done for logistic reasons. Blending is something different and involves 'commingling' oil with different qualities on board the vessel in order to make a new product. Blending on board is meant to create a blending margin and optimise logistics at the same time.

Commission

A payment made for services from an agent or broker who was involved in the process of the closing of a confirmed trade between buyer and seller. In oil business it is generally assumed that the seller pays such a commission. It does happen that an agent is used on behalf of the buyer. In that case the agent gets a fee from the buyer who instructed the agent to find the business. Such a commission is based on a certain price per ton or barrels related to the deal. See also 'brokerfee'.

Commodity

An article of commerce or a product that can be used for commerce. In a narrow sense, products traded on an authorised commodity exchange. The types of commodities include agricultural products, metals, petroleum, foreign currencies, and financial instruments and indexes. A basis for a good tradable commodity is a liquid market where a trader can easily buy and sell the product without causing big price movements in the market. Physical oil activity with standardised product specifications, like in the ARA barge market, can therefore also be seen as a commodity. But also in the futures market Brent, WTI, gasoil and Rbob are commodities in liquid markets.

Commodity Swap

A paper swap where the cash flow depends on the price of a commodity. See also 'swap'. The use of swaps or CFDs as a hedging tool is well used in the oil market. The swap market is an over the counter market. It is only futures that are traded on the exchange.

Commodity Trading Adviser (CTA)

A person who, for compensation or profit, directly or indirectly advises others as to the value or the advisability of buying or selling futures contracts or commodity options. Advising indirectly includes exercising trading authority over a customer's account as well as providing recommendations through written publications or other media. In the oil business traders get lots of analysis reports and talk directly with the market. On such a professional level advisors are not too much used. Traders create their own market view and make their own decisions. Brokers often try to give advice based on what they see happening in the prompt market. They want to involve the traders into the business to get deals done.

Common Carrier

A public pipeline or transport company supplying service under the authority and control of a government for oil transport.

Company Inspector

A company employee given the responsibility of determining the quantity and/or the quality of a volume of oil being moved or stored. Not necessarily independent.

Compatibility

The behaviour of oil when they are mixed together. Does it really blend and is there not an uncontrolled process on-going after blending the two oil grades? Forming of asphaltenes when blending two oil grades is the main reason to call such a potential mix not compatible.

Compatibility Test

A test to measure flocculation (molecules clumping together) or precipitation (molecules getting solid) of asphaltenes in oil as a result of blending two different oil qualities. The test is important as a bad outcome may affect further use or processing of the oil. This may occur when heavy oil is blended with light oil or when blending straight run fueloil with cracked fueloil.

Competence

The ability to perform a certain job/task in compliance with performance standards. Competence is very much linked to the knowhow and the experience of the individual. A person who knows the business and has the network is wanted by head-hunters. Competence is acknowledged when the trader delivers good results, when the trader performs, and shares information and knowledge.

Complex Refinery

A refinery which can maximise the production of high value petroleum products as it is processing the crude and other feedstock through many treatment units, cracking units and coker units. Feedstock for such refineries can be a combination of crude oil, VGO, fueloil and other straight run streams. Opposite of simple refinery. A simple refinery has a limited number of processing units and is therefore exporting feedstock (VGO or straight run fueloil) for further processing at other refineries. Have a look at 'simple refinery' and 'Nelson complexity index' as well.

Compliant Documents

Documents presented under a Letter of Credit that comply with all its terms and conditions. The banks are only obliged to pay the beneficiary if documents are totally compliant.

Component

An oil cargo or batch which on its own is an off-spec quality far from being called a finished product. Two or more different components may need to be blended in order to make an on-spec end-product. In a refinery gasoline does not come direct from distillation or cracking. All the units produce different qualities of gasoline components and some components may be imported into a refinery like MTBE, ethanol or other bio-components and additives. At the refinery these components are blended into a tank to make a finished gasoline which is ready for supply to its final destination, the petrol station. Blending at the refinery is also done with diesel and heavy fueloil or bunker-oil.

Composite Sample

A sample taken from more than one place of a unit, such as a vessel with different tanks. But also during pumping through a pipeline, different samples (hourly) may be taken in order to get a good average sample of a cargo. See also 'ship composite'.

Compulsory Stockholding Obligation (CSO)

Amount of oil which certain organisations are obliged, by law, to have in stock. This stock is meant to be available in storage on a continuous basis in case of an oil crisis happening. Deliveries (and common life) can continue if problems, as a result of a shortage in oil availabilities, arise. In most countries compulsory stock should secure supplies in an event of an oil crisis for at least 90 days. See also 'SPR'.

Compulsory Stock Ticket

Ticket or contract in which one company promises another company to cover for compulsory stock obligations. This ticket has to be approved by the ministry of economic affairs of the country where the oil is in storage before it can be issued. The seller of the ticket gets a certain value per Cbm/15 paid for this. Just look at 'compulsory stock' as well. In Europe different countries have agreements in place which makes it possible to have oil stocks in one country and based on that stock it is possible to sell a ticket to a company in another country. Tickets can cross borders. See also 'bilateral agreement'. In backwardated markets (empty tanks) these tickets will be more expensive than in contango markets (full tanks).

Condensate

A naturally occurring gaseous hydrocarbon that liquefies when cooled to surface temperature. Gas underground is warm and possibly at a temperature where C5 and a bit heavier molecules are gaseous as well. Once this gas is pumped up and the heavy molecules cool down it becomes wet. Condensate is considered to be a part of crude oil production. This definition is contested by some OPEC members who want to produce large quantities of this product outside official OPEC quotas. Condensate might on some occasions be considered as NGL. The naphtha content in condensate is often 75% or more. Some condensate is directly sold as feedstock to the chemical industry. Where gas is produced one will often find condensate as well.

Concurrent Bunkering

Vessel taking bunkers simultaneously with discharging or loading a cargo. By that, the vessel is not losing time for bunkers' intake. This is possible at some terminals when receiving bunkers from shore. Also in some harbours, barges deliver bunkers during cargo loading or discharging. There are terminals where it is not possible or allowed. Then the vessel has to get bunker at another place. A vessel may use roughly 12 hours of her time if the bunker delivery comes in time. Places receiving bunkers are at areas on the sea like Skagen area or Southwold in Europe. Concurrent Bunkers is the perfect way of saving time and money for ship owners and companies that have vessels on time charter.

Conductivity

Specification in jet A1 which is linked to static electricity. Related to static electricity, jet petroleum has a certain level where it could spark and ignite. Therefore a max conductivity specification is in place. When the jet petroleum does not meet the requirement it may be treated with additives like 'Stadis'. Often this treatment is done just before it is pumped through a pipeline to its final destination, the airport terminal. Relating to pipeline supplies in Europe, you should have a look at 'NATO pipeline' and 'CEPS'.

Conductivity Improvers

Conductivity improvers – or anti-static agents – are developed to prevent the building up of static electricity, which may result in sparks especially when pumping large volumes. When sparks are formed the risk of fire and explosion of volatile fumes in the surroundings is increased considerably. With the use of anti-static agents this danger will be greatly reduced. Static electricity is a consequence of friction. Jet A1 is pumped in the pipelines to airports. Before pumping the jet A1 may need treatment with a conductivity improver. The rules and regulations for transport or movement of jet A1 are extremely strict. Accidents can happen without good control. Empty gasoil tanks being cleaned may be static. The combination of gas, oxygen and a static spark needs to be avoided.

Condy Book

Condensate P&L. Condensate can be organised in a company in different units. I have seen it in crude oil departments, natural gas departments and naphtha departments (GL). Condensate may be hedged with crude paper, naphtha paper or a combination hereof. Condensate pricing is correlated with naphtha values. Light condensate could also be a petrochemical feedstock.

Condy Trader

Condensate Trader.

Confirmation

Confirmation of a discussion, agreement or recap. See also 'recap'.

Confirmation Statement

A statement sent by a futures commission merchant to a customer when a futures or options contract has been initiated. The statement shows the price and the number of contracts bought or sold. Sometimes combined with a purchase and sales statement.

Congested Market

A period of repetitive and limited price fluctuations within a tight trading range; the market is not really moving. Waiting for something to happen which creates more volatility.

Congestion

Shipping term for port/berth delays. Too many vessels may arrive for the same terminal. Rule is 'first come, first served'. Frustration with operators and traders is growing as 'demurrage' will most likely be the result. Someone in logistics did a bad job by accepting too much work at a terminal. However, in some cases a logistic plan can change quickly as vessels may be delayed for various reasons. With good communication operators and traders can anticipate any troubles to come. By that they can take action to find creative solutions before money is wasted on potential claims.

Congestion (Technical Trading)

When prices trade at similar levels over a period of time, the chart becomes cluttered with business at these levels and is referred to as 'congested'. Congestion areas are often seen as providing support/resistance. They are the levels at which, rather than breaking into new ground, prices tend to get bogged down and become trapped.

Consecutive Voyage

A vessel is ordered for a couple of voyages in a row for the same charterer. The charterer may have some freight benefits as the number of cargoes to be loaded may fit well in the logistic set up. Nevertheless, each cargo order has its own charter party. It is just the rate which is discounted in this case.

Consignee

The company to whom an oil cargo is consigned as stated on the Bills of Lading. Company into whose possession goods are to be delivered.

Consignment

Term of sale wherein a seller delivers goods to the buyer but retains legal ownership of the goods until they are re-sold by the buyer. The buyer is responsible for remitting payment to the seller at time of re-sale.

Consignor
The shipper/sender or seller of the cargo.

Consular Invoice
A document that is required in some countries. It describes the transaction details of a cargo, such as price, buyer, seller and commodity. In the country of origin this document is certified by a consul of the importing country. Customs might need it for import reasons and tax calculation. See also 'commercial invoice'.

Contamination
The result from unplanned commingling of a grade of cargo with a sufficient quantity of another grade to destroy the characteristics of the cargo. Contamination can happen on board a vessel, or in a storage terminal or refinery and occurs when the oil is pumped from one unit to the other. It may even be the case that the contamination happens in a pipeline that is used for the same product but with different qualities. Contamination of low flash product with high flash products is very sensitive. A little bit of naphtha may ruin a full tank of gasoil. The contaminated oil might have to be re-blended or in the worst case scenario it has to go through a distillation unit. Claims will most likely follow as these things are a result of non-performance on a terminal. However, an operator could give a wrong pumping nomination to a wrong tank.

Contango
Situation where the market expects that the forward market would be higher priced than the prompt market. In a contango market the prompt prices are low due to weakness of the market, lack of demand, oversupply. Traders would prefer to put their oil into storage and lock in a result further out in time. It is often a bit easier to make money in contango markets rather than in backwardated markets. Refiners may get nervous; their tanks are running full as the trader prefers to load the cargoes as late as possible to gain on the structure. Buy early pricing and sell delayed pricing is a good strategy if there are tools to lock in that result. Those tools are better available in the crude

CFD market where you can buy a 3 versus 5 day spread or by week. In the products market swaps are done per month average, not by days.

Contract

Legal agreement between two or more parties, such as that between a buyer and seller of oil, which describes the business to be performed, the agreed price of the oil, the delivery terms, the payment terms and other general terms and conditions. After a physical oil trade is done contracts are issued and often the contract departments of both the buyer and the seller are sending their text requirements on and on to each other until both companies agree on the final draft. With prompt cargoes it might happen that such discussion is still going on after the cargo is loaded, but details may be in demurrage clauses and other claim sensitive terms. A customer may still send a claim 60 to 90 days after loading or discharging.

Contract Month

The month in which delivery is to be made in accordance with the terms of the futures contract, also referred to as delivery month. Often the pricing time of a cargo is related to the contract month instead of the B/L date. Such terms have to be clear in a contract as it might cause trouble at month end situations.

Contract for Differences (CFD)

A crude swap based on short time periods, a week. Price is crude dated related. Tool to hedge a physical crude cargo and lock in a small timing difference. CFD timings are available as from 1 week after dated crude up to 6 weeks after dated crude. After those six weeks the market uses Brent futures for hedging purposes. With a CFD as hedging tool one can also hedge a couple of cents result when you buy on 5 days' pricing window and sell on a 3 day pricing window in a backwardated market. So every cent counts in trading crude and again "time is money".

Contract Risk

Risk of performance of both counterparties but also the interpretation of the different terms in the contract can be a risk issue. The willingness to cooperate in case something goes wrong and claims get out of proportion is another element. The risk of price changes and other commercial issues. I would rather call it trading risk.

Conventional Blendstock for Oxygenate Blending (CBOB)

Conventional gasoline blendstock intended for blending with oxygenates downstream of the refinery where it was produced. CBOB must become conventional gasoline after blending with oxygenates. Motor gasoline blending components which require blending other than with oxygenates to become finished conventional gasoline is reported as all other motor gasoline blending components. Excludes reformulated blendstock for oxygenate blending (RBOB).

Conventional Tanker

Vessel or tanker that can only load and discharge at terminals. Ship manifold is situated mid-ship, therefore oil terminal jetties are built to receive or load the oil basis mid ship. An offshore tanker can load from the bow and discharge from mid-ship. This is a special vessel, not conventional.

Convergence

The tendency for prices to approach each other at the same level. Brent and WTI may at some point converge when markets are changing. WTI used to be more expensive than Brent but at a certain point it converged and now WTI is much lower priced than Brent. Or perhaps it will have converged again after this book has been published.

Conversion

Calculation from one unit to another unit. Bar to kPa, metres to feet, cracks calculation. An overview of calculation methods is available on the final pages of this book.

Conversion Refining Capacity

The ability of a refinery to change oil products into a product with improved properties. Naphtha may be processed to gasoline with a certain octane. So the capacity we look for is the quantity of oil after primary distillation that can be further processed to upgraded products. Such a process is considered more complex than the first process in a refinery, the primary or atmospheric distillation.

Conway

Conway, Kansas. The main propane trading hub in the Midwest United States. See also 'hub'.

Correction (Technical Trading)

When prices move fast upwards or downwards there will be a moment when prices are adjusted at a certain level before they move on. The cause of such adjustment could be because of profit taking. But also when the price goes through a certain technical price level, corrections to support-levels or resistance-levels can be noticed.

Correlation

A statistical measure of how two products or two oil-related markets (shipping versus arbitrage) move in relation to each other. Correlations are used in advanced portfolio management. When people are checking pump prices for car fuels they most often follow the crude oil prices, as there is a certain connection between gasoline and crude. Keep in mind that the gasoline market has its own behaviour in Europe. The Euro/Dollar price has some effect as well.

Corrosion

Oxidation of pipes, tanks and tubes in an oil terminal or refinery under conditions of exposure or use. Aggressive properties of the oil such as salt, chlorides and acid increase the speed of corrosion. Such a refinery will buy the acid feedstocks at a lower price but might need a more regular maintenance programme. Tank bottoms in a storage terminal may be sensitive for acids as well. It may cause leakages after a certain time. But one cannot avoid it as some properties just belong to oil. See also 'TAN'.

Corruption Perceptive Index (CPI)

A list that measures the perceived levels of public sector corruption in 178 countries around the world. If you get a '10' then you are the most perfect performing country and if you get a '1' then you are the most corrupt country. Trading with a country with a low score increases the risk to a company's reputation in case business goes wrong. However, I must inform that a rating can be low in a country, but a lot of companies can still have a good reputation. Counterparty approval and IDD is very important if one wants to trade with a new company. But that counts for any company wherever they are. As a Dutch oil-man living in Norway, I am proud to mention that The Netherlands and Norway are on top of the rankings, which stands for good behaviour.

Cost and Freight

Shipping term included in a contract of sale (abbreviated as CFR or C&F) meaning that the seller is taking care of the supply of the oil by tanker to the agreed destination. The shipping costs are part of the sales prices (FOB plus freight). The risk of loss or damage to the goods is transferred to the buyer when the oil passes the ship's rail at the manifold at the port of loading. So even when the seller is the charterer of the vessel, the risk and title of the product are to the buyer.

COSP

Shipping abbreviation for Commencement Of Sea Passage. Vessel has left the port and is now steaming to her next destination. The speed of the vessel normally goes to 12 knots per hour. New ETA can be sent out from the vessel. See also 'break waters' and 'EOSP'.

Cost of Capital

The interest costs of money used as capital assets (like oil cargoes or oil in storage) are referred to as the cost of capital. When a market is in contango lots of oil is stored for a longer period. To store oil for such a long time one has to keep in mind that interest is part of the costs involved. Also when business is done based on delayed payment terms the calculated cost of capital ought to be incorporated into the price. When crude was at 147 USD per barrel in 2008 the costs of capital were extremely high. Some companies had to reduce their activity as a result of that financial challenge.

Cost of Carry

All costs related to a trade or trading strategy, such as freight, interest, tank rental, insurance, demurrage, inspection and many more. A trader must be able to calculate all those costs when making a decision. Often he would budget such costs especially when potential demurrage is part of the costs. The costs of carry are part of the trader's P&L.

COT Preparation

Cargo Oil Tank preparation that is done in order to reduce gas. Related to inert gas system of a tanker. Preparing to enter a port, ready for discharge.

Counter Offer

When the first original offer from one company to another company (buyer/

seller) is not acceptable, a counter or counter offer can be done. Basically the buyer and seller are negotiating a price and may keep sending counter offers until both buyer and seller agree on the price. Giving a counter offer automatically implies that the rejection of the original offer is in play. If a trader gets a counter on a bid or offer then he is at least assured of the counterparty's interest. However, if the counter is way off from a bid or offer then either the counterparty is trying to get a bargain or the offer or bid was not representing a real market value.

Counterparty
The receiver or supplier linked to an oil trade. Buyer and seller. Before business can be discussed the companies have to check if they are able to negotiate with each other. Major companies have to run an IDD check in order to get a new potential counterparty approved to trade with. See also 'IDD'.

Counterparty Approval
Strong requirement, as in many oil companies, that the company you do business with has to be approved by your company. Without that approval no deal is allowed to be done with that non-approved counterparty. With a new customer a deal can be done subject to counterparty approval. See also 'IDD'.

Counterparty Risks
The risk to each party of a contract that the counterparty will not live up to its contractual obligations. Risk is increased when the counterparty is based in a country that is low scaled on the CPI. The chance of getting a claim paid is relatively low. Companies located in financially challenged countries are lower credit rated; open credit facilities may get lost. Interest rates are increasing and so are the costs of issuing an L/C. Financing costs become more expensive related to the risk level.

Country Risk
Risk incurred by a seller of goods that a buyer in a different country will not be able to pay for the goods due to political or economic conditions in his country. The two components of country risk are 'political risk' and 'transfer risk'. The economic problems in Europe have, since 2011, caused some challenges for the oil business as a result of the increasing credit rates.

COW

Crude Oil Washing. The use of a high-pressure stream of crude oil cargo to dissolve clingage and sediments from cargo tanks of a vessel during the discharge operation. Due to a proper COW the oil remaining on board is set to a minimum. The operational oil loss versus the B/L is well controlled and not too much money is lost as a result of a potential negative differential between the B/L figures and the outturn figures.

CP Speed

The standard speed of the vessel that is agreed in the charter party. A vessel can get an order to deviate from that speed. If the cargo is required to arrive at a loading terminal with highest urgency then the charterer or seller can request for a higher speed. The bunkers' consumption will go up and the one ordering for faster sailing will pay for it. When a buyer has plenty of time or expects a long lay-time in disport then a request could go out to sail slower for the purpose of saving bunkers. The owner would probably keep TC speed and arrive at the normal planned arrival schedule. The income from demurrage is, for the owner, sweeter than the savings on bunkers.

CPA

Crude Processing Agreement. Basically renting refining capacity. A company pays a fee for processing crude to products. See also 'processing agreement'.

CPI

See 'corruption perceptive index'.

CPP

Clean Petroleum Products. When you charter a vessel you would often see what commodity such a vessel is meant for. See also 'clean oil'.

CQQO

Certificate of Quantity, Quality and Origin. Together with the B/L, this is the standard set of documents issued for a cargo.

Crack Box

The price difference between two crack-spreads. The position should be on the same product crack, but on different periods. It is called a box (rather than e.g. differential or spread) because the position is built on four legs and hence can be associated with a square. Example ("long position Jan/Feb Gasoline crack box"): Buy January crack and sell February crack. The four legs are 1) long January Gasoline, 2) short January Crude, 3) short February Gasoline, and 4) long February crude).

Cracked

Molecules broken by certain refining processes. The opposite of straight-run. Refers to a petroleum product produced by the processing units which are available at a refinery after primary distillation such as thermal cracking or vis-breaking processes etc. which yields very low quality residue. Long hydrocarbon chains are cracked into smaller pieces. Light material is processed from heavy material.

Cracked Fueloil

Residue remaining after a straight run fuel has been processed in cracker units at a refinery. See 'cracking'.

Cracking

The process of breaking down the larger, heavier and more complex hydrocarbon molecules into simpler and lighter molecules, thus increasing the gasoline yield from crude oil. Cracking is done by application of heat (over 380°C/716°F) and pressure, and in modern time the use of a catalytic agent. Principal cracking techniques are:

· Alkylation
· Reforming
· Hydro-treating
· Solvent extraction/Dewaxing
· Flexi-coking
· FCCU
· Vis-breaking
· Delayed cooking
· Thermal cracking
· Catalytic cracking
· Hydro cracking
· Steam cracking
· Co-cracking
· Plus more processes per refinery.

Crack Spread

A calculation of the value of a barrel of crude oil in terms of the value of its refined products such as gasoline and heating oil. Crack spreads may be based on a variety of refinery models, and also depend on the type of crude input. Expressed usually in Dollars and cents per barrel of crude. To calculate the spread, the cents per gallon product prices are multiplied by 42 (gallons per barrel), and subtracted from the crude oil price. For example, when heating oil futures cost US$2.475 per gallon and NYMEX light, sweet crude oil is priced at US$100 a barrel, the heating oil crack spread in Dollars per barrel = US$2.475 x 42 = US$103.95 – US$100 = US$3.95. Or following European numbers if price gasoil 795.25 US$ per ton = 795/7.65= 103.95 minus US$ 100 = 3.95 US$ crack. Some more crack conversions are available in the back of the book.

Cramming

When a customer is charged or billed for additional services without their knowledge or consent. Pipeline fee, additional harbour dues etc. When you commit to a trade then make sure what is included. That counts for oil trades and for agreement with service providers.

Crash

An event where liquidity is lost and the market plunges in price. This loss of liquidity is caused because all of the participants turn to the sell side and there are not enough buyers to balance out the equation. As a result prices seemingly melt and go lower and lower as traders panic, throwing out their stocks or futures regardless of price in an effort to convert all of their holdings to cash. In 2008 crude oil crashed from 147 USD per barrel down to 35 USD per barrel in early 2009. Banks got into problems. It was a big event during the credit crisis, which started when house prices collapsed in the USA in the first place.

Credit Checking

The process where the trader is checking the credit status of the counterparty. The company he works for has credit specialists who are looking at the balance sheets of each business relation and at the rating of the companies. Based on that rating the company would give a certain amount of open credit. They also look at the credit rating of those companies. Often such rating is done by Standard & Poor (S&P). Major companies, often the listed companies, may get a higher credit compared with most other companies with little assets. Based on that data available to the trader, the trader would decide whether he requires an L/C or whether he can trade on open credit. Also called credit analysis. Counterparties can have an open credit up to a certain level. Without enough credit, the seller would require an L/C to cover credit risk. So if a company buys a 2nd or 3rd cargo it may happen that not each sold cargo to the same company can be available for open credit and therefore an L/C may be required. That buyer may have extra costs as the buyer has to open an L/C. As a consequence of that this buyer may approach a competitor which still has credit available. As oil prices are very much increased to very high levels it will become more challenging to give open credit to the different companies. A crude oil cargo has values which lie around 100 million Dollars when one barrel costs roughly 100 to 120 Dollars. In 2008 oil collapsed from 147 to 35 Dollars per barrel. At 35 Dollars per barrel on cargo had a value of 25 million Dollars. Here you see that crude oil prices and the uptrend as we see today will cause more credit challenges in the near future. Therefore proper credit checking is very important. If your buyer does not pay the bill and credit was not covered as it should be, you can go bankrupt depending on the size of the company you work for. A credit loss goes straight into the trader's P&L.

Credit Insurance
Insurance against losses in case a buyer is not able to pay his bills. Often it does not cover 100% of the bill – there is some own risk as well. The higher the risk the more expensive such insurance will be. Increasing oil prices are causing an increased risk profile.

Credit Line
The amount an oil company is willing to give as open credit to a company. This amount is therefore part of accepted credit risk. It is a specified amount of unsecured credit to the buyer of oil. Also called 'line of credit'.

Credit Rating
A published ranking, based on detailed financial analysis by a credit bureau, of one's financial history, specifically as it relates to one's ability to meet debt obligations. The highest rating is usually AAA, and the lowest is S. Oil companies use this information to decide whether to approve open credit up to a certain level or to give no credit at all. Over time we have seen more

and more changes to the credit ratings of countries. Some South-European countries were very much in the picture. Companies like Standard & Poor are very important to follow; there are also other companies looking at this. Unfortunately the bad rating of a country has big consequences related to the credit position of the companies in that country. Companies with a good business reputation in the business are suffering a lot because of that.

Credit Risk

The risk that a financial loss will be incurred if a counterparty to a derivatives or physical oil transaction does not fulfil its financial obligations in a timely manner. A big example from the past is 'Enron' – suddenly no financials were available from a well listed company that had some open credit with certain companies. See also 'commercial risk', 'contract risk', 'financing risk', 'political risk'.

Credit Terms

At a sale of oil it has to be decided if a company gets 'open credit' or not. Therefore traders have to check if the buyer of the oil cargo is able to pay the invoice or whether there exists any risk that the counterparty may not be able to pay the invoice in the future as some companies do not have or are lacking assets. The financial strength is checked by the credit department and will be rated. Companies like most majors are considered reliable on their financials as they are high enough rated to get open credit. Other companies can be lower rated and get limited or no credit. In that case the seller can require a Letter of Credit to make sure that money will be available to cover credit risk of the business committed. Remember the company Enron. They were big in the oil business with good people and a great performance. But then suddenly they got into trouble and became broke. They disappeared from the scene. Enron was a huge company, but an L/C was still required. If a company would have given open credit one could count on it that not much money would have been paid. Also take a look at 'credit rating'. In a trade the credit terms are either on open credit or stand by L/C. It happens rarely that pre-payment is required. If that happens then the buyer might have proposed it.

Crew (Ship)

Officers including the master and seaman working on a ship.

Critical Zone

This refers to measurement zones in a floating roof tank. It is defined as the point where floating of the roof begins to the point where the roof is fully floating. Measurement between those zones may be impossible or inaccurate. Therefore storage companies prefer to stop pumping just before or just after such levels in tank are reached. Sometimes the critical zone is known as the 'inaccurate zone' or 'partially floating region'. The critical zone is identified on tank calibration tables where appropriate.

Cross-Hedging

Hedging a cash commodity using a different but related paper contract when there is no paper contract for the cash commodity available. The cash and paper market follow similar price trends, e.g. Straight run fueloil hedged by Brent and gasoil futures.

Cross Month Cargo

When a cargo is loading at the very end of the month it can happen that the Bill of Lading date slips from the current month to the next month. Sometimes it happens on purpose by delaying or slow pumping the vessel. That is done for commercial pricing purposes. Paper related hedging may be done in a profitable way depending on the date B/L, called 'month end option' trading.

Crude Distillation Unit

An oil refinery unit that separates crude oil into different products according to their individual boiling point ranges. Distillation allows for the materials to be separated without being subjected to conditions that would cause cracking or decomposition. Often you see in reports the abbreviation 'CDU'. Also called atmospheric distillation unit (ADU) or primary distillation.

Crude Imports

IEA member countries submit monthly registers of their crude oil imports, showing quantities and prices for each of more than 100 separate crude streams. The IEA publishes the volume information for key crude streams after aggregation by OECD region. Publishing numbers is done on a weekly basis. The outcome causes price fluctuation, volatility. Especially when the numbers differ a lot from the expectations.

C

Crude Names

Over 3000 crude names can be found on the internet; some examples: Troll, Forties, Oseberg, Kirkuk, Saharan, Bonny Light, Arab Heavy, Azeri, CPC, Basrah, Big Foot, Black Gold, Cotton Wood, Crazy Horse, Mars, Quiriquiri, WTI, Brent, Tabasco, Volve and many more to mention. See also 'Brent name'.

Crude Oil

Raw and unrefined oil being produced by drilling onshore and offshore. Crude oil ranges from very light (high in gasoline) to very heavy (high in residual oil). Sour crude is high in sulphur content. Sweet crude is low in sulphur and therefore often more valuable. It can be classified as aromatic, asphaltic and naphthenic or as high TAN or low TAN crude oil. All different possible properties of crude oil combined with the location where it is produced, makes it a complex, challenging and interesting oil to deal with. It is a fluid mixture of petroleum hydrocarbons, yellow (very light) to black in colour, and also containing small amounts of oxygen, nitrogen, acids and sulphur contents and other impurities. Crude oil was formed millions of years ago as a result of a natural process where bacteria, heat, and pressure on ancient plants and animals were converted to hydrocarbon being crude oil. Crude cannot be used as consumption product. Therefore it has to be processed in a refinery to final products for consumption and to feedstock for the petrochemical industry. Crude oil is an extremely important product which has a huge impact on the economy when prices fluctuate as result of production changes in the world. The OPEC tries to control prices. Wars and challenges in the Middle East are therefore everybody's concerns. High oil prices and environmental requirements entice investors towards the production of clean and alternative energy. Crude oil is sold and prices based on the assay or yield. See 'assay' or 'yield'. But also have a look at 'vanilla crude'.

Crude Oil 1 Lot

1 lot is 1,000 barrels. If the screen price shows 50 Dollars per barrel of crude oil then 1 lot has 50,000 USD value. To illustrate, a VLCC can load 2 million Bbls (2000 lots).

Crude Oil Demulsifiers

An additive that helps water separating from crude oil. High water levels may lead to off-spec crude oil. A refinery prefers minimum contents of water or BS&W. Disposal of water is costly and therefore the market sets a max specification for water in crude. This means the water separation and the cost for disposal of water are costs related to production activity. Occasionally an offshore field has a small cargo with water or slops going out. Too much water also takes part of the storage offshore and onshore. Different types of demulsifiers are available in the market. A bit of heat works as well to let water settle. Only use a demulsifier when water does not want to settle and is bounded to the oil molecules. Sometimes it is cheaper to find a commercial solution in case crude is off spec on water. A receiver may accept an off spec cargo at a small discount. A refinery has easier methods to get the water out of the oil; they are used to it as part of the refining process.

Crude Oil Washing (COW)
The use of a high-pressure stream of crude oil cargo to dislodge or dissolve. A crude oil washing is done to ensure that the vessel is discharging every drop of oil. Oil that stays on board after discharging is seen as operational loss at discharge. Not all types of crude requires a crude wash on board. It is most common for heavy and high paraffinic crudes. Experts in companies have a list of recommended crudes that are candidates for a crude oil wash. Often a vessel takes crude in a slop tank and heats that up. This stock in the slop tanks will be used for the COW operation. One needs to save time in disport so preparations can be done during the voyage of the vessel.

Crude Classification (Density)
See 'classification crude (density)'.

Crude Oil FOB Price
The price of the crude oil at the loadport in the country of the producer. That price may be a Brent, WTI, ASCI or Dubai crude related number. Often in the Middle East an OSP will be set as premium or discount. The choice of benchmark crude might also depend on the destination of the cargo. The buyer nominates such a destination at an agreed date in time based on B/L or loading window, e.g. 7 days prior to the first day of the nomination window. The buyer charters the vessel and takes risk and title at loadport.

Crude Oil Input
The total crude oil input into processing units at refineries. It is not the maximum processing capacity, but more an overview of crude input over a certain period. By month, quarter or year.

C

Crude Oil Landed Cost

The price of the crude oil based on a delivered basis including the costs of losses which most often are obtained after discharging. If the buyer bought the cargo on delivered basis then the freight costs were already included. If the buyer bought the crude on FOB basis then all cost of transport has to be included to calculate the landed costs. The cost does not include charges incurred at the discharge port (i.e. Import tariffs or fees, wharfage charges, and demurrage).

Crude Oil, Refinery Receipts

Receipts of all crude oil at a refinery. Crude oil of foreign origin held in bonded storage is excluded.

Crude Oil Losses

Losses which occur during logistic operation of the crude oil. It may be caused by transport per vessel or by pumpover from one to the other tank. At a refinery oil losses may also be seen as refinery losses. Other losses may be caused due to human failure such as contamination, fires and spills. With current oil prices loss control is very important. More attention is paid to losses that result from oil movement. The use of logistics which starts at loadport where the B/L figures are established until the receiving terminal which measures the quantity received. In my view a loss of 0.1% can be considered as an operational loss but every drop more than that should get more attention when it becomes a structural matter. More inspection and sampling may be required. See also 'operational losses' and 'apparent losses'.

Crude Oil Production

Production of crude from onshore and offshore reservoirs during a certain period of time. Agencies are following the production on a global basis and report it in groups such as OPEC production and Non OPEC production plus production per country. It is reported in barrels per day. OPEC is organised in such a matter that they are able to control the market price range by increasing or decreasing the production.

Crude Oil Qualities

Used to refer to two properties of crude oil, the sulphur content and API gravity, which affect processing complexity and product characteristics. High TAN or low TAN get more attention as well. As new fields show an increase of very heavy crude oil production the focus is now even more challenging and market talks about very heavy crude and light crude (Yes, that is still related to gravity).

Crude Unit
The initial refining operation in which the basic cuts of fuel are distilled out of crude oil. Same as the atmospheric distillation or primary distillation unit.

Crunching
The oil futures prices are crunching through a certain price level. It means the oil price passes the support levels as if the level did not exist. Prices are falling rather fast. See also 'crash'.

CSO
See 'compulsory stockholding obligation'.

CST
Centistokes. A way of measuring and reporting viscosity at 50° Celsius/122° Fahrenheit.

Cumulative Revolving Letter of Credit
Revolving Letter of Credit that permits the seller to carry over any amounts not drawn into successive periods.

Cup Tank
A cup tank is a metal wall surrounding a tank, or a 'tank-in-a-tank', which serves as containment area in case of leakage. The cup tank design replaces bund walls resulting in less surface-occupation for a tank farm. (From the Oiltanking website.) Unfortunately they exist for very small tanks only. It would be doubly needed for steel if such a tank would be a new built tank. That becomes a very expensive investment.

Cup with Handle (Technical Trading)
The cup and handle is a unique bullish continuation pattern. It starts after futures stages a lengthy rally. The futures prices then pull back and start to level off. The futures then rally back up to the point at which the previous run ended. The futures reverse once more from the same level, creating horizontal resistance. The futures level off after pulling back, attracting buyers, but this

time at a relatively higher price. It returns to the horizontal resistance once more and breaks out, continuing its bullish trend. If you would look at the bar-chart, you would notice the shape of a cup with a handle. A technical trading signal saying something about the price direction for the next few days.

Curve
The curve or the forward curve. The line in the graph of oil prices showing the oil values in the weeks or months to come, the forward market. The derivative prices from month to month forward in time as they are traded based on the market's bids and offers. A line going up from a low price to higher prices indicates a contango market, a weak prompt market and strong expectation later on. A line going down from a high price to lower prices later in time indicates a backwardated market, a strong prompt market with weaker expectations in time. Traders talk about the curve when the forward market is getting stronger or weaker, the curve gets steep, a steep contango or a deep backwardation. Or they talk about flattening curve or flat market. Take a look also at 'structure', as the curve indicates the structure of the market.

Cushing
Cushing, Oklahoma, is a major hub in oil supply connecting the Gulf Coast suppliers with Northern consumers. Cushing is famous as a price settlement point for West Texas Intermediate on the New York mercantile exchange (Nymex). Cushing is a small city where about 9 pipelines are connected enabling crude oil to be pumped to many directions across the USA. Cushing is connected to the Gulf Coast and also to Canada. It is not only crude oil which is pumped through Cushing, also products like gasoline makes this an important hub. The challenge at Cushing is that there is more pipeline capacity going into Cushing than pipeline going out of Cushing. Crude oil checks in but not all crude oil checks out. They call it the 'roach motel'. Cushing is a village of probably 9,000 people and a crude storage capacity of 60 to 68 million barrels. That much oil can cause a low price for WTI. See also 'landlocked'.

Custody Transfer Measurement
An oil stock measurement which is done to collect information about the exact quantity and quality. This measurement may be used as the basis for a change in ownership (risk and title) for materials. See also 'in tank transfer'.

Custom of the Trade

An expression sometimes used to describe an action or procedure that is not committed to writing, but which has been followed for a long time, and is considered 'standard practice' by practitioners in the trade.

Customs

Government agency charged with enforcing the rules passed to protect the country's import and export revenues. Customs is not always fast enough (related to trading) at informing the traders and companies what the options are to avoid paying too much import duties although you can contact customs and ask for information. Companies have specialists who may advise on the possibilities. However, it would be better if a trader knows what the possibilities are with preference certificates from different countries for oil products. Preference certificates such as a 'Form-A' or 'INF-3' can be presented to Customs when importing oil. See also 'nomenclature website'.

Customs Classification of Mineral Oil

Customs has classified the taxation numbers of oil products based on the distillation curve, sulphur content, lead content and the use of the product. Hereunder a simplified overview:

- **Light oils:**
  Naphtha and gasoline. Product from which at least 90% would evaporate (distillate) at a temperature of 90° Celsius/194° Fahrenheit.

- **Medium heavy oil:**
  Kerosene and jet A1. Product from which less than 90% evaporates at 210° Celsius/410° Fahrenheit and from which minimum 65% evaporates (distillates) at 250° Celsius/482° Fahrenheit.

- **Heavy oil:**
  Diesel and heating. Product from which less than 65% evaporates at 250° Celsius/482° Fahrenheit and from which at least 85% evaporates at 350° Celsius/662° Fahrenheit.

- **Heavy fueloil:**
  Heavier oil than gasoil and less than 85% would evaporate at 350° Celsius/662° Fahrenheit.

See also 'nomenclature' with tax number attached to products.

Cut I

Fraction in a distillation unit. Cut between naphtha and jet, cut between jet and gasoil.

Cut II

The water level marking on the measurement tape which has been coated with water indicating paste. 'Taking a cut' is taking a measurement of the oil or water level. Based on the millimetres of water level marking in the tank one can calculate free water in the tank with the use of the calibration table. From product tanks water can be drained. Crude oil tanks cannot be drained. Water is to be separated in the coalescer at the refinery before it is fed into the column for processing purposes.

Cut Point

If two or more oil batches are pumped through the same pipeline after each other, one batch will push the other batch through the line. The cut point is there where the quality from batch 1 changes to the quality of batch 2. Some contamination may be a consequence of that activity. It would normally not harm the quality that much. However, one has to take this into account. If the qualities between the two batches would differ too much, a line flush may be required. Pipeline business requires a lot of logistic organisation activity in order to get it done in the right way. Most pipeline business makes use of one standard quality. See also 'landlocked'.

Cutterstock

Fueloil blending component with a very low viscosity. This oil can be light on density but also heavy on density. The viscosity is the most important property of the blendstock. Russian cracked fueloil, which is the most important fueloil in the barge market, has a viscosity of roughly 600 Cst. at 50° Celsius/122° Fahrenheit. The bunker barge specification has a maximum requirement of 380 Cst. at 50° Celsius/122° Fahrenheit. Therefore any type of cutterstock is important for blending purposes in fueloil. Cutterstock is not necessarily cheap. This makes profitable blending for bunkers a real challenge. Diluent material, light oil used for blending the oil to lower the viscosity. Condensate can be used in heavy crude or LCO can be used in heavy fueloil. The choice of type of diluents depends on price and the new value of the blended oil.

Often the diluent has a much higher value than the oil that needs to be made commercially on spec. The heavy oil often has a very low value. Never use too much diluent as often you create a spec that is too good and you never get that value paid out. Avoid 'giveaway'.

D

D2

Russian diesel. It does not say anything about the quality of the diesel but it has an assumed standard specification and in certain cases one can be lucky if there is a lot of giveaway. Unfortunately this term, 'D2', is used in fake offers combined with huge and unrealistic quantities and prices that are not even close to market value. Nevertheless D2 is used in the business when talking about diesel and its origin in general.

D&H

Abbreviation for 'dangerous and hazardous' cargo.

DAF (Delivered at Frontier)

Delivery term used when the goods are transported by rail and road. The seller pays for transportation until frontier. The buyer has the responsibility for the costs and logistics from frontier to final destination. Change of title and risk is passed over at the frontier. DAF deliveries are done in big countries like Russia where a lot of refineries are located inland close to the crude oil production fields. Since there are no products pipelines available to sea ports most products are transported by railway system. See also 'INCO term'.

Daily Range

The difference between the high and low price during one trading day. It indicates the daily volatility in the market.

Daisy Chain
The process by which a cargo of crude oil or oil products is sold on many times before being delivered to the customer. The term is used to describe the paper chain formed by the passing of a 25-day Brent cargo (i.e. 25 working days ahead of its loading date) from the equity holder through a sequence of deals. E.g. In crude oil it can be a daisy chain from producer to one or more traders till end user, refinery.

Dark Spread
The difference between the market price of power and the cost to produce the power burning coal. The gross margin between the sales price of electricity and the cost price of making electricity where coal is used a feedstock. Other feedstock can be gas or heavy low sulphur fueloil.

Data Required for Crude Oil Survey (Measurement)
Tank number; tank reference height; dip innage (sounding) or ullage; free water dip (FW); oil temperature (C or F); oil density or API; BS&W volume in percentage (as per analysis result). Further to instructions, I would also point to standard procedures for crude inspections which include I.P. and API standards; instructions for reporting, how to report, when to report and to whom to report; invoicing instruction including reference numbers. Cargo operators send many inspection orders and the invoice follows a month later. Also, indicate how to split the bill. Often it is 50/50 buyer/seller and so much more to think of, sampling, retain samples etc. etc. etc.

Dated Brent
Brent cargoes are known as dated Brent cargoes once they acquire a specific set of loading dates, usually at a point about two weeks from loading. Before this point, Brent cargoes are typically traded generically as so-called 15-day Brent. The dated Brent market, which Platts/Argus assesses on a 10-25 day forward basis (10-27 days on a Friday), generates prices which have become a key benchmark for contract pricing of crude oil worldwide. The dated price is then the quotation of the day. Physical crude oil cargoes are pricing on these quotations often B/L related. Cargoes pricing in and out on dated Brent may be hedged by CFDs, so take a look at 'CFD' as well.

Dated to Frontline (DFL)
A swap based on Brent dated versus the first available Brent futures contract

on the exchange (ICE). The first leg is the floating price of the Brent dated and the second leg is the settlement price of the Brent crude oil futures. You buy one leg and sell the other leg. The price is the differential. You can also buy or sell a DFL which relates dated to a 2nd, 3rd or other month. Basically these are crude time spreads, physical oil price versus paper contract. Dated Brent is the price for physical cargoes when they are loaded and start pricing. Please note that the settlement price on expiry date of the futures contract is not included.

Dated Strip

In Platts and Argus a trader can see the prices of oil on a certain day. Quotations of a fixed group of different crude traded in one area can be, like a North Sea dated strip, or Mediterranean dated strip. The reference value of a strip depends on a reporter. Platts uses a strip of the 10th until the 25th day after actual date of trading. So the reporter would create or calculate a curve for the strip and reports the average values. To this the reporter has to look at the prices traded and makes clear assessment rules like Platts/Argus windows.

Day Order

An order that if not executed expires automatically at the end of the trading session on the day it was entered. If the price of the day order is hit, then the order is automatically executed. This is paper related.

Day Trader

A speculator who will normally initiate and offset a position within a single trading session. Also called 'scalper' or 'jobber'. A day trader prefers to be active in the most volatile markets. Even on daily activity a day trader can make his decision based on technical analyses. A day trader is better to sit in front of his screen during the whole day, looking for a good opportunity or waiting for the right moment to liquidate a profitable position, or cut the loss. Trading discipline is required.

Dead Cat Bounce

A rebound in a market that sees prices recover and come back up somewhat. Markets can be volatile and therefore they are unpredictable.

Deadfreight

Non-utilisation of the cargo carrying capacity on a vessel. The unused tonnage multiplied by price per ton freight according to the charter party is deadfreight. If the deadfreight is caused by failure of the supplier of the oil, then this deadfreight can be part of a claim based on non-performance. If a buyer of crude oil nominates less oil than what has been agreed in a contract a deadfreight claim may be the consequence. So buying oil with a big tolerance of 10% may cause deadfreight if the seller cannot handle the maximum volume of 110% of the contractual agreed quantity.

Deadweight

Deadweight tonnage (DWT). The lifting or carrying capacity of a ship when fully loaded. This measure is expressed in long tons when the ship is in salt water and loaded to her marks. When loaded to her summer marks the value is for her summer deadweight (SDWT). It includes cargo, bunkers, water (potable, boiler, ballast), stores, passengers and crew. Traders would be more interested in the maximum loading capacity of the vessel.

Deadwood

In a storage tank or ship tank there are pipes and coils. They use a small proportion of the tank capacity. That volume in tanks used by pipes and coils needs to be subtracted from the total volume in tank to get to the right quantity. All equipment in a tank taking ullage is called deadwood. Check if deadwood is included in the tank calibration table.

Deal

An oil trade which is confirmed by both traders of either side of the contract. After a deal is done the whole process in administration starts. Back office needs to be informed and the contract must be issued. The operators of both companies will contact each other to fulfil the activity that has been agreed. See also 'recap'.

Deal Date

The date on which a transaction is agreed upon. Contract date. It happens that traders agree after a deal is done to set the deal date on the next day. By that they create more time to register the agreed terms into their systems. A deal done late in the evening can then be handled the next day. Lots of companies require that a deal done has to be administrated on the transaction day into the trading system. A deal not pricing yet and done after office hours therefore gets a deal date on the next trading day. Also traders want to go home in the evening. The traders will reconfirm the trade during the next morning.

Decanting

Disposal of water from an oil cargo. Some offshore fields where water injections are used for crude production may have a lot of water in the produced crude oil. This water can be decanted to a slop-tank on board the floating storage unit at field. Although tankers may receive crude oil including a certain percentage of water in their cargo. Free water will settle to the bottom and if the percentage of water is too much, instructions may be given to get rid of the water onshore. A tanker may heat up the crude oil until roughly 40°C/104°F to speed up the process of water settling. A process called decanting. Costly when the water contains a lot of H_2S. Decanting can be time consuming. The first batches of water go fast out of the tanker. But from about a water content of roughly 2.5% it takes more time for water to settle down to 1%. The lower the water percentage the higher the possibility that emulsion of water and crude is decanted. This is when to stop the operation as here one starts losing oil. A refinery would be able to handle water as well, but there can be high costs attached to it. 1.5% water content can be acceptable for most refineries; nevertheless they want a discount for it – of course, nothing goes for free.

Deemed B/L

To agree on fixing the B/L day of a certain cargo on a fixed date before the cargo is loaded. By that the buyer and seller agree to set the pricing dates so hedging can be done more precisely. Deemed B/L does not necessarily have any effect on the payment due day. The payment due day is related to the real B/L day. Deeming is done for cargoes that are sold based on B/L pricing. This is in the interest of both the buyer and the seller.

Deep Water (Drilling)

Drilling for oil at sea, offshore at a depth of more than 150 metres (500 feet). Although this may vary from area to area. As I understood this 150 metre level is based on activity in the US Gulf area. The deepest drilling is at the offshore field 'Perdido', drilling at a depth of roughly 2,435 metres, 7,989 feet (one foot is 0.3048 cm). The deep-water platforms are floating platforms. In the North Sea and the Norwegian Sea oil is drilled at a depth of 60 metres (un-depth); however a bit further out at sea it is already 600 metres and deeper, as a result of a kind of underwater cliff. Latest developments in deep-water is 'subsea' production where production of oil is done on the sea bottom. The oil produced is pumped through underwater pipelines to the shore where it is treated to be commercialised. A system which is very good to use in the Arctic which has challenges enough due to weather conditions and possible threat of icebergs.

Deep Water Port

A terminal which is able to receive vessels without any draft restrictions. Large vessels such as ULCCs, VLCCs and Suezmax can load a full cargo without any problem. A full VLCC would require a draft of at least 22 metres. Nevertheless a full cargo in such a vessel cannot be discharged at every port. One has to look at port restrictions at disport as well. There is a 'big belt' in Europe or draft restrictions in Singapore. And even if in both the loading and the discharge port deep water is available there might be air draft restrictions. Logistics has many angles to think of.

Defence Pipeline Organisation (DPO)

The organisation regulating and controlling the logistics for jet A1 pumping through NATO pipeline system in Europe, The Netherlands. See also 'CEPS'.

Deferred Payment

Delayed payment. Crude oil standard payment terms are 30 days after B/L. The market gets the oil first but pays much later. Some buyers require a payment term of up to 60 days after B/L. When you as trader buy and sell on the same payment terms then there would be no financing costs calculated. A refinery receives their crude with late payment dates, 30 days after Bill of Lading. Then the refiners need time to process the crude oil. The products which become available to the market get a 3/5 day payment term, 5 days after Bill of Lading or 3 days after notice of readiness, whichever comes first. By that, the invoice of the crude has to be paid at roughly the same time as they receive the money for the products. The refinery minimises the financing costs for oil processing. If you buy your refinery feedstock from a location with a long delivery time (voyage) away from your refinery, then there may be a good reason to require deferred payment, e.g. Crude purchase from WAF with destination NWE or USA. Refiners prefer to pay at the same time they cash in the invoices after sales of products. This to avoid financing costs at a refinery.

De-hazers

Small amounts of water (usually above 200 to 300 ppm) can cause a gasoil to become hazy. As a result, a certain batch may fail the specifications. De-hazers let small water droplets be coalesced into larger droplets, importantly decreasing settling time. Hazy gasoil is often a winter issue in storage where oil is cold and water does not settle that easily. Refinery production is warm, therefore most often the diesel or heating oil from the refinery is often not that hazy. A de-hazer is a kind of demulsifier. Have a look at 'demulsifier'.

Delayed Coking

Process to produce cokes. A process that uses heavy crude and heavy straight run fuels as feedstock which is cracked by heat and pressure. The production is a range of lighter oils and petroleum coke. The liquid product may be used for blending programmes or further processing in other units in order to meet specifications of the final oil for export. The coke is a green coke. See also 'green coke', 'needle coke', 'shot coke', 'sponge coke' or 'coking'.

Delivered Place X Plus Options

When a CIF or CFR deal is done then the sales price is based on a certain discharge port. The buyer does not know or does not want to inform yet where the cargo is going to be delivered and needs the option for other places within the geographic market area. The extra cost or the discount on the price will be calculated from the basis destination. See also 'freight payable as per charterparty' and/or 'charterparty differential'.

Demand (Law of)

Demand is linked to the price, just like the supply side. If demand is bigger than the supply side, the price would increase immediately. It will cause a strong market and that means that the market will be backwardated. If the demand falls away then prices decrease and the market turns into contango. Such change of structure does not happen on a daily or weekly basis. Once the market changes from contango to backwardation or vice versa, it will take a long time before the market structure will change again. Backwardation or contango market may last for a few months up to several years.

Demulsibility

The resistance of oil to emulsification, or the ability of oil to separate from any water with which it is mixed. The better the demulsibility rating, the more quickly the oil separates from water.

Demulsifier

Additive used to separate water from oil. Most often used in crude, an activity just before the crude will be processed. It is most important to remove salt or sodium as that may cause corrosion in the refinery equipment. If water does not settle then the first idea is to heat the oil, and often the water will settle. But if the water is bound with the oil molecules the use of a demulsifier may be the best solution. See also 'coalescer'.

Demurrage

Overtime or extra time used by a vessel based on the time agreed according to the charter party for loading and discharging. If a vessel gets 36 hours for loading and discharging and uses 48 hours for the whole operation, then 12 hours for extra time needs to be paid at a rate which has been agreed according to the charter party. If such delay is caused by a third party then a demurrage claim should be expected. In most contracts the demurrage can be claimed up to 60 to 90 days after the event happened. The claim has to come first from the owner and that can take time. As a result many claims departments in many oil companies do have a big workload chasing the money from events which happened a long time ago. Traders might suddenly see their P&L going down when a claim is settled. All communication related to the logistics should be in writing and should be filed in a professional way. That information may be needed 3 months later when a claim comes in. Some claims are not solved and it may take more than a year plus a visit to court to collect the money.

Demurrage Protection

From time to time a vessel arrives before the loading window at loadport. In that case, a terminal prefers to optimise and load early. As a consequence of that, the vessel will also arrive earlier than planned in the disport. The receiver may give allowance to load early, but only when he gets demurrage protection for the time gained at loadport. It can also be that the receiver does not allow loading earlier since this has an effect on the bill of lading date. In backwardated markets, the buyer prefers a later B/L. When you give demurrage protection to a buyer, make sure that the terminal who wants earlier loading is covering for that cost. Else, the demurrage protection is a cost in your own P&L. Help and favours have a price. If the B/L date would be the reason for not allowing early loading, then traders can decide to make a deemed B/L date. See also 'deemed B/L date'.

Demurrage Rate

A fixed sum, per day or per hour, agreed to be paid for the detention of the vessel under charter at the expiration of laytime allowed. The demurrage rate per day is important to know in case a trader plans a big trade with a lot of ship-to-ship activity involved. The trader might budget a certain number of days of delay in his calculation. Days of delay multiplied with the demurrage rate are the costs that the trader will take into account when he makes a decision. In a tight shipping market the demurrage rate can be rather high. Demurrage levels follow the worldscale levels.

Density

The weight of one litre of oil at a temperature of 15° Celsius. Density/15 = Kilos per litre at 15° Celsius. Density is reported in a number with 4 digits behind the decimal point, e.g. Gasoil 0.8465. When a sample is taken the temperature of such a sample will never be exactly 15° Celsius. Therefore a conversion table of densities at different temperatures is available in order to find the correct factor to convert the findings to a temperature at 15° Celsius. B/L figures always show cubic metres at 15° Celsius. That conversion table may also be used to find a new density at heated temperatures. This is done when a full tank of fueloil is to be heated. Density goes down when the product gets heated and as result of that the actual volume will increase and may cause a logistic problem. In the USA we use a standard density of 60° Fahrenheit. Hereunder different types of density.

- **Absolute Density**
  The mass of a substance per unit volume at a specified temperature, often the actual temperature. Important with fueloil to calculate the actual Cbm. The actual Cbm is related to the capacity of the logistic tools.

- **Relative Density**
  The ratio of the mass of a given volume of fluid to the mass of an equal volume of pure water at the same temperature and pressure. Relative density replaces the term 'specific gravity'.

- **Relative Density at 60°F / 15°C**
  Fluid relative density measured against water with both materials at 60°F/15°C and reference pressure of 14.696 psia (or equilibrium pressure). Equivalent to 'RD 60/60' (15/15).

Did you know that the density of water is 1.0000 at 4°C/39.2°F?

Density (De)Escalator

For some grades of oil the standard density is fixed as in the consumer market the oil is sold per litre while the trading of cargoes is done in tons. For gasoline the standard density is 0.755 which affects the price positive (higher price) when a delivered cargo has a density below 0.755 because 1 ton of gasoline contains more litres when density is low. Blending low density products may give some extra money in the P&L. In Russian crude oil (Urals or REBCO) a density escalator is set around the API number of 32. The density (de) escalator is always described in the contract and is an important part of the price of the oil.

Departure Ballast

Ballast taken on board prior to departure. If loaded into tanks that have previously been used for a cargo it may contain traces of oil. See also 'dirty ballast'.

Density Vac/Air 11 Points

Vacuum weight is heavier than weight in air. Rule is 11 points difference between density in air and vac. When density in vac is 0.7550 than density in air is 0.7539. Most terminals use density in vacuum as the basis for all quantity measurement. However, some terminals use density in air. Just bear in mind that your loadport and disport can have a different standard. When calculating oil losses it is best to look at volume. Volume is volume. It is on mass that is reported in vac or air.

Depth Gauge

A device that allows for measuring the amount of liquid in a train tank car or land tank.

Derivative

A financial (paper) instrument, traded on or off an exchange. Paper contracts such as futures, options and swaps. They are used to hedge/limit risk or to exchange a floating rate of return for fixed rate of return. Derivative trading does not involve physical oil logistics. Only when one does not liquidate a futures position physical oil supplies may be executed if no cash settlement is agreed. Derivatives available on exchanges (futures) are reported and can be followed on the screen and are therefore used for technical trading purposes. And therefore next to hedging these paper contracts are popular to trade for speculative purposes. Swaps are traded on the OTC market. Brokers provide Excel sheets with overviews on a day to day business. A great overview to see the forward market for products.

Derv.
Diesel engine road vehicles.

DES
Delivered Ex Ship. This term has been changed in the 'INCO terms' to 'DAP' Delivered at Port/Place. It still has the same meaning. The seller charters the vessels for the oil supply and during sailing the risk and title of the product on board the vessel belong to the seller. When discharging into the terminal the risk and title go over from seller to buyer. The received quantity in tank is the product that will be invoiced. As the chance is high that there will be losses at discharging, the DAP price is often a bit higher than the CIF price. As an exception it can be agreed that the B/L quantity counts as official invoicing quantity. See also 'DAP'.

De-Salter
Unit in the refiner which is meant to extract water and sodium from crude oil before the oil enters the crude oil unit. Water in the column is something that needs to be avoided. It would cause real troubles during distillation as steam from water and gas from oil do not match and disturbs the distillation process. The water is extracted in flows through a kind of electric field and also through the use of a demulsifier. See also 'coalescer'.

De-Salter Demulsifiers
De-salter installations at refineries are often working with different blends of feedstock, varying the quality to be treated. It is important to use the right type of demulsifier to achieve best efficiency in crude oil washing operations.

Desk

Desk or trading desk is a term referring to a group dealing with a specific oil/gas commodity. The crude desk or the gasoline desk. Each desk has its own P&L. See also 'book'.

Desulphurisation

The removal of sulphur, as from molten metals, petroleum oil, or flue gases. Petroleum desulphurisation is a process that removes sulphur and its compounds from various streams during the refining process. Desulphurisation processes include catalytic hydro treating and other chemical/physical processes such as adsorption. Desulphurisation processes vary based on the type of stream treated (e.g. naphtha, distillate, heavy gasoil, etc.) and the amount of sulphur removed (e.g. sulphur reduction to 10 ppm). See 'catalytic hydro treating'. Refineries with limited desulphurisation capacity would rather process low sulphur feedstock unless they operate in a high sulphur market of course.

Det Norske Veritas

A Norwegian classification society which certifies seagoing vessels for compliance to standardised rules regarding construction and maintenance.

Deviation

Any departure from a true value. So you can deviate from your logistic plan and supply to other locations. But you can also ask for a waiver and deviate from the quality requirements (if not crucial) or testing method.

Deviation, Point of

Position of a vessel at sea where the decision has to be taken to sail a certain route to a certain port. Until the point of deviation the trader can change his mind and let a vessel sail to another port than was nominated in the first place without additional costs on top of the normal charter party differential. Of course the new port of destination has to be part of the earlier agreed charter party or may be agreed when the opportunity arises.

Dewaxing

When high paraffinic straight run products or crude oil are stored in tank, a layer of paraffin, wax, may be formed on the bottom of the tank or cavern. When that layer gets too big, the possibility of pumping oil in and out of the tank may be affected. Something must be done to get rid of the wax in tank. The wax is often a good straight run quality which may be (re-)processed in a refinery. Therefore gasoil can be flushed, preferably at high temperature, through the tank in order to dissolve the wax in tank and pump it to the refinery for processing. The quantity of wax coming out of the tank can be seen as a plus, a positive stock difference, and therefore it gives a gain in the P&L.

Dew Point
Temperature at which humidity in air can be cooled down to condense into water.

DFL
See 'dated to frontline'.

D.I.
Abbreviation for document instructions. Oil logistic people are requesting or sending the d.i. Document instructions are needed to get the correct B/L format and other papers related to the cargo. Also distribution of documents is instructed in this order. All parties involved want to know numbers and time. B/L quantity and B/L day are the most important as that regulates the exposure of the deal. Together with the d.i., the sailing instructions are sent as well. Where is the vessel going and to which companies should the master of the vessel send the estimated time of arrival in disport and loadport? It is all in the d.i.

Diesel Engine
Inventor: Rudolf Diesel, 1897. A simple explanation: Combustion engine, through compression in the engine temperature goes up. Power is generated through ignition generated by this heat.

Dieselisation
The development as we have seen over the last years in Europe related to the consumption of diesel. The diesel engine for cars has been further developed. It became cleaner, faster and less noisy. Due to that better image the sales of diesel cars in Europe have been growing. Diesel at the petrol station is also often cheaper than gasoline, but that is a result of the tax regime. Diesel is

lower taxed on excises than gasoline. The demand for diesel in Europe is still growing. The dieselisation of the market.

Diesel Index

The ignition quality of diesel related to cetane index.

Diesel Oil

Heavy fuel for engines such as cars, tractors and pleasure boats etc. Diesel oil quality requirements may be different from country to country based on cold properties like cloud point and CFPP. Diesel oil with a certain minimum of bio components is called bio diesel.

Diesel Pool

The production of all diesel related components in a refinery. The group of diesel components a diesel blender has access to. The refiner or blender will use the products in his diesel pool to produce or blend on-spec diesel in the best economical way. Additional components can be imported or exported; that is a matter of blending optimisation. Components can be heavy gasoil, light gasoil, burning kerosene, clean LCO, off-spec jet.

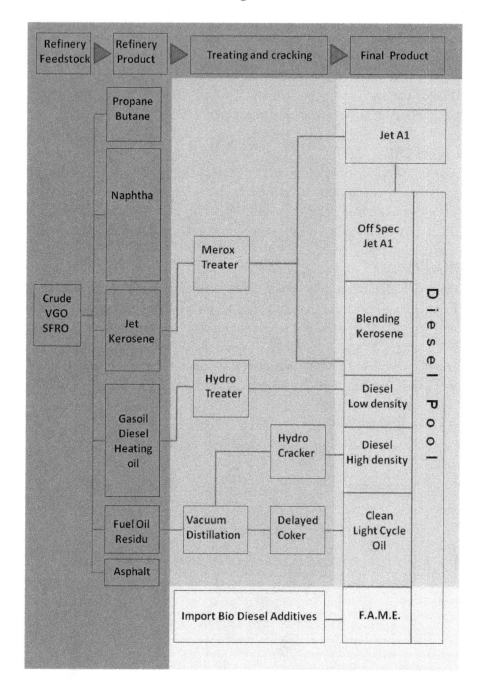

Differential(s)

Price differences between classes, grades, and delivery locations of oil products and crude oil. Also classified as the discount or premium versus the benchmark quoted oil value.

Dilbit

Bitumen crude blended with diluent in order to improve the viscosity so that it floats and can be transported through pipe and/or by vessel. Diluent is expensive, so one tries to minimise the use of diluent. Heating the oil is therefore also required to make the oil float. Most ports are able to handle crude receipts with high temperatures up to 70-80°C/158-176°F.

Diluent

Light low viscosity oil meant to be blended with heavy oil with the main goal being to make it possible to pump the heavy oil through pipeline and other logistic systems. The most used diluent used in extra heavy oil is condensate or naphtha. Heating the oil would also be a solution to lower the viscosity of heavy oil but most vessels and systems cannot handle a higher temperature than 70-80°C/158-176°F. Therefore heating the oil in combination with adding the diluent is a good solution.

Dip

The fueloil below the heating coils in a bunker barge. Due to its viscosity level it is impossible to empty the barge completely. Dip level in a barge is not fixed and can be different from time to time. It can cause product losses and contamination. Dips are always measured before commencement of loading and again after bunkers are supplied to a vessel.

Direct Access

Electronic access directly on the exchange by entering bids and offers into a system that is set up for that purpose. The ICE has such a system. Bids and offers plus required volume may be entered into the ICE system. That trader has to stay behind his screen as markets are moving and so does the bid-offer level as well. By using the 'electronic trading' system the brokers are out of the loop. Still many big oil companies choose to trade following the traditional way. Brokers give more information and the trader may respond faster when a trade or hedge needs to be committed. See also 'fat finger'.

Dirty Ballast

Ballast water, often sea water, taken on board of the vessel which is contaminated with the rests or clingage left in cargo tanks that previously were loaded with dirty oil. Dirty ballast has to be taken onshore to get through cleaning processes before it is allowed to be pumped back into the sea.

Dirty Cargo

Oil which is viscous and leaves significant amounts of residue in tanks. Generally applies to black oil such as crude oil and residual fueloil. Also called 'black oil' and opposite of 'clean oil'.

Dirty Ship

A vessel which is used to load dirty products or crude oil. When a dirty vessel is to be converted from dirty to a clean vessel then often LCO for bunker blending is to be loaded in order to get the most dirt out of tank. Cleaning a vessel is expensive and if it happens it would be applicable to smaller tankers of 5-10 kt. Most dirty tankers are ULCC, VLCC, Suezmax and Aframax size of vessels.

Discharge Specs

Specification of crude oil or oil products after discharging. When at a load point inspection is not possible or when certain parameters cannot be tested, then buyer and seller may agree to check the quality (split inspection cost) at disport. In the case that something would be off-spec, financial compensation might take place. Discharge spec may also be the qualities that the buyer requires upon arrival of the vessel. In some cases the buyer relies more on the inspection at disport than on the refinery qualities as reported at loadport. As a seller you run a risk of being off-spec on arrival. A commercial compensation may be needed if the quality of the oil does not meet the specification on arrival. The majority of oil cargoes are based on specifications at loadport. A sale based on discharge spec involves risk; a seller would then make products with better specifications than required to avoid problems at disport. That would be an expensive exercise.

Discharge Temperature

Weighted average cargo temperature before discharge. Hot product has a lower density which results in more volume. The trader and operator need to keep that in mind in case they are planning to use the maximum capacity of the shore tank. It still happens that a fueloil cargo is lacking ullage as the supplier has been reading B/L numbers that are stating cubic metres at 15° Celsius/60° Fahrenheit while the arrival temperature of most fueloil is 50 to 70°C (122 - 158°F). Hot oil can also damage the coating of a tank, cause emissions or other problems. Most terminals put maximum limits on temperatures of oil to be operated at discharging. See also 'hot oil'.

Discipline

The ability of the trader to follow the trading rules and act accordingly. "Cut losses and let profits run." "Do not fall in love with your position." Also stay within 'mandate'. You will find these words and expressions in this book. Discipline is the most difficult part of trading. No one would like to cut and take a loss. Traders like to believe in their view and expect markets to come back again and therefore they prefer to stay in their position which may become a bigger financial loss. Cutting losses too late results in huge losses. When a position looks profitable the trader would like to cash in quickly; they do not let profits run. As a result of that the traders cash in many times a rather small profit. To let profits run the strategy should be to cut loss from peak, the highest price. If they would follow the rule of trading discipline they would make much more profit. In many cases the many small profits do not offset the big losses they suffered earlier. That makes a trader a 'net loser'.

Disconnection of Hoses

The final disconnection of loading/discharging hose(s) or arm(s) from the vessel once loading/discharging operations have finished at the storage facility. Loading is ready, the vessel is waiting for last inspection reports and shipping documents are ready to sign off. The B/L day will be issued based on the reported day of 'hoses disconnected'. Not on 'loading completed'. Used laytime will stop when the vessel is ready for departure. That means when all documents are on board.

Discount

The amount, a price which would be reduced to purchase a commodity of lesser grade. Refers also to differential versus the benchmark.

Sometimes used to refer to the price differences between futures of different delivery months, as in the phrase "July is trading at a discount to May", indicating that the price of a July futures contract is lower than that of May. (Backwardated market.)

Applies to cash oil prices that are below the futures price. (Contango market.)

An amount agreed between buyer and seller to be subtracted from an existing benchmark. A small discount may be given as a result of a commercial solution when a product is off-spec or another problem has occurred.

Discrepancies
Differentials between requirements for certain documentation such as a Letter of Credit or a B/L and the presented documentation. Such errors may cost money or rights to claim. It is often in the details where discrepancies arise. In the oil business no mistakes are allowed.

Discrepancy Letter of Credit
An L/C which has not been issued according to the requirements to the seller or seller's bank. In such a case the bank will not and cannot process the L/C. The bank will inform the buyer and/or seller and wait for further instructions. A correct text of an L/C is crucial here. But also the loaded quantity on board has to be within the limits of the figures as stated in the L/C. Too much or too little oil on board a vessel may create a discrepancy Letter of Credit. In such a case it could happen that a vessel does not start loading. The nomination is then set on hold due to lack of a correct L/C based on quantity. The buyer has to be held responsible for demurrage caused by this delay. An operator may get a call when he is on duty and hear that a cargo has loaded a quantity that is not within the loading tolerances. In such a case the operator had better check what has been written in the L/C. An operator should never just say that it is acceptable without that check, also not when the call is in the middle of the night. Think about the consequences of having a discrepancy Letter of Credit.

Disposition
The components of petroleum disposition are stock change, crude oil losses, refinery inputs, exports, and products supplied for domestic consumption.

Distillate
Petroleum products from the refinery being produced at temperatures between 140° and 350° Celsius/284° and 662° Fahrenheit. Products we call distillates are often grouped in the same trading book or department. Products involved are jet, kerosene, diesel, heating oil or gasoil and LCO. Distillates are

clean products. Dirty LCO would become a blending component for fueloil bunkers. Other names for distillates in the market are ULSD, D2, Russian point 2, EN590 oil, AGO, DERV, fueloil (heating oil), TS1, ATK, bio diesel, etc. etc. When it concerns diesel then it comes in different qualities related to sulphur or aromatic requirements, but also cold properties from country to country and from season to season may differ.

Distillate Fueloil

A general classification for one of the petroleum fractions produced in conventional distillation operations. It includes diesel fuels and fueloils. Straight run oil that requires further processing in the refinery. Here we talk about clean oil, not heavy dirty fueloil.

Distillation

Primary distillation is the first step in separating crude oil into different oil grades by heating the crude oil up to 360° to 380° Celsius/680° to 716° Fahrenheit. The crude oil in the column will evaporate and the lightest molecules will condense in the top of the column. In the column, also called distillation tower, dishes (bubble caps) are placed on different levels. The heavier molecules will not be able to fly up to the highest dishes and will therefore condense at other dishes on different levels in the column. The condensed oil will float into a pipe which is at the same level as the dishes in the column. The oil from each different level streams into different tanks. The different products from high boiling point to lower boiling point are: propane, butane, naphtha, kerosene, gasoil and heavy gasoil. Those may be used for cracking purposes and further processing. The heavy material that does not evaporate is called residue, also called straight run fueloil or bottoms. This process is just the beginning in a refinery. All products are straight run products. Some may be used for blending, but most products will go into the next process of the refinery, 'cracking' or other treatment.

Distillation Curve

A graph that plots the percentage (by volume) of a given grade of crude or oil products that boils off as a function of temperature. Since the boiling points of the various crude cuts are constant, the distillation curve shows the percentage of each compound in a given grade or batch of crude. The temperature at which the first condensed drop of oil comes out is called IBP (initial boiling point) and the temperature at which the last drop of oil is condensed in the test is called FBP (final boiling point). Customs authorities would use the distillation curve to classify the oil with a correct customs code, linked to the excise duty system. See therefore 'customs classification for mineral oil'. The distillation curve for crude oil is also used to define the yield of the crude. See also 'yield' and 'E70'.

Distillation Tower

A tall, column-like tube in which crude oil is heated and where its vaporised components are distilled by means of distillation trays, bubblecaps. See also 'distillation'.

Distressed Cargo

Unsold cargo up on arrival at disport. The trader holding that cargo will have a problem when he has a cargo so promptly available without logistic solution to place the cargo in own storage. The trader will probably have to make a choice in taking demurrage on the vessel or selling it at a discounted price. This deal may end up with a considerable loss. The market is ready to help the trader get rid of the cargo – at a big discount. Renting storage could work as a type of insurance to avoid being a trader holding a distressed cargo. See also 'back up'.

Distributor (Wholesale)

A wholesaler that buys and owns (takes title to) oil products prior to reselling them to its customers. Integrated oil companies are holding or renting storage facilities in order to create a logistic service to a lot of end consumers. Based on the logistic and on the shorts created to the consumer market, such a company may be able to create a significant trading position. A good position to add trading value.

Diversify.

Spread risk. Never put all your eggs in one basket.

Diversion

When the original planned route as according to the charter party is changed and accepted by the owner of the vessel the new charter party relates to a 'diversion'. Markets can change rapidly and in some cases one can be lucky with freight optimisation by change of plan for a cargo to be delivered. Such diversion may often be done before or at the point of deviation. See 'deviation, point of'.

DLC
Documentary Letter of Credit.

DMA
Marine diesel fuels. Density up to 0.8900, sulphur max 0.1%. This is SECA area bunkers oil. Bunker in the past was heavy fueloil with a specification up to 4.5% sulphur. The sulphur limitation went down to 3.5% and in Europe it went down to 1.5% to 1%. As from 2015 the max sulphur for bunkers in Europe (Seca) is 0.1%. Vessel load DMA of still heavy fuel oil when using a scrubber.

Doctor Test
A qualitative method of detecting undesirable sulphur compounds in petroleum distillate in order to determine whether oil is sour or sweet. The doctor test is also a requirement in the gasoline specification. The required outcome for gasoline has to be 'doctor test: negative'.

Documentary Instructions
Instruction, in a nomination to load a vessel, with regards to the documentation to be issued and placed on board the vessel. The following documents are required: Bill of Lading, ullage report, timesheet, certificate of quality, certificate of quantity, certificate of origin, master's receipt of documents and some other documents. Often the vessel or the master gets one copy of each document on board. The originals plus some copies are sent by courier to the owner of the oil who sent the nomination including the document instructions.

Documentary Letter of Credit
Another way to refer to commercial Letters of Credit.

DOE
Department of energy in USA. The US federal government agency establishing programs and policies regarding national energy matters.

Doji (Technical Trading)

Observation in the graph of a futures market which is seen as a technical indicator. In a candlestick chart we see each trading day being represented by a stick. The sticks are made up as follows: A very small horizontal line (nearly a dot on the left side of the doji) which shows the opening of the futures market. Attached to that line it shows a vertical line. The highest point is the highest traded price of the trading day and the lowest point is the lowest price of the trading day. On the right side of the vertical line there is again a very small line (nearly a dot) which represents the close of the day. So the candle stick shows you the opening of the trading day, the high and the low, and the close of the day. A doji looks like a cross. The opening and the close are equal while the trading day had a high and low. Depending on the trend over time the doji indicates if the price is expected to go up or down during the next couple of days. Technical traders would notice the indication but would use more technical tools and indicators to make their decisions.

Dolphins

In oil jargon a dolphin is a sea bottom fixed mooring pole for a vessel. This mooring pole is not connected to the shore. Can be made from wood (e.g. 3 piles in the seabed), but for big vessels they are made from concrete and steel, a fixed structure. Also a relatively cheap solution to extend a normal berth. By that a terminal is able to receive bigger vessels. You find also mooring buoys in some harbours which are floating connection points. Of course a cable to the sea bottom connects the buoy; however, this is less stable than a dolphin. The port of Rotterdam has many locations where a charterer or agent can rent dolphins and buoys. They do this for temporary parking of a vessel in the Rotterdam harbour. However, the buoys are mainly used for logistic purposes like ship-to-ship operations or cargo treatment. In a busy harbour like Rotterdam, it is the perfect logistic solution and therefore it is well used. Anyone can make a reservation, but be in good time as Rotterdam is a busy port. The dolphin in the middle of a jetty is called a breast dolphin. The dolphins at the front and aft of the vessel are called mooring dolphins. The service of renting out dolphins generates more work and more income from port duties in for Rotterdam.

Domestic Inland Consumption (USA)

Domestic inland consumption is the sum of all refined petroleum products supplied for domestic use (excludes international marine bunkers).

Consumption is calculated by product by adding production, imports, crude oil burned directly, and refinery fuel and losses, and then subtracting exports and charges in primary stocks (net withdrawals is a plus quantity and net additions is a minus quantity).

Done

Deal done, a deal or a trade has been agreed. You're done! I take you out. When a deal is done a recap will follow. Look at 'recap' for a list of contract details to be confirmed on a taped line.

DOT-111

Non-pressure tank cars designed to carry a wide range of products including hazardous and non-hazardous materials. DOT Department of Transportation (USA). In 2015 there were about 335,000 active tank cars available from which 228,000 are DOT-111s. 92,000 cars are used in the USA for transport of liquids like crude oil. The biggest competitor for the train system is pipeline transport. See also 'AAR'.

Double Bottom

A general term used for all watertight spaces contained between the outside bottom plating, the tank top and the margin plate. Double bottoms are usually sub-divided into a number of separate tanks and can be used to hold clean ballast, potable or boiler feed water, or fuel. They also provide a measure of protection for cargo tanks if bottom plating is damaged in the event of grounding. Chances of pollution may be diminished due to this protection. For all new build tankers there is a general requirement for the vessel to have double hull and double bottom. Many companies have stopped using the old vessels. Single hull and single bottom vessels are being phased out.

Double Bottom (Technical Trading)

A bullish reversal pattern characterised by two lows at roughly equal value. Sometimes these lows are tested a 3rd time making it a triple bottom. The bottom may be seen as a strong resistance level. It is probable price will move up.

Double Handling

Executing twice the same operation for the same cargo, e.g. Supplying a cargo to Rotterdam and loading it again in Rotterdam to ship it to USA. Double handling can result in extra cost, but on some occasions it can still be part of logistic optimisation, e.g. Collecting a number of cargoes for a bigger vessel size, making bulk.

Double Port Discharge

A vessel discharging in two ports at the place of destination, e.g. Rotterdam has a large number of receiving terminals. Double port discharge may be done for logistic reasons. That can be because of lack of storage capacity a cargo can be too big for one receiver only or the second port has draft restrictions. Receivers suffering from draft restrictions often pay a small premium to the supplier, due to the extra cost they cause for deliveries in smaller lots.

Double Top (Technical Trading)

A bearish reversal pattern characterised by two highs at roughly equal value. At the tops the market meets a certain resistance for further increase of prices. There might be too many sellers in the market. Prices may move downwards.

Downgrading

Blending to reduce a 'too good' quality of oil in tank to a 'just in spec' quality in order to gain blending value and avoid selling product with 'giveaway'. If a gasoline has an octane of 97 and the specification is minimum 95 then there is room to add some lower octane fuel into the tank until the minimum of 95 is reached without spoiling any other specification to be met. The low octane component is cheaper than gasoline with an octane of 95, so some blending result is created in this case. See also 'giveaway' and 'upgrading'.

Downstream

All activity that comes after the production of different oil products. When the product leaves the refinery and trading of refined oil, retail, shipping out etc. Terms applying to functions or facilities closer to the end-user. Refining and marketing are generally downstream processes in the oil patch while exploration and production are upstream. Retailing is downstream or terminaling. Refining is to be seen as midstream. Crude sales from production belong to upstream, although the exploration and production groups prefer to call crude marketing a downstream activity.

Downtrend (Technical Trading)

A price pattern characterised by successive falling highs and falling lows. Do not forget to follow the trend when taking trading decisions. Most traders always talk bullish which can be challenging during a downtrend period.

DP

Dom Pérignon – What a good trader can drink when he is successful and is awarded with big bonuses.

DP (Shipping)

Dynamic Positioning. A system on board a vessel that controls the position at sea to keep the vessel stable. Very important when loading offshore. Offshore loaders are therefore classified as DP 1, 2 or 3 vessels. They all have automatic position control under maximum environmental conditions. The other way to keep position is by anchoring, but that does not work in deep-water.

DP Classifications

DP1 Vessel has no redundancy, one error and loss of position may occur, e.g. generator failure, computer failure, etc.

DP2 Vessel has redundancy; one error would not cause problems in positioning.

DP3 Vessels would even stay in position in the case of a fire or flood on board the vessel.

DPP

Dirty Petroleum Products. When you charter a vessel you would often see what commodity such a vessel is meant for. See also 'dirty or black oil'.

Draft

The depth of a ship in the water. This distance is measured from the bottom of the ship to the surface of the water. Draft at a port is the measurement of the depth of the water from surface to bottom. The outcome, how deep is the water, determines if a vessel is able to berth safely without grounding. Opposite is air draft which is important in case a vessel sails empty under bridges or electricity lines. See also 'AA', always afloat.

Drain

Pit, pipe or trench used in tanks to collect and dispose of free water in tank.

Most products' tanks do have such a connection as water is not wanted in consumers' products. Crude oil tanks do not need a drain system. Water is separated from the oil in the refinery before it is processed. See also 'Coalescer'.

Driving Season

Driving season refers to the summer vacation time in USA, when families step in their car and enjoy their holidays. Gasoline demand is increasingly significant and gasoline cracks go up. Gasoline prices increase and as a result the arbitrage from Europe to the USA may open up. During this season refineries avoid being in shut down or turnaround. The refineries want to cash in on the good refinery margins when available.

Dry

Empty. A refinery running dry causes a trader to work for finding crude or other oil to feed the refinery. Often a prompt issue caused by delays of supplies to that refinery. However, running dry is a consequence of bad logistics, too much risk in timely supply is taken or a matter of poor anticipation of problems that may arise. When feedstock is not available then the trader may have waited too long with buying the oil, maybe because the price was not right. A risk in a tight market. Running dry will cost a lot of money. The refineries will most likely circulate the production in order to keep the processing units warm until new feedstock arrives. I am sure that if running dry occurs due to bad planning, all hell breaks loose in your department.

Dry Chain Book Out

Same as a wash out. A cargo is sold and the buyer sold on that cargo and that buyer sold on the cargo and at the end the first original seller buys the same cargo in the market again. It does not make sense to move molecules if the cargo was a FOB cargo. The book out or wash out is done on paper, no liquids are moving within that chain, a dry chain book out. The chain can also exist of two companies only. X sells to Y and Y sells back to X. Nevertheless, the oil was produced and a physical delivery must occur. Therefore, the chain is washed out and the original seller may have sold the oil to another end receiver. Each company in the chain may have gained or lost some money on the deal. The quantity used for a washout can be the deal quantity or the B/L quantity. Traders to agree on that.

Dry Density

This is density in air; 11 points lighter than density in vacuum. API is always in air, like crude oil barrels API @ 60 °F. Numbers of barrels is volume. Volume is not reported in air. Only weight (mass) is reported in air or vac.

Dry Gas

Natural gas which does not contain liquid hydrocarbons. Gas is usually priced on a dry basis. Opposite of wet gas which may contain some C5.

Dtd

Dated, the price quoted at today's (now) value. Brent dated or Brent value on this day. Pricing reporters such as Platts and Argus are reporting the dated price quotations in their pricing reports. Physical oil cargoes in Europe and Asia are most often pricing on the Brent dated quotations plus or minus a differential. Discount or premium.

Dual Trading

Dual trading occurs when:

· A floor broker executes a customer's orders and, on the same day, trades for his own account or an account in which he has an interest.
· A futures commission merchant carries customer accounts and also trades, or permits its employees to trade, in accounts in which it has a proprietary interest, also on the same day.

Dubai Crude

A leading benchmark crude oil produced in the United Arab Emirates, used for pricing exports of sour Middle East crude oil to Asia. Crude with more than 1.0 per cent by weight of sulphur is sour crude; with less than 0.5 percent sulphur it is said to be sweet. Between 0.5 and 1.0 per cent is called a medium grade. Dubai crude has a gravity of 31° API and sulphur is 2%.

Dubai Market

A widely traded international forward market in Middle East Dubai crude oil that emerged in the mid-1980s and is used as both a risk-management tool and a benchmark for crude oil pricing East of Suez. Forward trading usually extends for two or three months. Nevertheless this market is not yet liquid such as the WTI and Brent futures markets.

Dubai Mercantile Exchange (DME)

DME, a 50-50 joint venture between Nymex and Tatweer, is the Middle East's first energy and commodity futures exchange. Some time to go before it is well traded. Currently many cargoes may be priced on Dubai crude. However Brent dated is still one of the main benchmarks for crude oil supplies from the Middle East.

Due Diligence

In an offering of securities, certain parties who are responsible for the accuracy of the offering document, have an obligation to perform a 'due diligence' examination of the issuer, issuer's counsel, underwriter of the security, brokerage firm handling the sale of the security. Due diligence refers to the degree of prudence that might properly be expected from a reasonable man, on the basis of the significant facts which relate to a specific case. See also 'IDD'.

Duration

Time span of an agreement. Often an expression in a term contract.

Duty

A tax imposed on imports by the customs authority of a country. See also 'preference certificate' and 'customs'.

Duty Types

· **Excise** – Regulated tax per country (consumer paid).
· **Quai** – Private companies might require this.
· **Harbour** – Local port authorities, maintenance and pilot.
· **Fairway** – Maintenance fairways in Sweden.
· **ICE** – Place where ice breakers are needed require ice duty.
· **Import** – Product from other geographic areas are due to pay import duties.
· **Export** – Product leaving a country cannot be cheaper than for own use, therefore export tax as income for a government.
· **VAT** – Value added tax. Vat numbers are often required and due to good administration of that VAT is not necessarily to be paid. Companies can get it paid back and the final payer is the end consumer. At petrol stations VAT is also paid over excise duties. Tax over tax.

DWT

Dead Weight Tonnes. Related to vessel size. You find information about the vessel deadweight in the vessel questionnaire (Q88). Just be aware that the deadweight of the vessel is not the same as the max capacity. Then volume, density and temperature need to be taken into consideration as well. Also, do not forget to think about draft restrictions at certain load or disports. Harbour authorities may have rules and regulations for vessel types and their size. Use 'DWT' in right way.

Dyes/Markers

Dyes and markers are usually used combined to identify a batch of gasoil or diesel. For example to indicate when excise duties are not paid on a certain batch of gasoil, depending on the end use of the specific batch, legislation requires the gasoil to be marked in order to prevent fraud. Often by use of furfural to make red diesel. If a private person avoids paying tax by using red diesel, then that person can have a problem. After 10-20 times refuelling a car with normal tax-paid diesel the inspection can still find traces of furfural. Therefore, some terminals prefer dyeing of gasoil in a barge when loading rather than dyeing gasoil in a land tank. From a land tank, the furfural traces may get spread in the terminal's pipeline system. Dyeing of diesel is also done to avoid or track theft of oil. See also 'fingerprint'.

E

E&P

Exploration and production. All majors and oil producers have this department in their company. Huge investments, big decisions and well skilled personnel. Searching and drilling for success and dollars. In my view, they need the expertise of traders and operators for the finishing touch of a project. The oil has to come to the market and operators' and traders' expertise is to squeeze the last dollars and cents out of the commodity planned to produce. It is important to understand that some oil quality is difficult to sell because of bad properties. It can most likely only be sold at a discount and it has to be seen if the market is willing to buy the new crude oil. Know what quality you want to drill. Bad quality oil is more challenging, not only on price but also on logistics.

E-4

Russian high sulphur straight-run feedstock. Formerly called F-10. Nowadays traders talk about M100 which is available as cracked and straight run quality. Nevertheless, E4 still exists and is very good quality for M100 blending purposes.

E10

Fuel that is 10 per cent ethanol, mixed with 90 per cent gasoline. E10 is the biofuel mixture that has been on the market for years. As long as the ethanol concentration is 10 per cent or less, it can be used in standard automobile engines without causing problems.

E15

Finished gasoline containing 15 % fuel ethanol by volume.

E20

Finished gasoline containing 20 % fuel ethanol by volume.

E70

The E70 means evaporation at 70°C/183.6°F. In a distillation curve the evaporation is registered at IBP, 10%, 20%, 30% up to FBP. But is also important to observe the percentages of oil being evaporated at fixed temperatures. Customs needs that to determine oil classification and indicate tax applicable to the oil. E70 is important to calculate the vapour lock index for gasoline. See 'distillation curve', 'classification of oil', 'nomenclature determination codes of oil' and 'vapour lock index'.

E85 Bio Gasoline

Mixture of 85 per cent ethanol with 15 per cent gasoline. This mixture won't work in standard cars, although several models are now sold and can run on E85 without damaging the engine. E85 is the new gasoline and started its development at the petrol stations in Sweden.

E93 Bio Gasoline

Mixture containing 93% ethanol, 5% methanol and 2% kerosene, by volume.

E95 Bio Gasoline

Mixture containing 95% denatured ethanol and 5% gasoline, by volume.

E200

The percentage of fuel evaporated at 200°F.

E300

The percentage of fuel evaporated at 300°F.

E-Commerce

Electronic trading using the internet. The ICE is a big example for it. See also 'fat finger'.

EAD

Electronic Administrative Document. Replacing the AAD. When goods are loaded within Europe from one excise warehouse to another customs warehouse, the customs documentation must be in place. Since January 2011 the old paper document AAD has been replaced by the electronic version. When a barge or vessel is loaded it can only leave when the final destination is known. Once the destination is known the excise numbers are noted and the vessel can sail. In the ARA area that may be a challenge as traders may change their mind or the operator sees a good chance to optimise freight. The barge will then set for another disport as there might be congestion at the original destination. When destinations are changed after a barge has sailed the customs registration has to be changed as well. It requires some cooperation in the market to make those arrangements. For some background related to customs documentation in Europe see 'AAD'.

Early Exercise

Exercise of an option prior to the maturity date.

Early Payment

Also called accelerated payment. Early payment means a payment which is to be done earlier than the business standard. Crude oil payment terms have a standard of 30 days after Bill of Lading date. A seller could ask for early payment, which is then related to a payment day after Bill of Lading before the 30th day after Bill of Lading. The seller will have to give a discount in exchange for that as there are financing costs for that with the buyer. Often such a discount is bigger than LIBOR on its own. Money in the account of the buyer also has value related to the balance sheet. The invoice from the seller to the buyer is a provisional invoice and it may happen that prices are coming off with the result that at reconciliation the seller has to pay money back to the buyer. In that case there is a credit risk with the buyer. How is that covered? Just to make clear, an early payment is done after B/L date and after receipt of relevant shipping documents. A pre-payment is done before commencement of loading a cargo. Opposite of early payment is 'deferred payment'.

Easing

Modest decline in price.

East West
In fueloil trading it is the arbitrage level between the forward paper markets of barges Rotterdam 3.5% and 180 Cst. fueloil in Singapore. It is often seen that the East/West levels are linked to the shipping market. When the arbitrage is open the shipping will get more expensive and the arb may close. In case of a short in Singapore the East/West may widen even further and more ships are needed. When the Arb is closed then the market is often waiting for freight cost to come down or market levels to change.

Easy in/Easy out
A trader prefers to deal in a liquid market. A market that he can step easy in and easy out at targeted price level.

Easy Money
Money a trader can earn with little effort and trading activity. In contango markets a trader can basically fill up a tank, hedge the long position in the forward market and go on holidays. When back in the month in which he secured his result, the hedge, he starts selling the oil and cashes in the profit. The profit locked in minus logistic cost is net profit. Easy money made while drinking some cocktails on the beach. Cashing in easy money is also referred to as 'harvesting low hanging fruit'.

Economic Steaming
A vessel that is slow steaming in order to save consumption of bunkers. In a slow market this would be a good solution to keep costs at low level.

Economy of Scale
The principle that larger production facilities have lower unit costs than smaller facilities. Often all about being efficient. Creating the maximum by using the minimum number of tools. In many systems with overcapacity the potential to make use of economy of scale is still present. The trader who sees this opportunity can create a perfect optimisation within his system.

Ecospeed
Economic speed. Reduced sailing speed in order to save bunkers consumption. When a vessel has an ETA before her loading window then the vessel would be idle on arrival until she is allowed to tender notice. Therefore, it is sometimes

better to slow speed and save bunkers and exhaust in atmosphere will be less as well.

EDP

Early Departure Procedure. A procedure related to shipping paper routines in order to let a vessel sail earlier instead of keeping her waiting for all documents. An agent could be entitled to sign for B/L and shipping documents on behalf of the captain. It could work well at a refinery or fixed supply points. The vessel sails early and the berth is available earlier for the next cargo. A matter of logistic optimisation. The electronic B/L helps a lot in this procedure. Also, counterparties must agree with such a system. If one counterparty in a chain of buyers and sellers does not agree with the EDP or electronic B/L, then a standard printed B/L must be issued, with loss of efficiency. B/Ls are also often linked to an L/C so also banks are involved. Still a way to go, but I am optimistic about it. Electronic B/L issuing will work in the future.

EFP

Exchange of Futures for Physicals. A transaction generally used by two hedgers who want to exchange futures for cash positions. Also referred to as 'against actuals' or 'versus cash'.

EGP

Excise Goods Place. A place to store or trade non-excised products. To obtain a permit for EGP rigid administrative and organisational requirements must be met. Moreover, a security must be given to customs in the form of a bank guarantee. Within an EGP production can also take place. See also 'AAD' and 'EAD'.

EHO

Extra Heavy Oil. Crude oil with an API below 20. Contains a lot of heavy fueloil and is therefore most often sold with a discount versus Brent or WTI.

Electronic B/L

Loaded quantities at a terminal are communicated with the captain of the vessel by IT tools. The captain gives his approval for the signing of the B/L on behalf of him. The B/L is then signed and stored in a computer and can be forwarded or endorsed through that system. Such a system has to be waterproof – no double set of original B/Ls should be printed in the market.

IT is the future and this system is getting used more and more. All parties involved in a trade of one cargo have to approve the use of electronic B/Ls. Can be including banks when it relates to L/Cs. Challenge is not to have too many different IT-systems from various terminals and locations. Then we lose overview and control.

Electronic Order
An order placed electronically (without the use of broker) either by the use of the internet or an electronic trading system. In oil trading, we often refer to 'The ICE'. See also 'fat finger'.

Electronic Trading Systems
Systems that allows participating exchanges to list their products for trading. This way of trading took over after the close of the exchange's open outcry trading hours. See also 'fat finger'.

Elliot Wave Theory (Technical Trading)
A theory based on the notion that the market moves in waves, which consists of trends followed by partial corrections. The Elliot Wave theory states that there are 5 waves within an overall trend. See also 'ABC' and 'Fibonacci'.

Embargo
Order to restrict the hauling of freight. Can be caused by financial matters or occasionally political or environmental matters. When such an embargo is executed on an international scale against huge oil producers in the Middle East, then it disrupts oil supplies. The OPEC may respond and adjust their production plans. Nevertheless the oil market may assume an increase of oil prices.

Emerging Markets
New upcoming markets. The business looks at new market development: how fast they grow and what impact this new business would have on the oil price. Is there increase of demand or new production? How is the Asian demand developing? How is Africa performing? A lot to cover and to watch market sentiment around these issues. Confidence level in emerging markets may set forward market prices.

Emission

Exhaust gas. Emission is bad for the environment and gets a lot of focus concerning CO_2 exhaust. Also in diesel, especially the sulphur and particles emissions are the main focus. In storage facilities tanks contain floating roofs to minimise the emission level for light and gaseous products such as gasoline, naphtha and crude oil.

Emission Trading

Trading model in which 'CO_2 tickets' are bought and sold in a market that should create a pollution control by providing financial incentives to companies investing in a cleaner production and by fining companies which do not adhere to the maximum allowances for exhaust of CO_2. See also 'CO_2 tickets'. Of course the economic reward for having a clean operation should encourage other companies to invest.

Emissions Cap

A limit on the amount of greenhouse gases that a company or country can legally emit. See also 'CO_2' or 'emission trading'.

Emulsion

Oil and water commingled which does not readily separate. The water is bounded with the oil molecules and may only be separated by treating. Heating may help but a demulsifier would speed up the water separation.

EN (590/228)

European norm. Related to oil qualities in Europe. Gasoil is related to EN590 and gasoline to EN228. The number is related to the specs belonging to the commodity. Those specs are updated following EU regulation on oil qualities. In those norms the testing methods are also defined. Automotive bio diesel (FAME) fuel has code EN14214 and ethanol blend component is EN15376. Heating oil is often related to a DIN code. See also 'DIN'.

End User

The buyer who consumes the oil for practical use. The consumer at the petrol station. In crude trading the end user is also seen as the refiner, as the consumer of crude oil is the refinery. For products trading the end-users are the marketing companies and wholesalers. For bunkers the end-users are the vessel owners and for low sulphur fueloil the end-users are the utilities.

Ending Stocks

Oil in stock as per end of the month. Incoming balance or end stock of the month before plus produced oil, plus imports minus export plus corrections on stocks is oil in storage as per end month. For planning purposes in oil-production, this formula is used to calculate availabilities to load next month. End stock or in that case expected stocks in the next month to come. The formula, end stock plus expected production, becomes availability to load next month. In crude this calculation keeps on going to a second month and availabilities are real estimations based on expectations which the producer or the crude field operator keeps calling ending stocks. So interpretation of ending stocks related to availabilities can be complicated.

Endorsement

A legal signature usually placed on the reverse of a draft. It signifies transfer of rights from the holder to another party.

Energy Information Administration (EIA)

The EIA is the statistical arm of the US Department of Energy. It produces numerous market moving reports on US energy supply and demand, most notably a weekly report detailing crude and product inventories in various geographical areas known as PADDs (Petroleum Administration for Defence Districts). The report covers US refinery throughput, as well as crude and product imports and exports. Information is also provided on international oil markets, gas and electricity. See also 'PADD'. Oil analysts are always very interested in the reports and announcements from the EIA. That information may have a fundamental effect on oil prices.

Engler Degree

A measure of viscosity. The ratio of the time of flow of 200 ml of the liquid tested, through the viscometer devised by Engler, and to the time required for the flow of the same volume of water gives the number of degrees Engler. Most fueloil traders have a special conversion lineal on which they can read Engler and convert it to Viscosity at 50° Celsius/122° Fahrenheit. Viscosity in Engler is most often used with Russian fueloil. Engler is reported at 80° Celsius/176° Fahrenheit. Look also at the conversion calculations in the final pages of this book.

ENI Number

European Number of Identification or European barge identification number. Registration number for inland barges in Europe. The ENI number is attached to the hull of the barge and stays there as long as the barge exists. The ENI number was introduced in October 2006. It can be compared with the IMO number system for sea going vessels. See also 'IMO number'.

EOSP

Shipping abbreviation for commencement of sea passage. A vessel or vessel agent would use such abbreviation in the time sheet. Indicating the time a vessel leaves pilot stations on her way to the berth. This time used is not for the account of the charterer or receiver of the oil, it is considered as sailing time. It will therefore not be deducted from the available time for loading and discharging as set in the charter party. If a vessel has plenty of time to sail to next loadport, then there would be idle time. The vessel better sails at 'eco-speed'. See also 'breakwaters' and 'COSP'.

ERRV

Emergency Response and Rescue Vessel. HSE related readiness when accidents happen.

Equity

The value of a futures trading account if all open positions were offset at the current market price.

Ownership equity, the value of an ownership interest in property, including shareholder's equity in a business (assets).

ESD

Emergency ShutDown. This is when someone must punch the red button in a refinery to prevent the refinery or terminal from damage or accidents. Trading logistics are now challenged, as this is completely unplanned. Traders want to keep it quiet in the market as they may have to covers shorts and maybe sell planned imports of feedstock. A PR-department in a company may have an interest to be open to the shareholders and other stakeholders and will make an announcement in public. A clear conflict of interest, therefore the commercial department needs to handle it fast, before Dow Jones, Platts and other reports start calling you to get information and report the issues in the news. The sharks in the market are waiting to help you with repositioning.

ESPO

Eastern Siberia Pacific Ocean. A Russian (Transneft) pipeline for crude oil from Siberia to the East Pacific Coast. Total length is roughly 4700km or 2900 miles. Meant to export Russian crude to markets like Japan, China and Korea. Russian crude oil loads in Asia from the port of Kozmino and other places. The pipeline does not reach Kozmino, so the crude will arrive there by train.

ESPO Cargo

Russian crude oil cargoes, mainly Urals/REBCO, which are supplied through the ESPO pipeline onto vessels at Kozmino, typical size 100kt. Most oil is sold through tender processes.

ETA

Estimated Time of Arrival. Date plus time is given by the vessel. If the ETA is before the loading window then the vessel has to wait tendering NOR. But if the vessel is coming after the loading window then the charterer has the opportunity to cancel the trip and book another vessel. Most often it is the owner changing vessel when they see that they are too late at loadport. ETA information sharing or updating is always mentioned in the voyage orders. It is needed as operators may have to update the B/L dates in the P&L. B/L updates can have exposure and result effects.

ETA Notices

Notices of vessel(s)'s estimated time of arrival. After the chartering of a vessel a stream of communication related to the planning begins. The vessel might have one or two more voyages to do before it can proceed with the agreed voyage. There might be delays in other ports or weather conditions may delay the vessel. When it seems that the vessel's ETA is deviating too much from the agreed laytime then it might be that another vessel has to replace the original agreed vessel. That vessel needs to be approved again by all counterparties involved related to the logistics.

ETB

Shipping abbreviation for Expected Time of Berthing. It is not the berthing prospects – those come from the terminal. ETB comes from the vessel planning. The master of a tanker sends out the position of the vessel and shows loading times, expected time of completion of loading or discharging a cargo, expected time of arrival, expected time of berthing and departing. The owner, charterer, terminal and other market participants with an interest in a certain cargo can make their planning based on that information from the vessel. ETB is given based on the information from the berthing prospects. The vessel agent in disport or loadport is continuously updating the master of the vessel.

ETBE

Ethyl Tertiary Butyl Ether, a high octane, low volatility, oxygenated fuel component made by combining alcohol with isobutylene from oil refineries. ETBE is a good replacement for MTBE. ETBE is also seen as a bio gasoline component.

ETC

Estimated Time of Completion. In offshore it is seen a lot that the day and time of completion is set as B/L date. Normally one would say that date and times of hoses disconnected is the B/L date, but that counts mainly for loading from onshore facilities. Hose disconnected at offshore and onshore is the time that the use of the vessel or lay-time stops.

ETD

Shipping abbreviation for Expected Time of Departure. The time and date that the vessel is ready to leave the terminal where the vessel loaded or discharged. Just be aware that this is not the moment that sets the B/L date. Lay-time of the vessel stops when hoses are disconnected. ETD is to use for logistic purposes – the vessel can now calculate and plan when the vessel arrives at her next destination. The master will send out a new ETA based on ETD.

Ethane (C_2H_6)

A normally gaseous straight-chain hydrocarbon. It is a colourless paraffinic gas that boils at a temperature of -88° Celsius/-127° Fahrenheit. It is extracted from natural gas and refinery gas streams. Ethane is considered as NGL and can be a petrochemical feedstock to produce Ethylene.

Ethanol

Alcohol and often seen as biofuel. Ethanol is used as biofuel blending component in gasoline. It has a high RVP and a very high octane number. It is produced from sugar, grain, potatoes, etc. Ethanol is often stored in well protected tanks surrounded by fences. This is to make sure that not too many samples are taken for purposes other than gasoline blending and testing.

Ether

A generic term applied to a group of organic chemical compounds composed of carbon, hydrogen, and oxygen, characterised by an oxygen atom attached to two carbon atoms (e.g. methyl tertiary butyl ether).

Ethics

Good behaviour according to common values in life and market. Often companies set rules of what activity is within or without company values. An employee not following those ethical rules is risking his career in that company. In oil contracts we see more and more anti-corruptions clauses, which is a positive development.

Ethylene (C2)

An olefinic hydrocarbon recovered from refinery H4 processes or petrochemical processes. Ethylene is used as a petrochemical feedstock for numerous chemical applications and the production of consumer goods.

EUR1

EUR1 is the name of a document, which is used in international commodity traffic and it is used as a preference certificate for customs purposes. The holder of this certificate can get import duty reduction or can import oil into the EU import duty free. Countries where EUR1 documents are issued: South Africa, Chile, Mexico, Bosnia and Herzegovina, Croatia, Iceland, Liechtenstein, Norway, Serbia, Switzerland, Algeria, Egypt, Israel, Jordan, Lebanon, Morocco and Syria.

Euro 4 and 5 Products

Russian classification for gasoline and diesel. Euro 4 products have a 50ppm sulphur cap., while the limit for Euro 5 is 10 ppm.

EuroBob

Bio gasoline, oxygenated, traded in the Rotterdam FOB barge market. Quality is EuroBob grade EN228 material 95 research octane number (RON) after the addition of 4.8% ethanol of minimum 98.7% purity. It is trading in the ARA barge market in lots of 1,000-2,000kt. This quotation replaced the premium unleaded assessments.

Eurograde

A term for 10ppm sulphur unleaded European gasoline. Most often loaded in cargoes out of refineries. It is not the same as EuroBob.

European Option

An option that can be exercised only at its expiration.

Even Keel

A vessel may inform the operator about the expected draft of the vessel on arrival in disport, e.g. 14.2-metre even keel. It means that this is based on the vessel floating straight (horizontal if you like). When a vessel is not flat/straight floating the back of the vessel lies deeper in the water. The master of the vessel may talk about a trim of 1 metre, the difference between the biggest and lowest draft of the vessel floating. When the vessel needs to get rid of some free water it may arrive in disport with a trim of one metre. Water disposal is then easier. The captain just needs to know if there is any draft restriction in disport. In a port with draft restrictions the total cargo would be more when a vessel arrives with draft even keel. With a trim, the vessel is deep drafted in the aft and therefore has less oil in the front.

Evergreen Contract

Revolving contract for supplies of crude oil or oil products; both buyer and seller can cancel the contract within an agreed notice of time.

Ex

'From', used as delivery term in order to confirm which loading figures count. Supplies by pumpover are called ex-tank or when STS operations occurred the term ex ship is used. For both examples it is clear that the ex-tank figures are used and not the figures in the receiving tank. For the STS case ex ship means the receiving ship takes over the exact B/L figures from the supplying vessels, a consolidated B/L. It also indicates that the quoted price is related to the point of origin.

Exchange Contract
An agreement between oil suppliers who deliver petrol to each other in different locations. By that action both companies save a lot of money on logistics or investments for storage of petrol to supply their petrol stations. It is very common for companies holding petrol stations especially in very large countries with different areas of close population. When the exchanged quantities are out of balance the parties will invoice each other. Also the market value per area may be different from each other. This is also settled in cash.

Exchange for Physicals (EFP)
A transaction generally used by two hedgers who want to exchange futures for cash positions. Also referred to as 'against actuals' or 'versus cash'.

Exchange-Traded
Futures or options that are traded on an exchange such as NYMEX or ICE, with standard contracts and rules.

Exercise
The action taken by the holder of a call option if he wishes to purchase the underlying futures contract or by the holder of a put option if he wishes to sell the underlying futures contract.

Exotic
A less broadly traded quality of oil. Often a tailor-made or blended oil. A bit special. See also 'boutique crude'.

Exotic Cargo
Vessel carrying different small parcels of oil products with different qualities. More often called a 'combi-cargo'.

Exotic Option
An option that is well out of the ordinary, i.e. not a 'plain vanilla' option.

Expeditor

Specialist controlling or witnessing all operational work to be done on a terminal for a certain order who sees to it that all work is done according to the right procedures. The outcome of a certain operation will be described and reported to the organisation who ordered for this service. Inspecting the inspection. Expeditors are often used as part of loss control programmes. Checking quantities that are stated on the B/L and control the activity and measurement when stating discharge figures.

Experience Factor

A compilation of the history of the total calculated volume (TCV) vessel measurements, adjusted for on-board quantity (OBQ) or remaining on board (ROB), compared with the TCV shore measurements. It was designed to be used, primarily, as a loss control tool to help assess the validity of quantities derived from shore tank measurements.

Expired Futures Contract

When a trader still has his futures contract at expiry date then a physical delivery or off take has to be executed. On most occasions traders balance their position by a cash settlement or EFP. Heating oil for example in ARA area in Europe can be traded by the use of futures, although it is not that much quantity and often part of a small trading strategy that can only be fulfilled by the bigger trading companies and producers. A result of a barge trading game sometimes. Often it gives more stress to the operations department than to the trader. The loading schedule is extremely tight; being off-schedule results in lots of re-arrangements with the exchange. At physical delivery, fulfilment of the futures contract, the exchange will mention the counterparty so that the logistics can be arranged. A balance quantity which cannot be loaded on a barge will need a cash settlement, EFP.

Expiry Date

Last date a contract or L/C is valid. When a tank rental contract expires the tank must be left empty on that day and in the same condition as it was when entering the tank unless different agreed according to the contract. If you still have a futures position after expiry you may be at risk or have an obligation to supply or deliver oil.

Expiration Date
The end of the life of a futures contract. Also the last day on which an option may be exercised. It is not uncommon for an option to expire on a specified date during the month prior to the delivery month for the underlying futures contracts.

Exploration
The search, discovery and drilling of oil and gas. Exploration operations include: aerial surveys, geophysical surveys, geological studies, core testing and the drilling of test wells. Trading crude oil originators are also searching for crude, but the only difference related to the upstream activity is that the originators are sourcing crude oil without drilling. They commercialise long term crude flows, buy and sell; they do not trade, but they develop long term business.

Export
Shipment of oil to a foreign country. Moving oil out of the country.

Export Licence
A government document which permits the 'licensee' to engage in the export of designated goods to certain destinations.

Export Oil
Crude oil of a standard of a country's export blend.

Export Oil Price
The price per barrel of export oil free on board ('FOB') at a fixed delivery point.

Exposure
Exposure is the amount of risk the oil trading book is faced with as a consequence of holding physical and paper oil positions. For traders exposure is the potential to make a profit or loss from fluctuations in market prices. To minimise default risk most traders work with a certain mandate which is monitored by a controller. A disciplined trader knows how to handle his exposure. See also 'discipline'. Two types of exposure are outright positions, being long or short, and spread positions based on time, market and products or cracks.

Exposure Effect

All changes in risk after a deal has been registered. When a cargo has a B/L related price then the operator has to register the best estimated B/L date in the P&L. Changes before the real B/L date may have an exposure effect on the hedge covering the deal. If the B/L date is updated and changed after the loading then suddenly the pricing will change and the risk position has changed as well. Same counts for quantity. Cargoes are often sold with a tolerance of +/- 10%. Here the operator must enter the expected cargo size based on tolerance according to contract but also based on eventual draft restrictions when a vessel loads less than expected. Errors of wrong pricing elements after a deal has been registered will have an effect. However, if the hedge was wrong due to that fact then it also has an exposure effect. When it concerns production companies, changes in refinery production or crude production can cause an exposure effect, e.g. when the production turns out to be less than anticipated the P&L will get short. When it relates to marketing systems the exposure effect may be observed when the market expects half way through that month that more or less oil has been sold. I based that on the fact that in most companies' oil to the marketing department is sold on month average prices and marketing departments update expected sales and realised sales on a regular basis. Sudden exposure changes will give an uncontrolled resultant effect. You can be lucky and achieve a gain, but it can also work against you. Controllers and traders are checking the P&L on a daily basis. Operators are important because of input of operational details. Understanding the P&L is a must when your work is related to the traders' P&L. At the end of the day, the trader working for his bonus has to be in control. They see it when sudden changes happen and will challenge that, when mistakes occur.

Ex Rack

Supplies of finished product to the consumer market such as the petrol station are based on ex rack prices. The price is a sum of the product market price plus the logistic costs, an ex-rack fee. The INCO term used in the contract is basis FCA.

Extrinsic Value

The difference between the price of an option (premium) and its intrinsic value. Also known as time value.

F

°F

Degrees Fahrenheit. In the USA the standard for temperature is measured in Fahrenheit while the standard in Europe is Celsius. Conversion calculation is available at the back of the book. Crude oil barrels are standard barrels at 60°F and most oil products are measured at 60°F. In Europe measurement is calculated at 15°C. Although in Europe trading activity for crude also goes in barrels at 60°F and API gravity is used. Nevertheless in European terminals the density measured goes at 15°C also for crude oil logistic calculation. Therefore, a conversion needs to be kept in mind as 15°C is 59.5°F or 60°F is 15.5°C. Therefore, from US Barrels to European Cubes we use 6.293 as factor. Barrels divided by 6.293 is cubes and cubes times 6.293 is barrels; the 0.5 degree temperature correction is included in this factor.

FAME

Fatty Acid Methyl Ester, blending component to make a bio-diesel from diesel.

Fahrenheit

Temperature scale used in USA. At 32°F water would start freezing and at 212°F water would start boiling – 180°F difference where Celsius has 100°C difference, zero to 100°C. Conversion to Fahrenheit from Celsius (centigrade) temperature scale is by the following formula: F = 9/5 x °C + 32, where °C is the temperature in Celsius degrees and vice versa: °C = (°F minus 32) /1.8.

Farm-in

The process whereby a company joins another company or joint venture participating in a block or field. The company farming in is granted a working interest in the field or block in return for cash and/or a carry through an exploration programme.

Farm-out

The process whereby a company reduces or disposes of its interest in a block or field. The company farming out grants a working interest in the field or block to another in return for cash and/or a carry through an exploration programme.

FAS

Free Alongside Ship. Product is sold when the goods in question are placed on the quay alongside the vessel. Same principle as CIF but here the cargo is delivered directly to a ship. Any STS costs are for the account of the buyer. The B/L figures for the delivery are taken over by the receiving vessel.

Fat Finger

Error in a paper trading order caused by a trader giving the wrong input. A typing mistake on a keyboard when entering an order has been committed. This can have a big financial impact on market prices, e.g. Someone gives an order for 10,000 futures purchase or sale instead of 1,000. The market will move due to a mistake caused by a 'fat finger'. Often we see a sudden peak or dip in prices as the market will correct quickly.

Fat Pitch

The perfect moment at which a trader takes a position in the market, just before prices are moving in his direction. The trader is holding an excellent position making lots of money from the moment of entering the market. Is this luck? No, luck is what you get in a casino. A fat pitch is a combination of a good view and a good trading decision, which apparently resulted in taking a position at the perfect timing.

FBP

Final Boiling Point. The last observed drop being condensed when testing a boiling range or distillation curve of an oil quality. FBP is reported in temperature. Naphtha has a lower FBP than fueloil. The first drop condensed is called IBP and is also reported in temperature. From IBP to FBP is called the boiling range or distillation curve. It can happen that not the full 100% has been condensed. The last bit, 0.1%, is called residue, can be sediments in crude oil production.

FCA
Free CArrier. The rail- and road freight equivalent of free on board. See also 'ex rack'.

FCCU
Fluid Catalytic Cracking Unit, or 'cat cracking unit', is the basic gasoline-making process. Cat cracked naphtha is the gasoline component produced and in most cases that is the basis blending component in a refinery to make gasoline. Most important feedstock is VGO or straight run fueloil. See also 'catalytic cracker'. Cracked naphtha has a relatively low octane number which needs further upgrading by blending with higher octane gasoline components such as reformate and alkylate.

FCO
Full Corporate Offer. Be aware that this term, between many other terms and abbreviations, is used a lot by jokerbrokers and there are a lot of those in the market. This is how I see it from a trading point of view. Does not mean that an FCO by definition is used in a wrong way. Of course there are also real FCOs.

Feedstock
The crude oil, straight run fueloil and naphtha from primary distillation which is needed in a refinery or petrochemical plant for processing purposes. For a refinery this may be crude oil, natural gas liquids, or natural gas. For a petrochemical plant it may be naphtha or clean condensate. As most refineries have lots of cracking capacity they may import straight run oil for further processing. Some cracking units may have overcapacity and therefore such imports of straight run oil may be very attractive for further processing. Crude is the most important feedstock, but the term feedstock is also related to the need for raw materials. Examples of those are: VGO, catfeed, naphtha, condensate and straight run fueloil. Straight run oil is produced and exported by the less complex refineries, also called simple refineries. Have a look at 'complex' and 'simple' refinery.

Fender

A cushion, placed between boats, or between a boat and a pier, to prevent damage when mooring. Used for vessels for protection when mooring at a jetty, but also used for ship to ship operation, e.g. A Suezmax pumping fueloil into a VLCC at Skår also called 'Skagerrak' or 'Skaw'.

FFA

Freight Futures Agreement. Paper contract for shipping where a freight price for a future voyage is agreed at today's value. A tool to lock in freight costs. See also 'long' and 'short' freight.

FFA Trade Symbols

FFA paper contracts cover different freight routes and different cargo sizes. Therefore here's an overview.

- **TD = Tanker Dirty**

TD3	VLCC AG – Japan	260kt	index Baltic
TD5	Suez WAF – USAC	130kt	index Baltic
TD7	Afra North Sea – UKC	80kt	index Baltic
TD8	Kuwait – Singapore	80kt	index Baltic
TD9	Afra Caribs – USGC	70kt	index Baltic
TD11	Afra Cross – MED	80kt	index Baltic

- **TC = Tanker Clean**

TC2	MR UKC – USAC	37kt	index Baltic
TC4	MR Singapore – Chiba	30kt	index Platts
TC5	LR1 AG – Japan	55kt	index Platts
TC6	MR Alg.–Euro MED	30kt	index Baltic

FFV

Flexible Fuel Vehicles. Vehicle being able to use different fuels. Probably needs 2 systems. In the Netherlands a lot of gasoline cars also had a gas system. Gas (butane/propane mixture) is much cheaper than gasoline. So a good saving.

Fibonacci (Technical Trading)

Fibonacci levels are commonly observed ratios between the size of a main trend and retracements. The main ratios are 38.2%, 50%, 61.8%, 100% and 161.8%. These ratios are derived from the number series named after the

Italian mathematician Fibonacci: 1, 1, 2, 3, 5, 8, 13, 21... If the first term is divided by the one to the right of it, the result gets closer and closer to 0.618, a ratio that recurs in nature and art. Fibonacci levels are used in the weird and wonderful Elliott Wave theory.

Field

A geographical area under which one or more oil or gas reservoirs lie, all of them related to the same geological structure. Fields are numbered and get a name when crude is produced, hence all the different crude names. Some fields produce 5kb per day and some 100kb or even over a million barrels per days. The huge fields are also called 'elephant fields'. Smaller fields may be connected to other fields which results in blended crude production. Combined field production can be a challenge as qualities are not often as stable as a single field production. As a trader you need to be aware of that and therefore sometimes they need to look at the specifications of the latest cargo. That gives at least an indication of what can be expected. Fields can be onshore and offshore. Brent is waterborne and WTI is landlocked. See also 'quality bank'.

Field Production

In crude oil activity, this relates to the production or the produced quantity of crude oil. The crude production goes per field and is used for investments, statistics and planning related to logistics. Traders like to know the field production and the behaviour of the field production. Each month the field operator sends out an overview of field production and therefore the availabilities for loading. Based on the forecasted field production a loading plan for the following month will be issued. This has to be as good as possible since the planning is meant to avoid a tank top situation. The statistics are used to look back at how the field has performed so far, but a forecast can also be calculated. New drilling techniques can prolong the lifetime of a field. Different fields can be connected to one load point. The total production of different fields together becomes a bigger loading plan. The oil sold from that loading point is called a crude blend. Brent, Ekofisk, Forties is crude produced from many fields. The lifting plan of a crude quality becomes known in the market so that the market can show their interest in various cargoes. Most planning of all oil comes out in the same timeframe so that they can be seen by the buyers. The buyer can then make up their plan and show interest in various crude cargoes for their refinery. Some qualities are of more interest than others are. Waiting too long is a risk as a crude programme can be sold out, but being too eager can also drive a price up to higher levels. A buyer must have a backup plan. Most oil is purchased and sold around 6 weeks before it is loaded. Field production programmes may need to be adjusted in the meantime. This may have an effect on the operational schedule of the buyer. Therefore plenty of challenges in the commercial side of the oil business when logistics are changing unexpectedly.

Field Testing

The term 'field testing' is here related to the shipping side. Each vessel loading at an offshore field must have the approval to load. A vessel has to go through a testing session. Can it connect in a safe manner and how is the communication with the field? Each field may have their own system. IT technicians have to be on board and see to it that a vessel has the correct programs installed on board and the system must work as well. Field-testing can take a day and is very costly. The vessel has to sail to the field with the IT people on board before testing. Also here time is money. The day rate of a shuttle tanker can vary between 50,000 and 100,000 USD per day. Then the vessel has to be tested with each offshore field before it can load. Most vessels will therefore be limited to a small number of fields. Who pays for the field-testing can depend on many things. Is it a brand new vessel or a brand new oil field? Or, is it just another vessel that needs more options for loading? The owner, charter and the equity holders of the field can sort it out. Best is to test a vessel in idle time.

Final Boiling Point (FBP)

The highest temperature in the boiling range from a crude or oil product. The temperature where the last drop condenses after a cooking process in a lab. Such a cooking process would go to a maximum temperature of about 360-380°C/680-716°F. The oil left over after the temperature is defined as residue. Naphtha has a lower FBP than gasoil. See 'boiling range'.

Final Price

Final price is the calculated price which includes all elements that were attached to the deal. It is the deal price from the trader based on all the terms connected to the pricing elements such as pricing quotations, density correction, others' quality corrections, freight corrections, etc. When all details are known, the buyer and seller countercheck the final price before sending the final invoice.

This counter check is often a function in administration. When both parties have different final prices and the administrations cannot agree, then the traders often get involved to agree on a solution.

Financial Year

The calendar year. The time in which the result (profit/loss) is measured. Should be equal to a tax year (1st Jan to 31st Dec). For many traders a bonus year.

Financing Risk

Term used to describe the increasing uncertainty that the buyer of goods will have the capacity to pay, when payment is due, the longer the time period he is given to make payment. In storage taking the financing costs have to be calculated as part of the total investment to take storage. Also with arbitrage cargoes, a long haul, some financing costs are due. See also 'credit risk'.

Finger Print

Specific oil additive which can be used to track the origin of a cargo. When a cargo has to be followed or when suspicious activity might occur an additive may be blended in the oil to track a cargo and its path to its final destination. When loading a barge or vessel with diesel or fueloil into a vessel or barge where shorts on shipping papers are big and structural, one could investigate if something has been pumped to the bunkers' tanks. The additive is easy to track. The oil with the finger print may end up in places or systems where it should not be. With good inspection, quantity and quality control, problems would not be expected to happen. The finger print will become the DNA of an oil cargo.

Finished Gasoline

Gasoline at correct quality ready as merchandise to the end consumers. Gasoline ready for the petrol station.

FIP

Free In Pipe. LPG is sometimes sold on this basis. But also oil supplies to refineries delivered from storage terminals by pipeline transfers are sold ex-tank or FIP. Risk and title goes over from seller to buyer as soon as the oil enters the pipe. If there are pipeline fees to be paid then it is the buyer who gets charged. If you buy delivered ex pipe then the seller takes all costs. The quantity assessment is also important. There are always operational losses so one can agree on quantity measurement from supply tank, receiving tank or share the operational loss over the average of both tanks. There are many pipelines for oil supplies and in the USA Cushing is one of the most important systems. Often pipeline capacity can be kind of rented as well. See also 'landlocked' and 'Cushing'.

Fire Point
The lowest temperature at which oil vaporises rapidly enough to burn for at least 5 seconds after ignition, under standard conditions.

Firm Offer/Bid
A trader being firm on an offer or bid is giving the buyer or seller a short time to make a final decision to confirm the deal. If the buyer or seller hits the deal it means that the business is confirmed. The risk of giving something firm for too long a time span is that the counter party can go shopping in the market. If the buyer or seller gets a better bid or offer in the market then the deal is not done. If you want to give a firm bid or offer it is better to do that at a competitive market level and at a limited time. If you are firm offering or bidding then the counterparty has the opportunity to take you out and accept the deal. There is no way that flaking is an option; in my view flaking is never an option.

First Foot Sample
When loading a jet A1 cargo it is important to know if the oil on board the vessel is not becoming contaminated with anything that was still in the line system of the vessel. After loading one foot of jet A1 into the vessel the pumping will be stopped and a sample will be taken. If the quality is good the loading will commence. If something goes wrong the vessel has to discharge the first foot out again. Thereafter the vessel has to be declared clean again and another attempt to load the vessel will be taken. Often then the first foot sample looks fine and the full cargo can be loaded. The off-spec jet A1 will be used for gasoil or diesel blending. It has lost a little bit of its value. But at least due to the first foot sample the off-spec situation was found before it would result in huge consequences related to the financials and the performance on the delivery.

First In-First Out (FIFO)

An accounting method based on an assumption regarding the flow of goods that older stock is disposed of first, in accordance with good merchandising policy. In oil storage it can be that import duties paid and non-paid are in the same tank. In that case the trader would nominate which parcel he wants to load. That choice will be dependent on the requirement for EU status or non-EU status deliveries. Something the fueloil market puts its focus on as bunker deliveries are free of duties, while deliveries to utilities are to be import duty paid supplies. Oil is blended in tank anyway, so it is not the molecules that leave the tank on a FIFO basis. Often each discharged cargo get an administrative cargo number.

First Oil

First day of oil production from a new field. When new projects are developed traders are often interested when the production is starting – they would ask when 'first oil' is expected.

First Refusal

In negotiating this are situations where the seller of gas has the right to solicit third-party bids for his gas; a right of first refusal provision gives the buyer of the gas the option of meeting the third party bid price and continuing the contract on such terms. In oil storage or with long-term oil contracts you might get the right of first refusal when it is time to discuss the renewal of the existing contract. The right of refusal is then given based on standard business practice or it is based on loyalty between the two counterparties resulting from good relations during the earlier term(s) of the contract. See also 'last look'.

First-To-Market Advantage

Also known as 'first-mover advantage'. The idea of first-mover advantage is that the initial occupant of a strategic position or niche (market segment) gains access to resources and capabilities that a follower cannot match. When the niche market is discovered and profits look attractive then in no time the competition in the market will jump on it and kill the business. Time to find a new niche. A good network is important to achieve such opportunities.

Five o'clocking

25 days before a cargo of Brent Blend crude oil loads at the Sullom Voe

terminal, the details of the cargo are passed by telex-telephone through the paper chains (see Daisy chain). If the cargo has not been sold by 17:00Hrs local UK time, then the last participant to receive the telex-telephone call with the cargo details owns the physical cargo and has been 'five-o'clocked'. Normally this is seen as a bearish sign, as it usually happens in a market with low crude demand. (Four o'clocking in the past.)

Fixed Price
Absolute price. Absolute number. Most often fixed prices are used in the ARA barge market, traded in small lots in order to set price quotations in Platts or Argus. Opposite is a 'floating price'.

Fixture
Moment that a vessel is booked for a certain voyage. The vessel is booked and fixed. Fixtures may be done on P&C basis; however, the market is often very inventive and soon the market knows. Most fixtures are reported for the purpose of creating the market quotation on Platts or Imarex. Fixtures are reported in the voyage (from x, to y), size (tonnage) and worldscale.

Flag (Ship)
Indicates for which country a ship sails. In some areas vessels sailing under a certain flag are not allowed to enter a port due to political issues. Often it could be cheaper for owners to let a vessel sail under a flag of another country because of taxes etc.

Flag (Technical Trading)
A price chart pattern that looks like a flag-pole with a rectangular 'flag' hanging off it. It is often seen as a signal that the trend is likely to continue after a brief consolidation. Also called 'bullish flag'.

Flaking
Being unaccountable. When a trader pulls back a bid or offer when he got hit in the market, then that trader is flaking on his deal. As a trader you do not want to be a flaker. If it happens too often the market would start ignoring that trader. It happens rarely – trading is still an honourable job and as a trader you prefer to keep your good reputation as a professional and reliable person. When you flake, people in the market will talk about you, complaining in the market.

Flare

The long thin sky high pipe/chimney at the refinery that is connected to different units and processing systems in the refinery. When the refinery produces too many gases as a result of overproduction of gas or as a result of problems in the refinery then the gas is routed in the refinery to the flare in order to handle the overpressure in the refinery. A huge flame of 10 to 25 metres high with lots of noise may be produced at the top of the flare. So if you see a refinery look at the flare – it indicates a bit how the refinery is doing (technically).

Flash Point

The lowest temperature under very specific conditions at which a combustible liquid will give off sufficient vapour to form a flammable mixture with air in a standardised vessel. Oil products are classified according to flash points related to logistic handling and HSE matters. See also 'classification of petroleum'.

Flash Title

Moment where title goes over from seller to buyer in a chain at loadport (CIF/FOB) or Disport (DES), e.g. A producer sells to a trader and the trader sells the cargo on to a refiner basis a CIF delivery. In that case, at title point, the oil which is on title of the producer goes over from the producer to the trader and then to the refiner. The trader would have title just in a split second as his cargo has been sold on. The trader never has, as a result of that, the risk and title of the oil on board the vessel. In case of trouble he would forward all discussions from the supplier to the off-taker and vice versa as if he would be an intermediary. But of course he needs to take care of his relations as well.

Flat/Square

Dealer jargon used to describe a position that has been completely reversed, e.g. You bought $650 then sold $650 thereby creating a neutral (flat) position.

Flat Price

The price as reported in the market without any premium or discount. As an example: Gasoline ARA Platts or Argus barges mean flat. Although no premium or discount is attached to the price it is often the average of the flat quotations of an agreed period. Flat price is also referred to as the futures price of oil on the screen. So dated crude price plus a differential is then the flat price (futures 1st month) plus the differential between the futures and the physical front market, dated crude plus the differential, a premium or discount versus the benchmark.

Flat Price versus Dated

The flat price is related to the futures as quoted on the screen. The October Brent futures or the April Brent futures price. The dated price is the price today as quoted on the daily price report. Platts dated or Argus dated. The dated price can be higher than the flat price, the first available futures on the screen. That means prompt high price and cheaper further out, a backwardated market. When the dated price is less than the flat price then there is a contango. However, between dated and the flat price there can be a period of 1 to 6 weeks. Those values per week are also quoted as 'CFD' 1st 2nd 3rd etc. week. It could well be that the dated until the 4th week is slightly in contango and that from there the structure is in backwardation. So in crude trading it is important to look at dated + the CFD weeks and then the futures market. That would give you the full picture of the forward market in crude, the curve.

Flat Rate

Flat rate is a shipping term to calculate the total freight for a cargo to be transported from A to B. The flat rate is a standard price in Dollars from port to port. These rates are set on a yearly basis and are dependent on the average freight market of the year before. Flat rate needs to be multiplied with the worldscale to find out the total freight cost. The level of the flat rate also depends heavily on the bunker prices over the last year. See also 'worldscale'. In some cases port dues are part of the flat rate, but in some cases one needs to add other different types of costs on top of the freight costs, such as ice dues and insurance. Worldscale multiplied with the flat rate is a lumpsum. The lumpsum divided by the cargo size is freight per barrel or ton.

Flexi-Coking

A thermal cracking process which converts heavy hydrocarbons such as crude oil, tar sands and distillation residues into light hydrocarbons. Feedstocks can be any pumpable hydrocarbons including those containing high concentrations of sulphur and metals. Feedstocks are the most heavy crudes and most heavy residual oils at the refinery. It converts the heavy oil to naphtha (coker naphtha), gasoil and cokes. Cokes may be needle coke, sponge coke or shot coke which is used to produce anodes for the aluminium industry. Heavy oil logistics can be expensive as heavy oil needs to be heated or blended to stay liquid enough to be pumped. Heavy crude oil may be supplied at temperatures between 50° and 80°C/122° and 176°F. Some extremely heavy crude grades are to be blended with diluent. See also 'dilbit'.

Flexi Short

Arrangement where the seller of crude has the opportunity to supply different grades of crude oil to a refinery. Often there is a basket of different crudes agreed with a refinery. But it could also be any crude within a certain range of specifications. If new crude is supplied then the refiner may need to re-approve the quality first. A flexi short can be based on sweet, sour or heavy crude. Depending on the refinery it may be a combination as well. A good opportunity for a producer or trader to optimise or create a length or short. The buyer often takes the advantage of certainty of supplies and a good financing arrangement. Most often the refiner takes care of the products sales himself or sells to a local trader or marketer, basically giving a length. Not a 'flexi length' as here the buyer just has to accept the produced qualities. In the case that the seller of the crude oil would also buy the products then this deal would almost become a processing deal. It would become a processing deal when the refinery margin risk is also handed over to the seller.

Floating Pipeline

A Russian company was planning to build a big crude oil terminal in Rotterdam Europoort with the main aim of creating a Urals benchmark. As a result of these plans it was be expected that shuttle tankers will move Urals crude oil from Primorsk or Ust Luga to Rotterdam. In the market we heard people calling it the floating pipeline. The terminal was supposed to become operational in 2015. Basically each activity from a production point to a fixed storage place for further delivery could be seen as a 'floating pipeline'. Bad economy and international trouble with Russia in 2014/2015 stopped the project. Nevertheless, the definition "floating pipeline" deserves still a place in this book.

Floating Price

Price which is calculated as average from a range of quotations. Such a range can be based on fixed dates like a quotation week Monday to Friday 1-5 May. It can be based on the B/L date like B/L +/- 2 days (5 quotations = 2 days before

B/L, the B/L day and 2 days after B/L). Other examples are based on monthly average or based on delivery dates or NOR at disport. The standard payment term in products is 5 days after B/L and at that day the price quotations may still be unknown. Then the preliminary invoice has to be issued and paid. As soon as the final price is known, the final invoice is prepared and the seller and buyer make the final settlement. When you buy a swap then you buy a fixed leg and you sell a floating leg.

Floating Roof

Roof of a tank that is floating on top of the products in tank. When a tank is full, the roof is high up in the tank and when the tank becomes empty the roof is down in the tank. A floating roof is used for tanks with products with high vapour pressure or low flash properties. As the roof is on top of the product it is nearly impossible that vapour, emissions, will leave the tank. Often crude can contain mercaptans and due to the floating roof the bad smell of oil will stay in the tank. When taking a sample it is important to know if the roof is high up or at a low level in the tank. The lower the product in tank the more gas will be on the roof with a high steel wall surrounding it. When a tank is empty then the roof is standing on its legs. To avoid further emission it is better not to empty the tank. Some terminals keep a heel in the tank to keep the roof floating. Most floating roof tanks can handle a product with a TVP of max 11.1 psi. Products with higher pressure should be stored in pressurised (bullet) tanks.

Floating Storage

Oil tanker used as stationary or temporary storage. Stationary storage is an activity done for example in Gibraltar 3 or 4 fueloil vessels, in Singapore at a certain stage up to 11 VLCCs being used as stationary floating storage; also in Fujairah floating storage is available. Often stationary floating storage is organised due to draft restrictions at shore jetties. Break of bulk is therefore most often seen as the main activity and reason for floating storage. Temporary floating storage is done based on forward markets in combination with low shipping rates. As long as the costs for temporary floating storage are below time value it certainly makes sense to utilise floating storage. A vessel waiting a long time for a berth is seen as a vessel in demurrage. Costs of demurrage per day are much higher than the price of floating storage per day. Stationary floating storage vessels have a different classification than normal transport vessels and are therefore not available to transport oil from one place to the other. Often those vessels are old vessels which are still good enough to squeeze out some money when used for floating storage. Floating storage is often lower priced compared with the rental of shore tanks. Keep in mind that when using floating storage there is an HSE element as well. Loading and discharging is executed based on ship to ship (STS) operations. See also 'FSU', 'FPSO' or 'sevan'.

Floor Broker
An individual who executes orders on the trading floor of an exchange for any other person. In the old days Brent futures were traded on the IPE (International Petroleum Exchange in London). The broker with the best and loudest voice was often able to get the best deal. Today the oil futures are traded electronically on the ICE.

Floor Trader
An individual who is a member of an exchange and trades for his own account on the floor of an exchange.

Flow
Production of oil from an area with different fields through the pipeline. The speed of the flow indicates how fast production goes; how well the pipeline is used; and it indicates disruption of production when the flow is down or in case there is no flow, e.g. Flow of Kirkuk fields.

Pumping speeds of oil in a pipeline for a certain oil commodity at a terminal.

The flow of crude into the market. Where is it produced and where is it shipped? Since USA is producing so much more oil, fewer imports are going from West Africa to the USA. The flow of crude has changed because of that. Europe gets more crude from West Africa. However, what would happen in the market when USA would start exporting crude, which is currently prohibited? Flows will change again, which may affect oil prices.

Flow Improver
This relates often to cold properties of diesel. Different formulations of CFPP-improvers (cold filter plugging point) have been developed to treat a wide range of gasoil and diesel fuels. During the winter period the n-paraffin in gasoil tends to form wax crystals at lower temperatures. When cooled down

further these wax crystals coalesce and will settle out of the fuel, resulting in blocking the engine filters (CFPP temperature). This will stop the flow of fuel to the car engine. Quality requirements are different per season for diesel.

Flow Meter

A device used to measure fluid flow. Based on pumping speed logistic timing can be calculated. On board the tanker and at shore side there are flow meters. While loading or discharging the shore side and the tanker can compare their flows. If a big flow difference is measured between the vessel and shore side, there may be a huge problem. Luckily the operational routines at most places are well organised and actions are taken very quickly before getting to such a problem.

Flow of Oil

The analytical overview traders would like to see. From where is oil exported, and where is it imported? Since the USA is producing so much shale oil, the flow of oil has changed in the world. West African oil used to go to USA, but now it flows to Europe and Asia. The flow into USA is much less. Oil producers have to find other destinations for the crude oil. Such big market changes have an effect on the way of trading. It could affect the way of organising a trading unit in a company.

Fluid Catalytic Cracker (FCC)

An oil refining unit in which a catalyst combines with a vacuum gas oil range feedstock at high temperatures to cause a reaction. This is the most popular design for catalytic cracking in a refinery. The feedstock used is VGO and straight run fueloil. The naphtha produced from the FCC is most often used as blendstock in the 'gasoline pool', also known as 'cat cracked naphtha'.

Fluid Coking

A thermal cracking process utilising the fluidised-solids technique to remove carbon (coke) for continuous conversion of heavy, low-grade oils into lighter products. See also 'coker' and 'flexi-coker'.

Flushing

Pumping product through a pipeline or tank in order to clean the system. See also 'dewaxing'. Flushing a line may also be done with (sea) water into crude. Such a refinery may need a good coalescer or de-salter before processing the crude. Flushing a pipeline may be needed to avoid contamination of different product qualities in a pipeline. Unleaded gasoline 98 and 95 may be pumped through the same pipeline into a vessel. The same may happen with different distillate qualities. The line flush material is then often pumped into the tank with the lowest quality.

FMV
Fair Market Value. See also 'arm's length price'.

FOB
Free On Board. In this case the buyer has the responsibility to charter transport at his cost to move the oil. B/L quantity counts as invoicing quantity. Title and risk goes to the buyer as soon as the product is on board the vessel. The quality and quantity are often as per shore tank certificate and measurement. On rare occasions the quality may be off-spec in the barge or vessel due to contamination with material that was pumped earlier through the same pipeline. A line flush should have been done.

FOB Price
The price actually charged at the producing country's port of loading. The reported price should be after deducting any rebates and discounts or adding premiums where applicable and should be the actual price paid with no adjustment for credit terms. The barge market in ARA is a FOB market. During the Platts and/or Argus window bids and offers are done. Deals are committed at market prices. These numbers will later become the assessment in different reports as FOB quotes for that day for FOB ARA Barges.

FOD
FuelOil Domestique. Term related to the French quality requirements for heating oil.

Foot
30.48 centimetres. Draft for vessels is often reported in feet. Feet times 0.3048 is metres. Metres divided by 0.3048 is feet. Always ask for the draft restriction at the location where the cargo is being supplied and know the draft restriction from your own loading places. And where it is relevant do not forget 'air draft'. Now you know what vessel size to charter related to the draft restrictions in different ports.

FOR

'Free On Rail.' The seller pays the logistic cost of loading including the activity at the loading rack. The seller most often has the control of the installation as such. The buyers get the price in which the seller has covered his costs and might make some extra money.

Forecast

Expectation of oil prices, oil consumption/production made by analysts. Those analysts may work for the big oil companies or consultancy offices. Analyses are used for investment decision long-term and trading decision short-term (although most traders make their own assessments). It concerns professional reported expectations based on actual status of actual and maybe expected world economy, market circumstances, and different situations per country. No guarantees given on outcomes. Some forecasts are made public and many are kept intercompany. How difficult it is to make a good forecast? Crude 1999 at 10 USD, in 2008 at 147 USD and in 2015 below 50 USD. There is so much happening in the world, economy and geo-politics, wars, nature, climate etc. etc. A short-term forecast is more secure than a long-term forecast.

Forecasting

Presenting the expected price development of oil based on a market view and expected fundamental changes in the future. A short term forecast is more precise than a long term forecast. Refinery LP models are most often based on short term forecasts. Big investments are often based on long-term forecasts. Such a forecast is most often executed by an analyses department in the major companies. A short term forecast as input to a model can also be done by a trader working for a refiner.

Force Majeure

Clause permitting a contract to be broken in the event of uncontrollable events, e.g. War, strike government action or act of god which precludes its fulfilment. See also 'Act of God'.

Form-A

Certificate of origin, used in a special programme for exportation of products by developed countries, in order to bolster the exports and economic growth from those countries. The Form-A is a customs preference certificate and when importing products into the EU, with a Form-A presented, import duties are discounted or import is free of charge.

Formula Price

A price for oil that is determined by a specified relationship to a benchmark oil or a group of benchmark oil grades or products. The formula also usually specifies the time leg from the point of loading at which the price is determined, the exact average to be used and other variables. (Like premiums or discounts.) Opposite is fixed price. See also 'floating price'.

For Orders

Logistic term for nominating where to let a vessel sale when the discharge port is still unknown, e.g. Rotterdam for orders. The vessel will have to sail to Rotterdam for further instructions. The trader has in this case not yet made the decision where to discharge the cargo. It could still go into many terminals in Rotterdam, to UK, Belgium, France or even Northern Spain. The different options related to final destinations are agreed in the charterparty. The nomination to the seller is often sent with destination 'for orders' to the seller 7 to 10 days before loading. The vessel is at that moment not yet distressed. By the time the vessel is loading the final discharge place is normally known. An unsold cargo will get a nomination with as destination location "sea", a certain deviation point "See deviation point". Otherwise, having a destination for orders on a Bill of Lading is fine. At least for a time the real disport can be kept quiet for some additional days. Hiding a destination is nearly impossible as vessels are easy to track in the market.

Forties

The first substantial crude oilfield in the British sector of the North Sea. Forties is traded during the Platts and/Argus windows and is extremely important as it is used to make the assessment for Brent dated crude oil quotations. See also 'BFOE'. Loaded at Hound Point terminal.

Forward (Cash) Contract

A contract which requires a seller to agree to deliver a specified cash commodity to a buyer sometime in the future. All terms of the contracts are customised in contrast to futures contracts whose terms are standardised. Forward contracts are not traded on exchanges. This is about physical oil trades, not about paper trades.

Forward Deal

A deal with a value date greater than the spot value date. Securing supplies in the future. The price can be floating average around supply date, but it can also be a fixed price based on price according to the forward market. A fixed price deal is easy to hedge and does not necessarily involve price risk. Forward deals may be of use in case one wants to 'play a leverage game'.

Forward Market

The market's expectation of a product's price at some point in the future. This expectation is based on current (prompt) price and fluctuates as you go further in time. Based on the curve of the forward market one can tell if the market is in contango or backwardation. See also 'structure'.

Forward Price

The paper price or value of an oil grade at a later date than today. The price of oil in the next months to come as indicated in the paper market.

Fossil Fuels

Fuels that originate from the remains of living things, such as coal, oil, natural gas, and peat. Crude oil is a fossil fuel.

FPSO

Floating Production, Storage and Offloading. Storage tanker used at an offshore field for production of crude oil. Such a unit may also be able to receive and store diluents which may be needed to blend heavy oil. Loading from such a floating unit does not work as a normal ship to ship operation with fenders. The loading activity from such an FPSO is done in the same way as from any other offshore rig. Bow loaders are required to load the oil. To give an impression, the loading point at sea is roughly 300 metres away from the FPSO. A FPSO may have a storage capacity 600 to 1000 kb. Size depends on the production and on the commercial logistics. Flexibility in cargo size does have better commercial value.

Fracking

Hydraulic fracturing, or 'fracking', is the process of drilling and injecting fluid into the ground at a high pressure in order to fracture shale rocks to release natural gas inside. The water brought in is mixed with sand and chemicals to create fracking fluid.

Fraction
A refinery distillation tower splits crude oil into separate fractions. A fraction is a mixture of hydrocarbons that comes out of the still at a particular level, according to its boiling point range.

Fractional Distillation
Separation process which uses the difference in boiling points of liquids. Separation of different fractions in a distillation unit depends on the design of the processing unit where dishes (bubble caps) in the unit are placed on different levels which cause different cut points. See also 'atmospheric distillation'.

Fractionation
The extraction by processing of condensate, LPG, ethane and other light hydrocarbon fractions from gas using a gas fractionation plant. Wet gas (mixture of gas and condensate) comes from production fields and is fractionated before it goes to the market. Gas and naphtha goes to 'consumers' – petrochemical industry – and condensate goes to refineries as feedstock for the column.

Fracturing (Frac-Job)
A process carried out to increase the permeability of a hydrocarbon reservoir, particularly those with relatively poor flow characteristics. This is essentially the pumping of special chemicals at high pressure into the reservoir, with the aim of causing fractures in the rock, thus increasing permeability and hence productivity. Linked to the technical way of production of shale oil. See also 'tight oil'.

Free Carrier (FCA)
An INCO term of sale meaning that the seller has delivered when the cargo is given to the carrier nominated by the buyer at the named place. The term FCA is commonly used for truck loading. Take a look at 'ex-rack'.

Free Water (FW)
The percentage of water that will settle out of an oil-water mixture in five minutes. This test is performed in a 100-millilitre laboratory cylinder. The measured volume of water in a tank not in suspension with the liquid in the tank at observed temperature. Expressed in cubic metre or/and barrels. Free

water from crude oil production can contain high levels of H_2S – I have seen up to 2000ppm. Some water is stored at production fields and is transported out of the system when needed. The cost of disposal of water can be expensive. Some fields produce oil and cannot avoid water mixture in the crude oil. A refiner does not want the water and may require a maximum acceptable percentage of water. Remember crude with a water percentage higher than 0.5 or 1.0% is regarded as off spec crude oil. Vessels may need to get rid of the water first before they can sail to the final destination. See also 'decanting'.

Free Water after Loading Vessel

On-board quantity of all free water measured in cargo and slop tanks after loading. Such measurements are important to keep track of the real quantity of crude oil. Loss of crude oil can become very expensive. See also 'crude oil voyage loss calculations' in the back of the book.

Free Water before Discharge Vessel

On board quantity of all free water measured in cargo and slop tanks before discharge. See also 'crude oil voyage loss calculations' in the back of the book.

Freight Optimisation

Use of the vessel's ullage or voyage plans in the most optimal way in order to have the freight per ton or barrel as low as possible. Communication and understanding between shipping departments, operations departments and traders have to be very professional to be best in class. Freight optimisation can also be organised by using a vessel by constantly loading and discharging it at ports which are nearby the next voyage order of the vessel. Using a vessel for a backhaul from a Trans-Atlantic trip is an excellent way to optimise freight.

Freight Payable as per Charterparty

Freight costs have to be paid as described according to the original charter party. Deviation cost and other services required by the charterer are described in the charter party. When a cargo is sold then the physical trade is also done as per charter party. The buyer of the cargo will pay the additional cost if the vessel deviates from the original destination. The charter party differential will be calculated by multiplying the differential of the basis flat rates with the agreed worldscale for the voyage. See also 'charterparty differentials'.

Freight Rate

The charge made for the transportation of freight. Freight rate is based on worldscale and flat rates. Harbour cost, ice dues and other related costs are also important to include when calculating the total freight costs. Traders calculate freight to the price per unit, tons or barrels.

Fresh Feed Input

Represents input of material (crude oil, unfinished oil, natural gas liquids, other hydrocarbons and alcohol or finished products) to processing units at a refinery that is being processed (input) into a particular unit for the first time. Examples:

· Unfinished oil coming out of a crude oil distillation unit which is input into a catalytic cracking unit is considered fresh feed to the catalytic cracking unit.
· Unfinished oil coming out of a catalytic cracking unit being looped back into the same catalytic cracking unit to be reprocessed is not considered fresh feed.

Front-Month Contract

Commodity futures have different contracts for each month onwards. Front-month contracts are the futures contracts whose expiration date is nearest to the current date. The front-month contract would be the shortest futures contract a trader could buy. Front month is first month available futures. Between dated and the front month there are CFDs available as paper tool for hedging of physical crude oil cargoes.

Front Office

In business, front office refers to sales and marketing divisions of a company. It may also refer to other divisions in a company that involves interactions with customers. See also 'back office' and 'middle office'.

Front Running

A process whereby a futures or options positions are taken based on non-public information about an impending transaction in the same or related futures or options contract. Taking in a trading position based on pre-information which has not been available to other market participants. Illegal practice where a floor broker executes an order for his own account before executing an order for a customer, with the intent of getting ahead of a market move precipitated by the customer's order. A broker who went long 10 contracts of December crude just before he executed a buy order for 500 contracts would be 'front-running'. The audit trail, which timestamps when orders are received, etc., is intended to make this practice difficult to get away with.

Front to Back

Traders like to talk about their front to back positions. They are long or short the front to back. That means they have a time spread position. One can be long in the front and hedge the length further out in time. Or one can be short the front to back, meaning short in the prompt market and hedged with length position later in time. Refiners and oil producers are always long in the front. Wholesalers (buyers) are short in the front.

Front Window (Front End)

'Front window' or 'front end' is a term used in the barge market during the Platts and/or Argus trading window. It means that the loading window of the offer or bid is based on the first 5 delivery days as set during the window session of that trading day. E.g. Company X bids 650 USD per ton for a HS barges ARA loading f/e. See also 'back end' and 'full window'.

Fronting

Trading positions in the nearest dates. Prompt market, first month. Smart to know what happens in the physical oil market. What is going on in the market, who is active and how prompt are buyer and sellers selling. Question and demand are affecting price levels especially in the front. You must know if there is a leverage game going on. The trader must be proactive as usual. See also 'leverage game'.

FSU

Former Soviet Union. After the big changes in the Soviet Union 15 countries were declared as independent states. The market started to call this geographic area the 'FSU'. You can call it a kind of slang as the official name is CIS countries. Commonwealth of Independent States. Take a look at 'CIS countries' to see to which countries this applies.

FSU

Related to the oil trade an FSU is a Floating Storage Unit. Storage on board of a stationary VLCC, suezmax, other vessel or sevan. These can be used related to oil production fields, offshore but also onshore close to sea based on draft limitations or even ice conditions. See also 'sevan' or 'FPSO'. In contango markets the demand for storage is huge. If the shipping market is weak then it can be profitable to use a big vessel as floating storage.

Fuel Additives

Various fuel additives are being added to fuels as gasoil, diesels, and gasoline to meet the standard characteristics set by the different receiving markets. Additives to improve the cold flow properties, to improve the ignition quality or to prevent excessive wear to diesel engines. Other additives improve the safety in handling and during transport like conductivity agents, H_2S-scavengers etc. So, it is not the same as blending components. I see blending components and oil products to be blended together in big quantities. Additives are a special type of chemical which cause a reaction that improves oil properties. It is added in small volumes and calculated in ppm. E.g. add 300-ppm flow improver. The use of the competence of a good inspection company would be a great outcome. Additives are expensive but worth the money. When adding additives at a terminal in tank, then the tank must be made homogeneous while adding. There are some costs attached in doing this. Too much additives can make the oil oversaturated and opposite results can then be achieved. One has to work with precision.

Fuel Ethanol (C_2H_5OH)

An anhydrous denatured aliphatic alcohol intended for gasoline blending as described in oxygenates definition. Alcohol and alcohol blends are added to gasoline in order to make it burn cleaner. It has a high RVP and a very high octane number. It is produced from sugar, grain, potatoes, etc. Call it a 'biofuel'.

Fuel Grade Coke

Coke used in the production of cement and with fluidised bed boilers (using limestone for sulphur removal) for generation of steam and electricity.

Fueloil (Heavy)

A name given to the heaviest grades of residual fuel used in marine oil burning boilers. The different fueloil grades are classified according to their viscosity and sulphur content. Fueloil is black and classified as dirty. It is high flash (k3) oil which is often stored in insulated tanks which can be heated. Often people mention 'fueloil' when they mean heating oil which is clean oil. This can be confusing, therefore it is better to talk about heavy fueloil if it concerns the dirty part of the business.

Fueloil Pool

The production of all fueloil related components in a refinery. The group of fueloil components a fueloil blender has access to. The refiner or blender will use the products in his fueloil pool to produce or blend on-spec fueloil in the best economical way. Additional components can be imported or exported; that is a matter of blending optimisation. Components can be heavy fueloil, light fueloil, fueloil with a certain sulphur or viscosity content, cutterstocks, dirty LCO, leftover straight run fueloil, etc. Blending would be done to supply the bunker market or the utilities market such as electricity companies or steel producers.

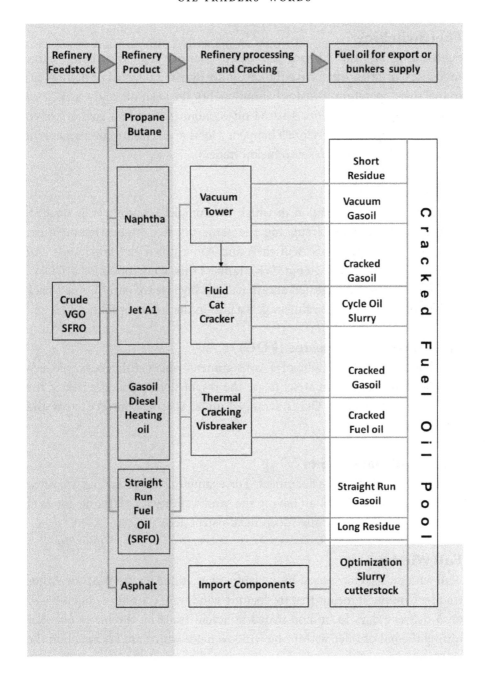

Fuels Solvent De-asphalting

A refining process for removing asphalt compounds from petroleum fractions, such as reduced crude oil. The recovered stream from this process is used to produce fuel products.

Fuel Switching

Substituting one fuel for another based on price and availability. Large industries, utilities, often have the capability of using oil, coal or natural gas to fuel their operation. Due to that optionality they can make the switch on short notice. That decision is based on economics. Gas and coal are often cheaper for burning. Therefore it happens a lot that electricity companies rent out their tanks in the market to fueloil traders.

Full Cycle Washing

Crude oil washing operation in which the complete cargo-tank is washed. Often by spraying or circulating the same oil at a higher temperature. Clingage, sticky paraffins, will melt and come down the tank walls. All products in tank should go out. With tankers this would be called a 'COW'. Tanks and caverns are treated occasionally. A big layer of paraffins gets back to the stocks. A trader or refinery gets a plus in the stocks or P&L.

Full Outturn Guarantee (FOG)

Guaranteed outturn weight of a consignment where differences between load- and discharge port weights are the responsibility and the risk of the FOG service provider. FOG is arranged under specific contract terms and conditions.

Full Set of Documents

All signed originals of a document. For example, Bills of Lading are often issued in three originals, all having the same validity for claiming goods at the place of delivery. See also 'document instructions'.

Full Window

'Full window' is a term used in the barge market during the Platts or Argus trading window. It means that the loading window of the offer or bid is based on 5 delivery days to be nominated at actual trade by the buyer or seller hitting the bid or offer within the window dates which are set based on the window session of that trading day. See also 'front end' and 'back end'.

Fully Disclosed

An account carried by a futures commission merchant in the name of an individual customer.

Fundamental Analyses
A method of anticipating future price movements by using supply and demand information. The study of specific factors, such as weather, wars, discoveries, and changes in government policy, which influence supply and demand and, consequently, prices in the market place. Each event is weighted differently. Market analysts indicate the market to be bullish or bearish based on their findings and their approach of the events which affect the oil prices. Traders have to choose what to read and what to use to make their view on the market. Without an own view a trader should not take a position. Some fundamental events have a long term effect. Traders prefer to look at short term effects. That includes the prompt activity including the behaviour of the trading activity in the product swap (paper) market. Network is important. The major events causing fundamental changes come as a surprise and market may move rapidly. E.g. Middle East changes in 2011 or the European financial crisis in 2011 – oil markets need a long time to recover from such events.

Fundamentals
The macro economic factors that are accepted as forming the foundation for the relative value of crude oil and petroleum products; these include inflation, growth, trade balance, government deficit, interest rates, OPEC production changes, oil findings, strikes, refinery shutdowns and many more events which may affect oil balances.

Fungible
Oil product on-spec. Most often related to pipeline deliveries. Tradable and acceptable in the market. Not a boutique crude or other crude with quality challenges. Oil is oil some say; however, not every quality is easy to market because of its properties. A commodity.

Furnace Oil
Canadian term used to describe high-sulphur No. 2 oil. Furnace oil in Canada is the equivalent of high-sulphur, off-road, home heating oil.

Futures
Type of derivative. Contracts on a recognised exchange to make or take delivery of a specified oil grade, at a fixed date in the future, at a price agreed upon at the time of dealing. Most futures positions are liquidated before expiry

date. If a position is open after expiry date the holder of the futures is obliged to supply or receive the oil. The alternative could be a cash settlement which may turn out to be expensive. Futures are used for hedging and speculation purposes. Deliveries on futures contracts in the oil business happen rarely. In the heating oil business in the ARA it may happen that a physical delivery is done. The buyer will load the oil from the seller's tank in the ARA, a barge business. The rules of loading the exact quantities combined with the timing can be very challenging. The exchange has a special set of rules for this activity.

Futures Contract
An exchange-traded contract that on its last trading day settles into a forward contract.

Futures Exchange
A central marketplace with established rules and regulations where buyers and sellers meet to trade futures and options on futures contracts. In oil those are electronic exchanges like 'The Ice'. In the past it was the IPE where crude and gasoil futures were traded on the basis of a system called 'open outcry'. The buyer and seller trade direct with the exchange. The buyer and trader do not meet or see each other, nor is their name mentioned. Exchange business is not an over the counter (OTC) activity. In the USA oil is traded on the exchange called 'Nymex'.

Futures Market
A trade centre for quoting prices on contracts for the delivery of a specified quantity of a commodity at a specified time and place in the future. Futures are available in the front market and in the forward market. The values of the futures of different months forward in time form the structure of the market. If prices are getting lower forward in time then the market is backwardated and if prices forward in time are getting higher, then the market is in contango. The volatility of the futures prices as such is what we can call the outright market. One can buy futures based on months or as strip of a quarter of even a full calendar year.

Futures Month Symbol
Not every letter on the screen is used for each month. This is done to avoid confusion connected to the commodities. Letter 'O' for oil is not used, like

'B' for Brent and 'W' for WTI. But also 'I' could look like a number one. This results in the following symbol-month combinations:

- F = January
- G = February
- H = March
- J = April
- K = May
- M = June
- N = July
- Q = August
- U = September
- V = October
- X = November
- Z = December
- Y = Cash

G

G/L

Grams per litre. If divided by 1,000 then g/ml. Used as a measure of contaminants and to specify density of refined oil products. Standard German grade gasoline, for example, is specified as 0.755 g/l. G/ml is the same as 'ppm Vol' (Volume based).

G/ml

Grams per millilitre. PPM volume (parts per million).

GAL

1 gallon equals 3.7853 litres. USA standard measurement for gasoline and diesel. Prices on Nymex for gasoline and heating oil are quoted in price per gallon. 42 gallons is equal to one barrel. Crude oil price minus 42 times the product price is the product crack value, the gross refinery margin per barrel of petroleum product. 1 lot of oil on the Nymex is equal to 1,000 barrels. 1 lot of oil products is therefore 42,000 gallons.

Gallon

Net or standard gallon (231 cubic inches at 60°F). 42 gallons is equal to one barrel. Gasoline, heating oil, diesel is priced in gallons in the USA. Measuring in gallon is a USA standard. In Europe the standard is in litres at 15°C. Gasoline and heating oil in the exchange in the USA is offered gallon-lots and priced per gallons. 1 lot of gallons is 42,000 gallons equal to 1,000 barrels. Crude futures are offered barrels and 1 lot is 1,000 barrels.

Gas
Any dry gas, rich gas (e.g. butane/propane), ngl, stabilised condensate and/or unstabilised condensate. So make sure which one you handle.

Gas Condensate
Liquid hydrocarbons present in casing head gas that condense when brought to the surface. The majority of condensate production is classified as a clean product. Very light condensate can be available to the petrochemical industry as feedstock. If the quality is heavy, then condensate can be dirty and needs processing in a refinery. Some refineries may blend condensate with heavy crudes before processing and in some refineries there might be a condensate splitter. Just to give an idea, condensate may consist roughly of 70 to 80% Naphtha, 10 to 15% gasoil and 10 to 15% kerosene. Some butane, propane and drops of fueloil can also be noticed in condensate. Condensate can also be used as diluent for heavy crude oil production. Very heavy crude oil does not always float unless it is heated at very high temperatures and blended with a diluent. By using condensate the heavy oil is enough diluted to make it available to move through logistic systems, pipelines.

Gas Free
An atmospheric condition in a tank when it is free from any concentration of inflammable, noxious or toxic gases and vapours. In case a tank needs to be inspected or if it needs maintenance the tank has to be accessible by people in a safe way. On terminals a person is only allowed to enter a tank when he is licensed by the terminal. Be aware that an empty tank is most often more dangerous than a full tank. Tanks which are still saturated with gas may be very sensitive for static electricity. Enough accidents have happened in the past with activity related to empty tanks, e.g. Empty gasoil tanks were often related to accidents such as explosions, as a result of static electricity generated from tank cleaning operations. Today those operations look much more safe than ever. It requires high HSE focus.

Gas Liquid Trading
Activity of a trading group dealing with naphtha, LPG and light condensate. One can be a trader at a producer (refiner, crude drilling), consumer (wholesaler) or purely a trader (margins related). Gas liquid trading involves paper trading as well. This is based on the purpose for hedging and speculative trading. Abbreviation: 'GL'.

Gas to C4

An abbreviation for the percent mass of hydrocarbon gases at normal temperature and pressure from C1 to C4 inclusive, present in crude oil.

Gasoil

An intermediate distillate product used for diesel fuel, heating fuel and sometimes as feedstock. The term is often used interchangeably with No. 2 heating oil, D2, AGO, ULSD or fueloil. Gasoil qualities are very much linked to sulphur, cetane and cold properties. High sulphur gasoil can be further processed in a hydro-treater which is basically a desulphurisation unit. After sulphur removal gasoil becomes a diesel quality. A liquid petroleum distillate having a viscosity intermediate between that of kerosene and lubricating oil. Gasoil refers to diesel and heating oil, density can vary between 0.8100 and 0.8700. Below the 0.8100 density we get towards kerosene or jet petroleum and above 0.8700 we get to darker products LCO, cutterstocks etc. It may need further treatment in a refinery to squeeze more light oil out of it. The refinery margin would be negative on heavy oil products. Gasoil is the most preferred product, as now also bunkers' specs for vessel require gasoil due to low sulphur requirements. Europe is short of gasoil and is therefore a big import market.

Gasoil 1 Lot

On 'The Ice' 1 gasoil futures is called 1 lot. 1 lot is equal to 100 tons of gasoil. If the gasoil futures cost 950 USD then 1 lot costs 95,000 USD. To illustrate, one cargo of gasoil in Europe can be 30,000 tons or 300 lots. On Nymex 1 lot of heating oil is equal to 42,000 gallons (1,000 barrels or roughly 135 tons). On the Nymex the gasoil pricing is in cents per gallon.

Gasohol

A blend of finished motor gasoline containing alcohol (generally ethanol but sometimes methanol) at a concentration of 10% or less by volume. Data on gasohol that has at least 2.7% oxygen by weight and is intended for sale inside carbon monoxide nonattainment areas are included in data on oxygenated gasoline. As the market moves more and more towards biofuel we see that ethanol becomes the most common gasoline blending component for the future. See also 'oxygenates'.

Gasoline

Volatile motor fuel used in cars. Gasoline does not come straight from distillation or cracking. Gasoline is a blend of different components which are produced in the refinery. A refinery is processing and cracking oil to create the highest valuable product or component. Components used for gasoline blending are cat. cracked naphtha, reformate, butane, isomerate, alkylate, ethanol, mtbe, plattformate, ic5-c9, debenzenised steam cracked naphtha, oxy-fraction, polymerate and other light oils. Gasoline blending may be done in refineries but also in storage – there are plenty of traders able to buy the different components and make gasoline. Gasoline has many different specifications depending on seasonality. Quality requirements can also be different from country to country. There are more than 100 different gasoline specification requirements in the world. Knowledge of quality and knowledge about the value of blending components or even knowledge of specification value such as octane value are very important to be a good trader or blending specialist in gasoline. Even though lead is not used anymore in gasoline, the customs classification still exists. The requirements for cleaner specification for gasoline are getting stricter. Until the year 2000 gasoline was allowed to contain a high benzene and aromatic content. Sulphur was high as well. Over the last decade a lot has changed and most bad properties of gasoline that were allowed in the past became limited or prohibited. Now we see a change to more bio-grades being blended in the gasoline. With the new standard, refineries will be further challenged. Gasoline is probably as clean as diesel, although it is still higher taxed at the petrol stations in Europe when you compare it with the tax for diesel. Europe is long on gasoline and short on distillates.

Gasoline Blending Components

Products produced in different refining and cracking processes which need to be combined and blended in order to create a finished gasoline. Examples are cat. cracked naphtha, reformate, butane, isomerate, alkylate, ethanol, mtbe, plattformate, ic5-c9, debenzenised steam cracked naphtha, oxy-fraction, polymerate and other light oils. It is clear that gasoline does not come direct from the distillation or cracking units. In many processes the different gasoline components are produced. Blending at the refinery is done to be able to supply on-spec gasoline.

Gasoline Engine

Inventor: Niklaus August Otto. First called the Otto engine, today gasoline engine. A simple explanation: Air and fuel combined with spark ignition result in power to let the engine run.

Gasoline Factor

Way of setting a price on gasoline components. The factor times the price of gasoline (unleaded 95) is the final price for the gasoline component. I have traded those for alkylate and MTBE. High octane gasoline components are important for gasoline blending. In the case of a closed gasoline arbitrage situation there will be more low-octane gasoline available in the European market. It might create a short of high octane gasoline components. MTBE used to trade (2000-2005) at an average of a 1.35 factor versus unleaded 95. But in tight markets it traded at a 1.90 factor and when ETBE started to find its way in the market MTBE became cheaper than gasoline at a 0.95 factor. Also when the specification of gasoline became stricter and sulphur went down from 50ppm to 10ppm and the aromatic spec came down from 42% to 35% alkylate became more important. Also here the factor was rising fast initially but came down later.

Gasoline Grades

Gasoline is classified by octane (RON) or octane ratings (average of RON+MON). Based on the octane we can mention regular gasoline with a typical RON/MON of 91/81, Euro grade or middle-grade gasoline with RON/MON 95/85 and premium gasoline with RON/MON of 98/95. These are the common grades. Each country may have their own specification requirement which may be based on geographic area, taxation, political, environment and seasonal level. E.g. RVP in the North of Europe is required to be higher than in the South of Europe. Germany RVP in gasoline during summer and winter is 60/90 and in Norway it is 70/100. That allows for more butane blending in Norwegian gasoline. A higher RVP makes it cheaper to produce gasoline.

Gasoline in USA

- **Conventional Gasoline**
  Finished motor gasoline, ready for marketing at the petrol station. This quality is not included in the oxygenated or reformulated gasoline.

- **Oxygenated Gasoline**

  Finished gasoline, other than reformulated gasoline, having an oxygen content of 2.0% or higher by weight. Gasohol containing a minimum 5.7% ethanol by volume is included in oxygenated gasoline.

- **Reformulated Gasoline (RFG)**

  Finished US gasoline formulated for use in motor vehicles. This gasoline is required in order to reduce smog in areas that exceeds the federal health standard for ozone in the USA. Emissions such as VOC (volatile organic compounds) and NOx (nitrogen oxides). RFG is specified to contain 2.7% oxygen. Due to this oxygen content in gasoline the exhaust of toxic air is significantly reduced. Some spec requirements to show that the gasoline became 'cleaner': Aromatic down to 25% max, benzene 1%, a requirement of 2% 2.7% oxygen. Oxygen comes from MTBE blending or from bio ethanol. Octane index to be 83.7 (R+M)/2.

- **Reformulated (Blended with Ether)**

  Reformulated gasoline blended with an ether component (eg: Methyl tertiary butyl ether) at a terminal or refinery to raise the oxygen content.

- **Reformulated (Blended with Alcohol)**

  Reformulated gasoline blended with an alcohol component (i.e. Fuel ethanol) at a terminal or refinery to raise the oxygen content.

- **Reformulated (Non-Oxygenated)**

  Reformulated gasoline without added ether or alcohol components.

- **PBOB**

  Premium reformulated Blendstock for Oxygenate Blending. Octane index to be 91.3 (R+M)/2.

- **CBOB**

  Conventional Blendstock for Oxygenate Blending. Octane index to be 83.7 (R+M)/2. There is also a CBOB for the Laurel pipeline which has another octane requirement of 84.0.

- **PCBOB**

  Premium Conventional Blendstock for Oxygenate Blending. Octane index to be 91.0 (R+M)/2.

- **GTAB**

  Gasoline treated as blendstock. Gasoline components. When imported into the USA the blendstock should be listed as such because of import regulations in the USA.

- **RBOB**

  Reformulated Blendstock for Oxygen Blending. This is the gasoline as listed on the Nymex in price per gallon. Quality is fixed and should allow 10% of ethanol blending. RBOB combined with MTBE at some refineries makes what we call RFM (Reformulated gasoline with MTBE). RBOB combined with ethanol at some terminals makes what we call RFE (Reformulated gasoline with ethanol).

- **Regular Unleaded**

  Low octane gasoline with octane index of 87.0 (R+M)/2. In Europe it would be MON 81 and RON 91 with a density basis of 0.745.

- **Unleaded Midgrade**

  Gasoline with an octane index of 89.0 (R+M)/2. In Europe it would be MON 85 and RON 95 with a density basis of 0.755.

- **Super Premium Unleaded**

  Gasoline with the highest octane and therefore the most expensive at the petrol station if available. Octane index of 93.0 (R+M)/2. In Europe it would be MON 88 and RON 98 with a density basis of 0.755.

Gasoline Pool

The production of all gasoline related components in a refinery. The group of gasoline components a gasoline trader or blender has access to. The trader or blender will use the products in his gasoline pool to produce or blend on-spec gasoline in the best economical way. Additional components can be imported or exported. That is a matter of blending optimisation. Components can be reformate, cracked naphtha, isomerate, alkylate, light naphtha, polymerate, mtbe, ethanol, etc.

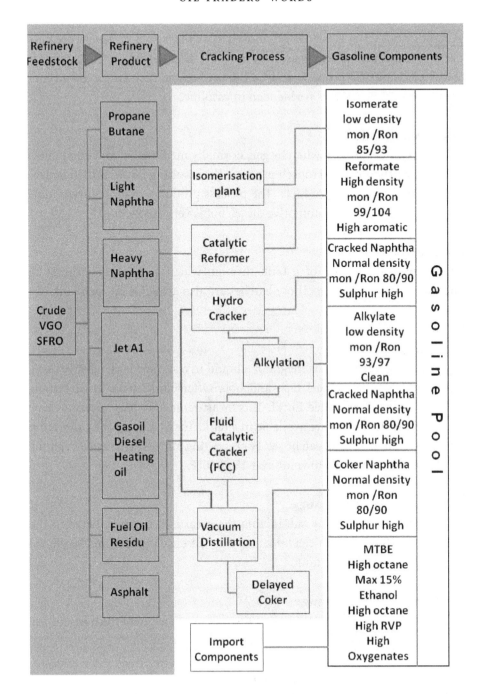

| Refinery Feedstock | Refinery Product | Cracking Process | Gasoline Components |

			Isomerate low density mon /Ron 85/93
	Propane Butane	Isomerisation plant	Reformate High density mon /Ron 99/104 High aromatic
Crude VGO SFRO	Light Naphtha	Catalytic Reformer	Cracked Naphtha Normal density mon /Ron 80/90 Sulphur high
	Heavy Naphtha	Hydro Cracker	Alkylate low density mon /Ron 93/97 Clean
	Jet A1	Alkylation	Cracked Naphtha Normal density mon /Ron 80/90 Sulphur high
	Gasoil Diesel Heating oil	Fluid Catalytic Cracker (FCC)	Coker Naphtha Normal density mon /Ron 80/90 Sulphur high
	Fuel Oil Residu	Vacuum Distillation	MTBE High octane Max 15% Ethanol High octane High RVP High Oxygenates
	Asphalt	Delayed Coker	
		Import Components	

Gasoline Pool

Gas to C4

An abbreviation for the percent mass of hydrocarbon gases at normal temperature and pressure from C1 (methane) to C4 (butane) inclusive, present in oil. C1 and C2 are often used as refinery fuel or at overpressure party or it will end up in the refinery flare. C2 might also be used as refinery feedstock. Gases C3 propane and C4 butane are commercial gases and may be traded/sold-on or they are blended in gasoline.

Gas-to-Liquids

GTL, a technical process whereby gas, normally methane, is converted into a liquid using the Fischer-Tropsch process. The resulting liquid is then hydro-cracked into synthetic products. The process produces high-quality middle distillates, particularly automotive diesel, but is very costly.

Gauge Hatch

The opening in the top of a tank through which gauging and sampling operations are carried out. Those hatches are also available on each tank of a tanker.

Gauging

A process of measuring the height of a liquid in a storage tank usually using a weighted graduated steel tape and bob. Often tanks have an electronic measurement system called Enraf. This measurement system calculates how many millimetres of oil are available in a tank. Then by using the calibration tables the volume in tank can be set. For reporting purposes the actual volume will have to be corrected to volume at 15°C/60°F.

- **Alternate Innage Gauge**

  The innage obtained by subtracting the measured distance between the surface of the liquid in the tank and the reference point from the official reference height of the tank.

- **Alternate Ullage Gauge**

  The ullage obtained by subtracting the measured height of the liquid in the tank from the official reference height of the tank.

- **Innage Gauge (Dip, Sounding)**

  The height of the liquid surface from the bottom of the tank (or datum plate).

- **Ullage (Outage) Gauge**
  The distance from the liquid surface to the top of the tank (or reference point).

- **Open Gauging Method**
  This is a method for obtaining measurements of the tank contents through an open gauge hatch. This is the traditional method of performing static measurements.

- **Closed Gauging System**
  A method for obtaining measurements of the tank contents without opening the tank. This may be accomplished by using automatic tank gauges or by taking measurements through a pressure/vapour lock standpipe. This type of gauging is done extensively on vessels with inert gas systems.

- **Stop Gauge**
  The final gauge reading for a transfer to or from a shore tank or vessel.

See also 'manual tank measurement'.

GBRT

Great Big Round Things. When a trader points to tanks or big units in a refinery.

Gentlemen's Agreement

Unwritten agreement between two parties based on mutual trust, behaviour and common business understanding. This type of arrangement is not popular with legal departments. One cannot draw any rights from this agreement. It is 100% based on a good relationship between two companies or rather the two traders of the two companies. For traders a matter of common sense, maybe a matter of honour.

Giveaway

Sold oil product with specifications that are much better by far than the minimum requirements. The buyer of the oil can take advantage of the product when blending. Too high quality oil products have a great blending value. Products with giveaway can therefore be downgraded. A missed opportunity to the seller. Giveaway is quickly obtained in density, sulphur content, octane, RVP and viscosity. There are of course more parameters to mention. Value of giveaway can be different per trader; it all depends often on what a buyer has available in his blending pool. Traders are always chasing for the component giving best value.

GL

Gas Liquids. LPG, naphtha and light condensate. Condensate can be marketed as petrochemical feedstock due to its high naphtha content. Heavier condensate may be traded through the crude trading book. However, that may differ from company to company. Condensate may also be traded through LNG offices.

Global Strategic Petroleum Reserves ('GSPR')

Crude oil inventories (or stockpiles) held by all governments of all countries, as well as private industry, for the purpose of providing economic and national security during an energy crisis. See also 'compulsory stock'.

Global Warming

Increase of the average temperature of the Earth's surface. Assumption is that due to heavy air pollution the world is changing. Weather is changing, more prolonged dry periods, more heavy rainfall and storms are the major changes. The ice on the North and South Poles is melting. As a result tankers are starting to sail through the Barents Sea to Asia, the Northern sea route; 34 vessels sailed north over to Asia in 2011 during summer. So far guided by nuclear ice-breakers. As a result of the change in the atmosphere, emissions have to be cut – CO_2 is the main focus. Fuels for burning have to be cleaner (lower sulphur), and renewable energy gets much attention. Can we save the planet in a world of economic growth?

GMT

Greenwich Mean Time, London, UK time basis. Greenwich was a royal park and place on a hill to the south of the River Thames, east of London. The line of 0° longitude runs through Greenwich and in 1884 this became the standard, also called meridian time. CET is Central European Time and is one hour ahead of GMT. CET is the time in Amsterdam, Paris, Oslo, Madrid etc.

Going Long

The purchase of a commodity for storage, supplies or speculation. If you own something then you are long. When you are long you are exposed to value changes, your position is at risk. To avoid risk one can sell derivatives in order to balance the position. See also 'long'. When a trader says that he is bullish, then he is probably taking a long position. He will probably try to find fellow traders in the market confirming his view.

Going Short

The selling of a commodity not owned by the seller. When you owe something to another then you are missing a product. You are short. To cover a short you need to buy something later in time when you have to fulfil your delivery. So if you are short you are exposed to price changes. If the price of the commodity goes down you can buy your commodity at a low price and you make profit. If the price of the commodity goes up you would lose money. If you do not have a market view then you better reduce your risk by buying derivatives for hedging purposes. A trader being short would tell the market and the reporters that he is bearish. If no one agrees with his view then the trader may feel less comfortable. Will he change his mind-set now or does he follow the rule of trading discipline?

GoM

Abbreviation for Gulf of Mexico.

GOST

Russian standard oil testing method. The 'gosudarstvennyy standart' is Russian language for state standard, created in Soviet Union period. Next to 'astm', 'din', 'en' also the Russians have their own set of testing methods. If you buy oil from Russia then 'gost' standards are used. The outcome of quantity reported can cause a small loss. One buys on gost-standards ex Russia while the receiving port in Europe uses different standards for measurements. It is not clear if that loss is calculated in the price of Russian oil. Maybe a trader is not aware of that. An operational loss they call it, even though in my view this loss is not caused by operations. It is an accepted loss since the market is not able to change the way of calculation or use of international standards in Russia. Just be aware of it; it should be part of calculations when taking a commercial decision, a relatively small standard loss.

GOV

Gross Observed Volume. See 'gsv gross standard volume'. Take a look also at the 'conversion calculations' in the back of this book.

GOV = TOV - Free Water

Gross observed volume of product on board a vessel minus the total observed volume of liquids on board the vessel. Free water is a cost for a terminal. When it is too much a vessel may be able to pump the free water into a slop tank on board or start a 'decanting' operation. 'Decanting' is described in this book.

GPH

Gallons Per Hour. USA standard measurement. Refinery production gasoline goes in gallons per hour. Alternatively, a vessel is loading or discharging gasoline in 'GPH'.

Grantor

A person who sells an option and assumes the obligation to sell (in the case of call) or buy (in the case of a put) the underlying futures contract at the exercise price. Also referred to as an option seller and/or writer. Involves more risk as now you have to deliver when the option is executed. Delivery of futures (paper contracts) in this case.

Green Coke

Residual product produced by the coker unit. Green coke is unprocessed coke. The green coke is to be processed to calcined cokes which are needed to produce anodes. Those anodes are used again in the aluminium and steel industry. So the refinery production of cokes finds its way to the steel and aluminium industry. Green coke can be classified as needle coke, sponge coke and shot coke. You can find those in this book.

Green Line

This term is used to describe the 'permit to pump' telemetry system installed on virtually all North Sea off-take tankers. Sensors are fitted to various systems on the tanker and it is only when all of these sensors are in the correct position that the permit to pump signal is given to the FPSO, which allows the cargo discharge pumps to be started. Offshore HSE gets highest priority;

mistakes like leaking lines and lack of communication between vessel and offshore unit are not allowed of course.

Greenfield

Oilfields from which we know there is oil available to be drilled but nothing further has been developed. Drilling for oil will be done when it makes economic sense. The reason for waiting with drilling can be because of logistic reasons or oil quality issues. Some crude oil has difficult marketable or low value quality and is expensive to produce. Only when oil prices reach a certain minimum price level would it make sense to produce it. Related to logistics I would use the Arctic as an example: no good systems, ice conditions, polar lows, darkness and much more. It has to be safe to drill and production of oil must be shipped somehow. A lot of work to be done, but apparently a lot of oil waiting to be produced.

Greenhouse Effect

The idea that certain gases in the atmosphere trap heat like the glass in a greenhouse was first proposed over one hundred years ago, and is now widely accepted. About half the sun's energy reaching the earth is reflected back into space or absorbed by the upper atmosphere. The other half is absorbed by the Earth's surface. Some of this energy is then radiated upwards where a portion is trapped in the atmosphere, warming the Earth. The rest goes out into space. The greenhouse gases, primarily carbon dioxide and methane, control the balance between the trapped and radiated energy. The air pollution contributes to a faster process of the greenhouse effect. World programmes are in place in order to better control and regulate rules about exhausts.

GRL

Gross Rail Load, related to gross weight, the total combined weight of a rail car and its contents.

Gross Input to Atmospheric Crude Oil Distillation Units

Total input to atmospheric crude oil distillation units. Includes all crude oil, lease condensate, natural gas plant liquids, unfinished oils, liquefied refinery gases, slop oils, and other liquid hydrocarbons produced from tar sands, gilsonite and oil shale.

Gross Observed Volume (GOV)

The total volume of all petroleum liquids and BS&W, but excluding free water, at observed temperature. Expressed in cubic metre or/and barrels.

Gross Standard Volume (GSV)

The total volume of all petroleum products and BS&W, but excluding free water corrected by the appropriate volume correction factor (VCF) for observed temperature and density to a standard temperature. Expressed in cubic metre or barrels.

Gross Standard Weight (GSW)

The total weight of all petroleum liquids and sediments and water (if any), excluding free water, determined by applying the appropriate weight conversion factors to the gross standard volume.

Gross Tons

Same as GSW. BS&W plus net tons are gross tons. In crude trading the gross tons are important for the shipping and other logistics. The net tons are the tons which are stated on the commercial invoice.

GSV

Gross Standard Volume on the Bill of Lading. The total volume of all petroleum liquids and sediments and water, excluding free water. See also 'crude oil voyage loss calculations' in the back of the book.

GTAB

Gasoline Treated As Blendstock. Gasoline components. When imported into the USA the blendstock should be listed as such because of import regulations in the USA.

GTL

See 'gas-to-liquids'.

Guarantees

Promises from the seller to the buyer that agreed parameters of the product will be perfectly on-spec, e.g. Sulphur max 1.0% or density max 991. Sellers would only guarantee those specifications if very sure that it will be fine. Opposite of guarantees would be 'typicals' or 'standard specs'. During negotiations the seller may be more firm on his offered price when giving guarantees. Giving guarantees in specs involves some risk on performance, which has to be paid for by the buyer. Look also at 'waiver'.

Gulf Coast

Trading hub in USA for crude and products as feedstock. Many refineries are based in this area. That results in good trading activity. US Gulf coast (USGC) is a market area with price quotations available in the quotation list of price setting agencies. USGC is United States Gulf Coast (Houston Area).

Gum

Kind of rubber sustained and formed in gasoline engine of an old car. Gasoline has a max gum spec. Gum is formed in the cylinder of a car engine. One will notice that when the car gets old or after many gasoline kilometres.

H

H$_2$S-Scavengers

H$_2$S in gasoil and gasoline is considered hazardous if the concentration in the vapour phase exceeds 25 ppm. Especially during handling and transport it can be extremely hazardous. H$_2$S-scavengers are used to reduce the H$_2$S concentration in the liquid phase. Most receivers of oil have a maximum allowance for taking in oil that contains high H$_2$S values. The cargo needs to be treated before it can enter the discharge port. It is just standard HSE rules per company. The closer a refinery is situated to cities and civilisation the stricter a receiver's requirement may be. People living close to a refinery would complain when a bad smell is observed in their back garden. Local authorities may have set maximum limits in the licence of a terminal. It is to protect civilians from exposure to bad smells. A terminal can be fined or can even lose their licence. Just as a reference, low ppm levels of H$_2$S smell like rotten eggs; 500 ppm H$_2$S does not smell at all and is so dangerous it can kill you; 1000 ppm H$_2$S and higher does not smell and is extremely deadly. People on terminals and vessels carry H$_2$S detectors. When the alarm goes off, they will walk away from it and report it immediately; the threatened area needs to be cleared and secured until the problem is solved. When I see high contents of H$_2$S reported in a cargo, I inform the terminal and surveyor about it. Most often H$_2$S levels are reported on certificates carried by the vessel. The shipping documents are often forwarded by email to terminal, agents and others who are interested in the cargo. So always read ship documents.

Hand Blend

When a trader is uncertain about a composition of a blend to be executed, he can decide to instruct an inspector to make a hand blend first and look at the outcome. The inspector will take samples of the different oil components to be blended and makes a small blend in the laboratory according to the blending ratios as requested by the trader. Such a blend is quickly done and when results and the reaction between the different components look good, the blending operations in the tank can be executed. Often the focus here is on the stability of the oil, the sediments tests, RVP and other specifications which cannot be calculated based on a percentage blending. It may delay the blending operation a bit, but it gives the trader some certainty when making his decision. Hand blends are also done to see if two oil grades together are compatible. See also 'compatibility'.

Harbour Dues

Various local charges against all seagoing vessels entering a harbour, to cover maintenance of channel-depths, buoys, lights, etc. All harbours do not necessarily have this charge. Harbour dues are the main income for a port. Therefore ports prioritise companies who want to invest in terminals with a lot of activity which guarantees a lot of vessel-traffic in a harbour. Strategic oil storage in a harbour is therefore often located in different places. Low shipping activity related to long-term storage does not generate much income from port duties.

Harmonised System of Codes

An international goods classification system for describing cargoes in international trades under a single commodity–coding scheme. Developed under the auspices of the customs cooperation council (CCC), an international customs organisation in Brussels. This code is a hierarchically structured product nomenclature containing approximately 5,000 headings and subheadings. It is organised into 99 chapters arranged in 22 sections. The basic code contains four-digit headings and six-digit subheadings. Many countries add digits for customs tariff and statistical purposes. Find codes in Europe. For oil use section V: Mineral products and go to chapter 27.10. Find in this book also 'nomenclature products'. Most oil products can be found there.

Website: *http://ec.europa.eu/taxation_customs/dds2/taric.*

Hatch

The opening in the deck of a vessel which gives access to the cargo hold. Samples may be taken from the hatches to create ship average cargo sample, ship composite. "What you do not see or smell you do not know." Therefore it may happen that in case a cargo has too high a content of mercaptans at departure, vessels may sail with open hatches on open sea in order to arrive with an acceptable specification of the oil. High mercaptans oil (H_2S) can be treated on arrival before it is accepted at the berth. Sailing with open hatches is something I would not fancy. Probably it is prohibited to do, but difficult to check.

Hazy Gasoil

In winter time water settles less fast in gasoil;, it starts binding. As a result of that a sample of gasoil can look hazy after it has been pumped into a vessel or barge. The receiver will not accept the product as it looks off-spec. Brightness is a visual test and easy to find out. When one keeps his hand behind the sample he will be able to see his fingers through the sample when the oil is bright and clear. When the product is hazy it is difficult to see what is behind the sample. Often when the sample is a bit warmer the water will settle and the sample is bright and clear. Hazy gasoil is a typical winter problem. In refineries this problem is less common as most production is still warm. Hazy gasoil challenges are more a storage terminal problem, where gasoil has been stored during a summer to winter contango. See also 'bright and clear', a visual test.

Head and Shoulders (Technical Trading)

A reversal pattern characterised by a high, a higher high, a lower high, and a break below the line joining the lows between the highs, the so-called neck-line.

Health, Safety, Environment (HSE)

Oil is a dangerous commodity to operate with. There is a lot of focus on how to behave when having a job related to oil. It is important that every single person working oil-related is aware of the risks attached to his activity and responsibility. So you are accountable for all your decisions, advice and judgements. The more people know how to behave the better likelihood of minimising any potential situation where accidents may happen. Next to that the company image of being HSE focused is becoming more and more important as well, certainly towards the stakeholders. Every company has its own programme concerning HSE. The bigger the company the more money is available to focus on and to invest in HSE. My advice would be to look around in your own area or company and see what activity is going on related to HSE It might be impressive as the HSE work in companies is increasing all the time. HSE regulations may slow down trading decisions, but a smart trader can anticipate that. Once HSE behaviour is well adopted in trading, as it should be, then it quickly becomes a routine within the work process. People need time to get used to new work processes, but it will finally work.

Heating Coils

Coils located on the bottom of cargo tanks in vessels and land-tanks in which steam passes through to heat up the cargo or to maintain the cargo at a certain temperature. The heat lowers the viscosity of the heavy oil and permits easier pumping of a cargo from the vessel discharge port or from the tank at loadport. Vessels in clean service normally do not have or need heating coils as the viscosity of the clean products (with the exception of some lube oil) is good enough to permit easy pumping at atmospheric temperatures. Heating coils are available in land tanks for heavy fueloil so that the viscosity can be controlled in order to reach a decent pumping rate and to not damage the pumps during loading a vessel. Oil in caverns can be heated by pumping the oil around through heat exchangers. Tanks which can be heated are most often insulated. Heating and keeping oil at temperature is very expensive as it costs a lot of energy. An insulated tank is therefore a good investment.

Heating of Oil

Heating of oil is sometimes required in case the oil has a high pour point or high viscosity. Without heating, the heavy oil would become solid and sticky; pumps may be damaged. Therefore most terminals have their requirements for oil viscosity at actual temperature. A viscosity of 380 Cst. at actual temperature is often well accepted and makes a good pumping speed possible. So a fueloil with a viscosity of 380 Cst. should be heated up to 50°C/122°F. Oil with a viscosity of 600 Centistokes requires a temperature of 56°C/132°F. High viscosity oil requires more heat to guarantee enough pumping speed. As heating of oil is very costly it is important that oil is supplied at a good temperature and that the oil is stored in insulated tanks. Heating is expensive.

Heating Oil

Heating oil is essentially the same product as gasoil, clean oil. Some people may also call it fueloil, which should not be confused with heavy dirty fueloil. Heating oil is traded on the futures market on the exchanges (ICE and Nymex). On the ICE, London, it is traded in tons and in price per ton related to the ARA barge market for supplies to Germany. 1 lot is 100 tons of heating oil. But deliveries generated from futures being expired does not happen that much. The heating oil is sold and bought in the physical market (OTC). Traders may take delivery and store the juice in tanks in the ARA area in case the market is in contango. Heating oil is a low flash product and can be stored in a tank with a fixed roof. Heating oil traded on the Nymex is traded and priced in gallons and is delivered at New York harbour. Lot size is 1,000 barrels or 42,000 gallons, roughly 135 tons.

Heating value

Also known as caloric value. The energy content of a unit quantity of fuel. There are two calorific values: the gross (high) and the net (low) calorific value. The gross value is that which is obtained when all of the products of combustion are cooled to standard conditions, and the latent heat of the water vapour formed is reclaimed. The net value is the gross value minus the latent heat of vaporisation of the water. Caloric value is saying something about the burning value and is important in gas. Heavy density gas or oil often has a better caloric value. Dutch gas has a high caloric value and the consumption system is based on that. Dutch people heat their houses with gas and heat their furnace or oven in the kitchen with gas. Norwegian or Russian gas has a lower caloric value and cannot substitute the gas from the Dutch consumption market. It would ruin the gas-burning equipment, which Dutch people use in their houses. However, the industry can use the gas with a lower caloric value. There is a price difference between the two types of caloric values, but that is obvious. Caloric value is also relevant when it concerns low sulphur fuel oil supplies to utilities. Also for bunkers caloric value is important. Fewer bunkers are consumed when caloric value is high. Get quality for money and know where you buy bunkers.

Heavy Crude Oil

A type of crude petroleum characterised by high viscosity and a high density or low API. It is usually difficult and costly to produce by conventional techniques. It has an API of less than 28. The lower the API gravity, the heavier the oil. As a result of low API the yield will consist of an increased volume of fueloil, bitumen or asphalt (less than 20 API). The viscosity is typically very high and sometimes this oil cannot be pumped without use of heating and/or blend with a diluent. See also 'diluent'. Not every refinery is able to run heavy oil. Therefore this oil is best to be processed by refineries that are designed for it. Those are complex refineries with FCC units, coker units and much more processing availability. Often those refineries produce bitumen, asphalt and green cokes, but of course also naphtha, gasoline, heating oil and diesel. Heavy crude oil is sold at a discount versus most benchmarks due to the bad yield and the challenging logistics.

Heavy Fueloil (HFO)
Residual refined fractions used as boiler fuel by industry, by large ships and in electricity generation.

Heavy Gas Oil
Heavy gasoil is still seen as clean oil although the colour may be dark brown. Heavy gasoil may be used for heating at utilities that do not use preheating for their burning installations. In USA often mentioned as no. 4 fueloil. Heavy is related to the high density. Call it an off-spec or unfinished heating oil which needs blending with lighter components such as kerosene or off-spec jet.

Heavy Naphtha
Higher density naphtha from the primary distillation density going direction 0.69-0.71. Light naphtha is classified as C5 and C6 (boiling range from 30-90°C/86-194°F) and heavy naphtha is classified as C7-C12 (boiling range 90-200°C/194-392°F).

Heavy Shit
The trader means heavy dirty black price discounted oil, heavy crude and very heavy fueloil. Even this is a product that can be traded, hedged and consumed. And traders can make money with it. Also fueloil traders may say that they have some some heavy shit to offer. Popular talk for discounted heavy oil.

Heavy Water Ballast
Additional ballast loaded into cargo tanks to enable the vessel to maintain a

safe sea-going condition under extreme weather conditions. Consider this as dirty ballast.

Hedge

A trade designed to reduce risk. When you are long physical oil then you sell paper for hedging purposes. When you are short physical oil you will buy paper for hedging purposes. When a trading book is flat balanced then there is no risk for price fluctuations, e.g. When you are long physical oil in storage you would sell paper. When the price goes down you lose money on the physical oil in storage and you gain money on the paper position. Your result is in balance because by hedging you reduced the risk versus price fluctuation. Works also vice versa if price would go up. Make no money, lose no money, but trade on margins.

Hedging

Locking in the value of the trading position. The purpose of hedging is to minimise risk (price, arbitrage, spreads). A transaction which reduces the overall risk of the company as measured by value-at-risk calculations, back-to-back contracts, pass-through costs, purchase of a put option to protect against fall in price of fuel inventory. In a contango market hedging is done with paper contracts which cover a value forward in time. In such a case the traders are hedging and locking in profit. Although there is always a basis risk and time spread in a trading book. The perfect hedge does not really exist.

Hedge Funds

Investment companies trading actively on the futures market and any other commodity market. A hedge fund contributes to the level of liquidity in the market and adds capital in the market as well. The hedge funds have a high risk profile. As hedge funds are active on many exchanges, their risk can be considered pretty much hedged. But a huge economic crisis could push all markets down simultaneously. The risk is based on spreads as the hedge funds take long and short positions in any commodity market. They trade bonds, options, futures, exchange rates, interest rates, cattle and much more. They can also invest in companies. They can go long oil and hedge with a short in oranges. Gold and oil or oil and the Euro/Dollar price seem to have good links. But also weather derivatives and coffee or cacao is a good trade off. If the market goes bad and the hedge funds pull back, just like in 2008, prices of oil and other commodities may fall and financial hell breaks loose. Just before the oil prices collapsed after hitting 147 USD per barrel the rumour came in the market that an oil fund was offering 10,000 lots of Brent futures. Apparently some institutes in the USA needed cash as the economy was crashing. Sea also 'crash'.

Hedge Ratio

The ratio of the size of a position in a hedging instrument to the size of the position being hedged.

Heel

Fixed minimum quantity which is required to be kept as fixed stored level of oil in tank. This quantity of oil must stay in tank for technical or anti-emission reasons. Can be because either the tank is not measurable or to avoid getting air between the oil and the floating roof. In some cases a refinery prefers to keep a heel in tank to avoid pumping of slurry and bottom sediments into the processing unit. A heel can be roughly 2 to 5% of the tank capacity. It would rarely harm the quality of a new cargo being discharged into tank, it's just a relatively small contamination. Also called 'tank-heel'. Net tank capacity minus heel is usable capacity of the tank.

Henry Hub

Pipelines interchange near Erath, Louisiana, where a number of interstate and intrastate pipelines interconnect through a header system operated by Sabine pipeline. It is the standard delivery point for the NYMEX natural gas futures contract in the US.

High

The highest price of the day for a particular futures contract. Peak of the day or part thereof. Opposite of the 'low'.

High Flash

Products with a flashpoint over 55° Celsius/131° Fahrenheit are called high flash products. Different rules for handling in logistics would apply for this type of oil compared with 'low flash' oil. High flash products are less flammable than low flash products. Examples are gasoil and fueloil. High flash products are the so called 'k3' products (low flash is 'k1'). See also 'classification of petroleum and crude oil (flash point)'.

High-Sulphur No. 2 Diesel Fuel

No. 2 diesel fuel that has a sulphur-content above 0.05 per cent by weight. Therefore referred to as distillate home heating oil. Some may call it 'No2 fueloil' but still meant as clean oil.

High-Sulphur Distillate Fueloil

Distillate fueloil having sulphur content greater than 500 ppm/0.05 percent by weight.

High Viscosity Crude Oil

A crude oil which, due to its viscosity, requires heating during transportation or COW at discharge. These types of crude oil generally may also be called aromatic or high paraffinic oil. High viscosity oil often has a high pour point as well. It is not necessarily heavy crude with a low API (or density). See therefore also 'aromatic crude oil'.

HILOS

Paper position where one speculates on the sulphur differential in fueloil. It is the 3.5% fueloil Rotterdam barge swap versus the 1% fueloil CIF cargoes NWE swap. If you buy the HS barge swap and sell the LS cargo swap you are short HILOS, you expect the sulphur spread to come down, meaning less difference between HS barges and LS cargoes. The spread differential can go from 0 (zero) up to 100 Dollars per ton, but I have seen down to minus 5 dollars per ton as well. HILOS are linked to the consumption/demand for low sulphur fueloil at the utilities. That demand may depend on their alternative feedstock prices. Most utilities can substitute fueloil with natgas or coal. They prefer the cheapest fuel. Of course the high sulphur bunker market can be tight or oversupplied as well, which often depends on the arbitrage opportunity to the Singapore market. The HILOS market is pretty much based on fundamentals. HILOS can be a good hedging tool when blending high sulphur fueloil to low sulphur fueloil, locking in a blending margin. Some cargoes of low sulphur fueloil are available with some giveaway and have a sulphur specification which can be much less than 1.0%. In that case it is possible to add some high sulphur fueloil which is very profitable. Making a blending margin by converting high sulphur fueloil into low sulphur fueloil. Low sulphur fueloil is higher priced than high sulphur fueloil, although occasionally it has been the other way around. In price quotation the high sulphur fueloil is based on bunker specifications (0.991 density and viscosity of 380 Cst.) and the low sulphur quotations are based on utility specs (0.995 density and a viscosity of 450 Cst.). As well as sulphur, density and viscosity, high and low sulphur fueloil qualities also differ on metal content and other small parameters.

Hinterland
Related to the barge activity. Cargoes arrive in Rotterdam and by break of bulk activity the oil finds its way over the rivers to Germany, the hinterland. This is one of the many reasons that makes Rotterdam the most important trading hub of Europe.

Historic Volatility (Technical Trading)
The change in the absolute value of a commodity or instrument over a certain period, expressed as a percentage of the lowest price recorded in that period.

Hit
A trader is said to be 'hitting' the bid when he initiates a trade that sells directly to the bid quantity. This trader probably believes that the contract price will fall and is willing to give the perceived edge to another trading by selling into his bid.

HO
Heating Oil, clean gasoil as traded on the futures exchanges on the ICE and Nymex.

Home
A company's refinery, storage place or marketing system. When a company sails a crude oil cargo home, it means that the oil, most often from own production, is used within its own system. It means also that no cargo value, a traded price, will come available in the market. Nevertheless these cargoes are well followed in cargo tracking systems. It gives information related to the consumption of certain crudes at different refineries.

Home Car
A train tank car on tracks of its owner.

Homogeneous
Well blended oil, in such a way that on each level of the oil in a tank the

quality is the same. A blend in tank is declared homogeneous after comparing densities in tank at the top, middle and bottom levels. If those 3 densities have a difference of less than 11 points (density difference of 0.0011) then the product in tank is officially declared as being homogeneous. Be aware that the blend in tank is declared homogeneous on density only. If three components with the same density are blended then the density says nothing about the layering of qualities in the tank. Depending on the quantity in tank, a minimum 6 hours of homogenation should be sufficient, unless the differential between top and bottom is huge. When the heaviest density is on the bottom of the tank and the differential between top and bottom is huge then to save time I would recommend pumping the tank over to an empty tank and then pumping it back again.

Homogeniser

A system at a terminal that is able the make an oil-blend of different qualities homogeneous. Can be a system that pumps oil around in the tank, low suction out and high suction in again. It can also be a propeller in the tank, or a compressor blowing air bubbles in the tank (only at high flash products). The time spent for homogenation depends on the composition of the blend. Pumping to another tank and back again may go faster in some cases. See also 'blending order'.

Hot Oil

Oil which is required to be heated to stay liquid. You do not want hot oil to stay too long in tank as heating costs a lot of money. Either it needs to be processed soon, in case it is heavy oil, or it has to be blended to a commercial low viscosity specification so end-users will buy it, e.g. Heavy fueloil to be blended to bunker specification (max 380 Cst.) or heavy crude blended with diluent to make it possible to pump it through a pipeline to a refinery. Hot oil may arrive at discharge ports at temperatures up to 80° Celsius/176° Fahrenheit. Just make sure that the receiving terminal can logistically handle cargoes at such a temperature, as you do not want to get stuck with a hot cargo. See also 'COW'.

Hot Work

Describes the hot work as it is defined in the latest edition of ISGOTT definitions: work involving sources of ignition or temperatures sufficiently high to cause the ignition of a flammable gas mixture. This includes any work requiring the use of welding, burning or soldering equipment, blowtorches, some power driven tools, portable electrical equipment that is not intrinsically safe or contained within an approved explosion proof housing, and internal combustion engines. Hot work can delay logistics until that job is done. Just a matter of HSE regulation at terminals or vessels. These planned maintenance programmes are always a pain in the neck. Stop production and delays in logistics costs money. We just have to respect that this is unavoidable, and you cannot always be commercially pleased. Terminal informs their operator about the maintenance plans and temporary shutdown of jetties. Therefore, demurrage cannot be charged to the terminal.

HS
High Sulphur. Fueloil with a sulphur content which is higher than 1.0% in volume. Or related to crude oil it would be also higher than 1.0%, also called 'sour crude'.

HSCR
High Sulphur CRacked which relates to fueloil for bunkers.

HSFO
High Sulphur FuelOil. As a trader you need to know if the HSFO is cracked or straight run (un-cracked). Russian M100, mazut, is available as cracked and as straight run fueloil. Straight run oil is a feedstock for a refinery and is higher priced than cracked fueloil. Still some straight run fueloil is used for bunkers consumption because of its qualities. On the contrary, some cracked fuel oil may have specifications that are close to straight run fueloil qualities. In that case some of the cracked fuel oil may be blended into the straight run fueloil. A good way to add some blending value into the P&L. Opposite is of HSFO is LSFO.

HSSR
High Sulphur Straight Run which relates to fueloil. M100SR, Russian straight run fuel, popular for arbitrage trades to USA and China.

Hub
Geographic oil price quoted trading area like ARA, NWE, MED, USAG, USGC, Singapore, WAF. Also called 'trading hub'. There are also other active trading areas or hubs which do not have a quotation on the reports but those

hubs often use a standard benchmark plus a differential. Basically a hub is a well-accepted place in the oil market based on its infrastructure which results in active trading activity at that location. A place without a logistic function, refinery systems or crude oil production activity will never be a trading hub – that would not make sense. Companies like to create their own hub around their own assets, their base giving them best value to trade from.

Hurricane Season

From August to November the US East Coast is threatened by many hurricanes. Remember the year 2005, August, hurricane 'Katrina' – that hurricane had a huge effect on all crude oil operations including refining activity. It caused a lot of trouble in the Gulf Coast area in industry and common life. Some traders may speculate on hurricane seasons but also a lot of books are completely hedged in order to minimise risk when a hurricane is on its way to the Gulf of Mexico. Risk analysts are often stress-testing the P&L in order to be prepared for the worst case scenarios. Due to hurricanes in the Gulf coast oilrigs have to be abandoned and get shut down temporarily. Production goes down and prices may go up during the hurricane season. Often the market has adopted that scenario already in the actual prices, resulting in no expectations of sudden spikes in prices such as in 2005. Only in case of real unexpected damages and longer shutdown periods the oil price may peak. Refineries in the Gulf Coast area can be in trouble as well but the traders in those markets never make those challenges public; they know what to do and are often well prepared.

Hydro Carbons

A large class of organic compound of hydrogen and carbon. Crude oil, natural gas and natural gas condensate are all mixtures of various hydrocarbons, among which methane is the simplest (C_1H_4). Crude oil consists of many different types of molecules. These are chains which can be long and heavy or short and light, including aromatics, benzenes and other challenging material. Butane has a short chain C_4H_{10}, lightest naphtha starts at C_5H_{12} and so on. During the refining process these chains will separate in the distillation columns. Short chains are light and can be found in the top of the column. Fueloil is the most heavy and with longest chains is in the bottom of the column. After primary distillation the long chained molecules (residue) will be cracked into smaller chains. That results in light cracked products and even heavier bottoms. Those bottoms may be cracked again. In a complex refinery they keep processing and cracking the oil till there is really no light material to get. The heavy residue may be cokes, bitumen or asphalt. The volume of the various products depends on the compositions of hydrocarbons in the oil. See also 'yield'.

Hydro Cracker

A refinery upgrading process in which light or heavy gasoil or residue hydrocarbons are mixed with hydrogen under conditions of high temperature and pressure, in the presence of a catalyst, yielding light oils. This unit converts heavy, processed feedstock such as vacuum gasoil into lighter products such as gasoil, kerosene and gasoline components.

Hydrogen

The lightest of all gases, occurring chiefly in combination with oxygen in water; exists also in acids, bases, alcohols, petroleum, and other hydrocarbons. Hydrogen is a very dangerous and explosive product if treated in the wrong way. Hydrogen can be used as fuel for cars. The CO_2 emission of hydrogen on its own would be zero.

Hydrometer

An instrument for determining the density of a liquid. Basically it is a thermometer that can float vertically in liquids such as an oil sample. One can read the numbers from the hydrometer at the liquid's surface. The numbers on the hydrometer are the density. Some hydrometers do also indicate the temperature of the sample. The obtained density on the hydrometer can now be converted to the standard density at 15°C/60°F. The use of hydrometers works for clean products only. With dirty black sticky products or crude it is impossible to read anything from a hydrometer. Today densities are measured in a laboratory in a much more sophisticated way.

Hydro Power

Energy or power produced by moving water.

Hydro-Treater

A refining unit whereby processed material from the crude units are treated in the presence of catalysts and hydrogen, often to remove sulphur and other unwanted substances. The hydro-treater is often the critical unit for producing jet fuel and low-sulphur diesel.

Hydro-Treating

Catalytic hydro-treating is a process in petroleum refining used to clean gasoil from nitrogen, sulphur, oxygen, and metals. This is done to meet the specs of clean diesel.

Hydrogen Sulphide (H_2S)

A poisonous gas associated with natural gas and heavy fueloil products. It smells like rotten eggs. If the concentration of H_2S in the air is at a very high level, one cannot smell it. No smell of H_2S is a dangerous situation and if in that case a person is exposed to it, that person might die. In most refineries there are systems available that can monitor it when H_2S comes freely into the atmosphere. In that case an alarm will go off. You had better stay away from that area. Sometimes fueloil contains H_2S. If that is the case some chemicals may be added into the vessel's cargo in order to neutralise the H_2S content. Thereafter discharging the cargo is according to the receiving terminal's rules and regulations safe for the people who have to execute the operational work at the terminal.

I

IBP

Initial Boiling Point. First condensed oil drop observed when testing a boiling range. The IBP is measured in temperature. A product with an IBP at a low temperature is light and has a low flashpoint. Naphtha could have an IBP at 20°C. Fueloil can have an IBP at 350°C. When all oil in a boiling range test is condensed the focus will be on the last drop to be condensed. That is called the 'FBP'. From IBP to FBP is called the boiling range or distillation curve. It can happen that not all of the full 100% has been condensed. The last bit 0.1% is called not condensed. It may be sediments in crude oil production.

ICC

International Chamber of Commerce.

Ice Class Vessel

Ship with a strengthened hull to be able to sail through sea ice.

- **Scandinavian classification:**
  - **1A*** - Extreme ice conditions. Ice floes of thickness 1.0 m are anticipated.
  - **1A** - Severe ice conditions. Ice floes of thickness 0.8 m are anticipated.
  - **1B** - Medium ice conditions. Ice floes of thickness 0.6 m are anticipated.
  - **1C** - Light ice conditions. Ice floes of thickness 0.4 m are anticipated.

With extreme ice conditions vessels would sail in convoy following an ice breaker. In the North at the Arctic the sailing route from Europe to Asia is opening up in summertime. Nuclear ice breakers lead the convoys. In areas where ice breakers are used, ice dues have to be paid and ice delays may occur due to slow speed sailing and other logistic challenges. In some cases ice class vessels are required to have an 'ice passport'. The local authorities make the decisions when the ice class vessels are required or not. Also during the wintertime without sea ice there can still be a requirement for at least ice class 1C.

- **Based on Canadian WMO Sea Ice Nomenclature**
  - **PC1** - Ice layer 3.0 metres, year-round operation in all Polar waters.
  - **PC2** - Ice layer 2.4 metres, year-round operation in moderate multi-year ice conditions.
  - **PC3** - Ice layer 1.8 metres, year-round operation in second-year ice, which may include multi-year ice inclusions.
  - **PC4** - Ice layer 1.3 metres, year-round operation in thick first-year ice, which may include old ice inclusions.
  - **PC5** - Ice layer 1.0 metre, year-round operation in medium first-year ice, which may include old ice inclusions.
  - **PC6** - Ice layer 0.7 metre, summer/autumn operation in medium first-year ice, which may include old ice inclusions.
  - **PC7** - Ice layer 0.5 metre, summer/autumn operation in thin first-year ice, which may include old ice inclusions.

- **Russian Maritime Register of Shipping**
  - **Arc9** - Ice layer up to 4 metres.
  - **Arc8** - Ice layer up to 3 metres.
  - **Arc7** - (formerly ULA) Ice layer up to 1.7 metres.
  - **Arc6** - Ice layer up to 1.3 metres.
  - **Arc5** - (formerly UL) Ice layer up to 1 metre.
  - **Arc4** - (formerly L1) Ice layer up to 0.8 metre.
  - **Ice3** - (formerly L2) Ice layer up to 0.7 metre.
  - **Ice2** - (formerly L3) Ice layer up to 0.55 metre.
  - **Ice1** - (formerly L4) Ice layer up to 0.4 metre.

- **American Bureau of Shipping**
  - **A3** - Ice layer greater than 1 metre.
  - **A2** - Ice layer up to 1 metre.
  - **A1** - Ice layer up to 0.6 metre.

· **A0** - Ice layer up to 0.3 metre.

Ice Clause

Clause in the charter party for the situation of sea ice on arrival at the destination as agreed in the charterparty. 'BIMCO general ice clause for voyage charter parties and delay' is used for that in most standard charter parties.

Ice Delay

Delays of vessels on arrival or at berth leaving as a consequence of ice conditions. With heavy ice conditions vessels may only be allowed to sail to certain harbours in convoy. It can happen that a vessel has to wait for the ice breakers when she wants to enter the harbour. She can also be delayed after loading when she has to wait for an ice breaker to leave the harbour. It has to be clear when time starts ticking. In some cases the notice of readiness can already be tendered at the place where the convoy will start, at ice edge. It will cause waiting time and demurrage. Question is always: "Who will be responsible for demurrage?" The trader needs to make that clear when negotiating a deal.

Ice Dues

Extra dues to be paid by a vessel charterer when a vessel is entering areas where most often harbours could be in a frozen condition. The ice dues are collected on a special account to pay ice breakers in case needed to keep the harbour open to get vessels in and out, e.g. Baltic Sea. Ice dues are paid during the whole year. During summer it is just a small fee and during winter the ice dues are higher priced. By that the extra cost for ice dues are during winter within a reasonable level and therefore there will not be a big competitive disadvantage for these cargoes due to an ice exposed location versus other cargoes in non-ice exposed locations.

Ice Edge

During winter times the Baltic Sea is freezing and ice starts forming. Vessels must be ice class certified and in some circumstances vessels are not allowed to sail into the ports by themselves. The vessel has to wait at ice edge to get permission to sail to the jetty. It can happen that a vessel must wait for ice breakers and that means that there may be waiting time. Related to that waiting time at ice edge the charter party contains ice clauses which tell us that waiting time at ice edge is for the account of the charterer. The trader who bought the oil and chartered the vessel is risking a demurrage bill. It is therefore important to agree with the seller of the oil at which moment the NOR is allowed and accepted to be tendered. From the time of tendering notice, the clock starts ticking for the seller who has to perform on his delivery and load within the allowed loading time. It is also important to have a good understanding about the arrival time. A vessel which waits a day for an icebreaker might miss her loading window. NOR tendering at ice edge is therefore important. When a vessel is ready from loading the seller stops the time. This means that any demurrage on a vessel when leaving the berth, caused by waiting for the ice breaker again, is for the account of the charterer, the buyer.

ICE Futures, Intercontinental Exchange
The ICE is an electronic exchange. A London oil futures market trading gasoil and Brent crude oil as well as options. In the recent past futures were traded at the International Petroleum Exchange (IPE), see 'open outcry'. Look at the website from 'The ICE'. Here one can post bids and offers into the screen and trade. The trader is here obliged to sit behind the screen and adjust his bid or offer depending on the market movements. Leaving the screen and keeping a position active can be dangerous. Markets may suddenly move in a certain (the wrong) direction. See also 'fat finger', another type of error.

Ice Passport
Requirement for ice class vessels sailing in special ice conditions. A manual for sailing through the ice has to be on board the vessel.

IDD
Integrity Due Diligence. The last few years have seen new opportunities arising for investors in new geographical markets. While potentially lucrative, these opportunities can have risks which, if not identified and addressed before a transaction or relationship is completed, can result in financial loss, reputational damage or criminal or regulatory sanction. The recent renewed focus from Western countries on combating corruption including increased action by law enforcement and regulatory authorities under relevant anti-corruption legislation has created a new impetus for conducting corruption-related Integrity Due Diligence. Sourced from the Chevron website.

Idle Capacity

Non-utilisation of capacity. A ship that is idle is waiting for an order and is therefore not generating any income. A refinery being idle does not produce oil or in the case of idle capacity it can mean the refinery has spare capacity. It can produce more oil or it can make a processing deal. Renting out some of the capacity. When refinery margins are low or negative a refinery would minimise production, causing idle capacity. The component of operable capacity that is not in operation and not under active repair, but capable of being placed in operation within 30 days; and capacity not in operation but under active repair that can be completed within 90 days.

Idle Time

A tanker ready after discharging and not having an order for next cargo. The time after hoses connected until notice of readiness at next port is for the account of the owner or time charterer. Then the vessel is lying in idle time. The operator gives the instruction to let the vessel sail at the most economical speed to the next loadport. Just to save some money on bunkers consumptions. In the meantime, a cargo operator could ask his supplier if it is possible to load a day or so earlier. Everything must be done to get the vessel back into commercial use. If that does not happens then money is lost in idle time. Idle time for offshore loaders may be utilised for 'field-testing' – look it up in this book.

IMO

International Maritime Organisation. United Nations specialised agency with responsibility for the safety and security of shipping and the prevention of marine pollution by ships.

IMO Number

Identification number of a vessel. Some vessels may have the same name, but the IMO is unique to the vessel. IMO stands for 'International Maritime Organisation' which administrates all registered vessels. When a vetting department is checking a vessel, they make sure to clear the correct vessel with the correct IMO number. Also when confirming a vessel to a customer they add the IMO number of that vessel. IMO numbers are unique, the id of the vessel. Rhine barges have also id numbers but do not use the IMO registration. Have a look at 'Eni number'.

Imported Crude Oil Burned as Fuel

The amount of foreign crude oil burned as a fueloil, usually as residual fueloil, without being processed as such. Imported crude oil burned as fuel includes lease condensate and liquid hydrocarbons produced from tar sand oil, gilsonite (kind of natural asphalt), and shale oil. In Asia there is a market for waxy high pour point, low sulphur crude oil to be burned in electricity companies. The efficiency of that is the easy way the heating can be switched on and off, which is more difficult when heating by fueloil. This type of crude is also not the easiest oil to refine and so by that there seems to be good economy for this set up.

Imports

Imports are oil cargoes brought into one place or country from another. Exports are oil cargoes sent to one place or country from another. Net imports are imports minus exports. Collectively, imports and exports are referred to as 'trade'. Trade may be denominated in volume, financial value, or both.

In Bond

Cargo moving under customs control where duty has not yet been paid. The oil will move in this case from one duty licence holder to another licence holder. In the ARA barges may move without issuing of customs documents. Administration there is well organised and the customs can follow the cargo on paper. See also 'bonded storage' and 'AED'.

INCO Terms

Series of international sales terms published by the International Chamber of Commerce. These terms may include lots of differences compared with general terms and conditions of the major oil companies. Be aware on what terms you buy or sell; in case of doubts talk with the contract specialists in your office in order to find out what is appropriate. The INCO terms describe the following delivery terms, many of which are described in this book.

- EXW = Ex works.
- FCA = Free carrier.
- CPT = Carriage paid.
- CIP = Carriage and insurance paid.
- DAT = Delivered at terminal.
- DAP = Delivered at place ex ship (old DES).

- DDP = Delivered duty paid.
- FAS = Free alongside ship.
- FOB = Free on board.
- CFR = Cost and freight.
- CIF = Cost, insurance and freight.

Indemnity Basis
The demurrage payable by a company to a principal shall not exceed a demurrage claim which the principal receives and pays.

Independent
Generally applies to a non-integrated oil or natural gas company, usually active in only one or two sectors of the industry. An independent marketer buys petroleum products from majors or independent refiners and resells them under their own brand name. There are also independents that are active exclusively either in oil or gas production or refining.

Independent Inspector (Surveyor)
A person or organisation of persons, acting independently, but on behalf of, one or more parties involved in the transfer, storage, inventory or analysis of a commodity for purposes of determining the quantity and/or quality of a commodity. They may also be assigned to the calibration of various measurement instruments and/or storage tanks ashore or on vessels. These inspection companies are organisational, neither connected to any oil company nor do they have an interest in an oil company and are not involved in any trading activity. Their only interest is to survey and sell their services.

Independent Marketer
A retail petroleum 'seller' or wholesaler, who is not involved in the refining of petroleum products and therefore must purchase its supply of petroleum products from a refiner or other supplying source.

Independent Storage Company
Storage company which is not linked to any other refiner, wholesaler or trading company. This storage company is also not participating in the market on its own account or on behalf of third parties. Information about stocks in tank is not public and not shared in the market. An independent storage company takes only orders from the customers who rent one or more

tanks. The core income of independent storage companies comes from rental fees and any other logistic services they provide related to storage handling.

Indicative Quote
A market maker's price which is not firm. A trader might give an indication in order to get feedback on his indication in the market. The market information which the trader gets is the counterparty bids or offers and a feel for the demand level in the market.

Inert Gas (IG)
A gas used by oil tankers to displace air in cargo tanks to reduce oxygen content to 8% or less by volume and thus reduce the possibility of a fire or an explosion. The inert gas used is usually nitrogen, carbon dioxide or a mixture of gases such as flue gas. A good working inert gas system on board a vessel is a real HSE requirement. Such a system reduces the likelihood of accidents. Gas in combination with air is explosive and that situation must be avoided.

Info Quote
Rate given for information purposes only. Not always a real quote, it is rather an indicative quote at the moment that you get it based on actual market circumstances. Markets are changing and are volatile. The information may be used for initial calculations of a potential deal but needs to be checked again before the trader is willing to go into the market to create the business and make the real deal.

Initial Boiling Point (IBP)
In a standard laboratory distillation, the temperature on the distillation thermometer at the moment the first drop of distillate falls from the condenser. With light products such as gasoline the IBP will be obtained at a very low temperature and with heavy oil such as gasoil the IBP will be at high temperature. The lower the IBP, the lower the flashpoint and vice versa. Opposite of 'FBP'; see also 'boiling range'.

Initial Margin
The amount a futures market participant must deposit into a margin account at the time an order is placed to buy or sell a futures contract.

Inline Blending

Loading a vessel from more than one tank at the same time connected through one pipeline. Different qualities, components, are pumped in certain blending ratio into the vessel. The vessel will receive the blend, which is the finished product, on board. During loading the quality in line may be monitored by infra-red systems etc. If one of the parameters of the finished product to the vessel is off-spec then the loading master in the control room can adjust the blending rate. During loading a drop-sample will be made which represents the sample for the cargo. Additional ship-composite samples might be taken as well as a back-up.

Innerfloater

Tanks with a fixed roof but also a floating thin roof within the tank. The innerfloater is placed within the tank in order to be very sure that no rain water can get contaminated with the oil and it is meant to reduce emission to a minimum level. Tanks that are used for jet A1 require a fixed roof with inner floater. Jet A1 has to be clean, free of water and safe for aircrafts.

Inspection

The buyer and/or seller may request an inspection for quality and quantity for all deliveries. This is done to ensure that the correct qualities as agreed according to the physical oil contract are placed on board of a vessel or discharged in the tank at the receiving terminal. A correct B/L quantity is very important. Most often the costs for such an inspection are shared fifty/ fifty between buyer and seller. In FOB contracts most often the tank quality is the agreed quality, then the seller is more interested in sharing the inspection cost for quantity only. With oil prices so high quantity inspection and loss control is important to invest in. Oil losses are expensive at current level, which is based on crude price between 100 and 120 USD per barrel.

Inspection Certificate

A document that is required by some purchasers and countries in order to attest to the specifications of the goods shipped. This is usually performed by an independent third party that will inspect the goods for conformity. Often costs of such inspection are shared 50/50 between buyer and seller. In the case of a third party being involved the bill may be split in one third each.

Inspector

A person or inspection company assigned to determine the quantity and/or the quality of a commodity. Most often the costs are shared 50/50 between buyer and seller or sometimes one third each when a third party is involved in the trade. The inspector takes the sample and does the measurement. He follows the complete operations and reports that to his office. The inspection company sends the inspection report to the companies who gave the instructions. The order for inspection is also to be given to the terminal and the vessel. Without the instructions the inspector would not be allowed to enter the terminal or to come on board the vessel to fulfil his task. See also 'time of analyses' and 'time of sampling'.

Insulated Tank

A tank protected against exposure to cold temperatures caused by weather conditions. A tank with an isolation layer around the steel wall of that tank. The purpose is to maintain the product at temperatures in tank and to minimise the loss of temperature when oil is stored. These types of tank are meant for high viscosity oil, often fueloil. It is easier and more energy saving to keep a fueloil tank at a certain temperature when the tank is insulated. Insulated tanks save a lot of energy for the terminal and heating costs to the owner of the product in tank. Products in insulated tanks can also be heated to higher temperatures if required. There are heating coils on the bottom of the insulated tanks for that purpose. Pay also attention to 'heating coils' or 'traced pipeline'.

Integrated Oil Company

Non-producing oil company but well established in marketing and sales systems such as big wholesalers and trading houses. Such companies do not produce crude oil or own any refinery. They may own storage facilities or other logistic systems. Often due to lack of assets business with an integrated oil company has to be covered by a Letter of Credit, although that is dependent on the credit risk willingness of each company.

Interface

The mixture which occurs in normal pipeline operations between batches of petroleum products or crude having different specifications. Also called 'slop' or 'transmix'. Sometimes when specifications of two oil grades are very different a line flush may be required to avoid a later contamination when the next batch is pumped through the line.

Intermediate Fuels
Light, residual-type fueloil with characteristics between bunker fuel and marine diesel fuel, typically used in motor ships.

Intermediate Grades Petrol
During seasonal changes from summer to winter and vice versa the specification requirements for gasoline and diesel are temporarily deviating from summer and winter spec, a transition quality. Cold properties and specifications related to exhaust are seasonally regulated. Have a look at 'vapour lock index' and 'transition period'.

Internal Pricing
Agreed prices for oil products between the different business units within an oil organisation. Can be very political and sensitive between internal parties as internal prices affect different results between different departments of a company, even though tax regulation may be the main reason for internal pricing agreements. Internal pricing between business units should be based on market prices or values. If not, it would affect the possibility to optimise within the value chain in a significant way, which should be avoided. See also 'value chain'.

International Energy Agency (IEA)
A Paris-based organisation of 26 leading oil consuming countries, operating under the aegis of the Organisation for Economic Cooperation and Development (OECD) that coordinates its members' energy policies, including the sharing of oil stocks in times of shortage. It also compiles energy statistics including forward supply-demand projections for countries both within and outside its membership.

International Ship and Port Security Code (ISPS)
It is an amendment to the safety of life at sea (SOLAS) convention (1974/1988) on minimum security arrangements for ships, ports and government agencies. Having come into force in 2004, it prescribes responsibilities to governments, shipping companies, shipboard personnel, and port/facility personnel to 'detect security threats and take preventative measures against

security incidents affecting ships or port facilities used in international trade'. An ISPS clause may be part of a physical oil contract.

Intraday
Small period within a single trading day. Traders might trade during these small periods. Brent is most often very volatile when the US market opens. The Brent price might move half a Dollar or more up or down first and after half an hour it settles again. A nervous start in USA. A moment of volatility where price goes up and down can be an interesting period to trade and cash many Dollars if you are a real specialist, an intra-day trader.

Inventories
Total inventories representing the value of the end-of-month stocks regardless of stage of fabrication (whether in the form of purchased materials and supplies, work in process, or finished goods). These inventories are valued at cost using any valuation method other than LIFO.

Inventories (Retail)
Merchandise inventories representing the value of stocks of goods held for sale. The inventories' estimates represent the value, at cost, of the merchandise available for sale as of the last day of the report period. Methods of valuation may vary according to the accounting practices of each firm.

Inverted Market
A paper market in which the nearer months are selling at premiums over the more distant months. Characteristically, a market in which supplies are currently in shortage. See also 'backwardation'.

Investor
A day trader not closing his position before the market closes will have an overnight position. The market would call such a day trader an investor.

IOC
International Oil Companies. Major oil companies without any (shareholders) link to a nation (state). Companies like Shell, ExxonMobil, BP, Conoco, Chevron, Valero and HESS are companies which are not owned by a government.

IP

Institute of Petroleum, merged since 2003 to the Energy Institute. Nevertheless the abbreviation we often see back in specifications of products as IP standards or as a well-known event, IP-week, which has a full focus on the crude and petroleum market.

IPCO

Irrevocable Corporate Purchase Order. Kind of binding letter of intent. Be careful with these kinds of terms. I see them most often in fake offers together with many other popular abbreviations. What you are doing here is basically giving someone the mandate to trade on your behalf. You give someone a short position while that trader has no obligation to supply. This is not at all the same as a 'flexi-short'.

IPE

International Petroleum Exchange. Based in London. The exchange for oil futures as it was in the past based on 'open outcry'. Today replaced by the electronic version called 'The ICE' (Inter Continental Exchange) based in London, UK.

IP-Week

During the 3rd or 4th week of February the Institute of Petroleum organises oil conferences. The people working or trading in the worldwide oil industry meet each other in London by organising lunches, dinners, receptions, one to one meetings and other events in order to discuss business, network, find new partners and/or maintain existing business relations and create business. Of course during that event there are many parties around till late in the evening. My advice during that week: "Avoid breakfast meetings!" You do that when you get older, wiser and when late parties are not on your agenda (not from own experience, or…).

Irrevocable L/C

Opposite of revocable L/C. Once issued it cannot be cancelled unless the receiver agrees with that. See also 'Letter of Credit'.

ISGOTT

International Safety Guide for Oil Tankers and Terminals.

ISO

International Standard Organisation. All companies need to have the working processes well controlled and described. When all procedures and archiving in companies are in place the company can apply for an audit and can get the ISO certification. Companies which are ISO-certified present good working standards. Some companies only want to be in businesses with companies that are ISO certified. Regular auditing is required in order to keep the ISO-certification status.

Isobutane (C_4H_{10})

A normally gaseous branch-chain hydrocarbon. It is a colourless paraffinic gas that boils at a temperature of -11.7°C/10.9°F. It is extracted from natural gas or refinery gas streams.

Isobutylene (C_4H_8)

An olefinic hydrocarbon recovered from refinery processes or petrochemical processes.

Isomerate

Gasoline blendstock. Made by processing naphtha in an isomerisation unit. Isomerate is a very clean gasoline component, high on RVP, small difference between RON and MON, no aromatics and low in density. Isomerate is pricing versus the gasoline quotation plus a premium. The better the octane the higher the premium will be.

Isomerisation

A refining process that alters the fundamental arrangement of atoms in the molecule without adding or removing anything from the original material. Used to convert normal butane into iso-butane (C4), an alkylation process feedstock, and normal pentane and hexane into iso-pentane (C5) and iso-hexane (C6), high-octane gasoline components. Isomerate is a gasoline blending component. Ron/mon is close to each other. Gasoline ron/mon is 95/85 and isomerate can be 93/87. Often the benefit for aromatics is the good mon number and the fact that it is clean material. No aromatics, no sulphur, no benzene and low density. RVP and Ron can be the limitation. Always add as much as possible. When I blended gasoline I preferred to use isomerate as the finishing touch – it added value, mostly on density escalation as gasoline is sold based on a standard density at 0.775; isomerate is lighter than that, at around 0.700 density .

Issuing Bank

The bank of the end buyer. The issuing bank is obligated to pay if documents are presented that comply with the L/C requirements.

ITT

In Tank Transfer. One can be the owner of a cargo in a tank and decide to sell the cargo in tank to another company which will, after the trade, keep title of the product in the same tank. When a trade is done with an intention to change title in tank then no logistic means are used and 'in tank transfer' (administrative pumpover) is executed. The buyer takes over risk and title in tank. The agreed due date and the exact quantity and quality are deemed when the deal is committed. Tank rental is not transferable. The buyer has to move the oil-cargo out of tank before a certain date.

J

Jacket

A thin outer shell over a tank used to contain insulating material. Heavy fueloil tanks are insulated tank and include heating coils.

JCC

Japanese Crude Cocktail. Average price of imported crude oil into Japan published by the Japanese government.

Jet Fuel, Jet A1

A high-quality kerosene product primarily used for fuel in commercial and military aircraft engines. Jet fuel is obtained by distillation and sweetening. The latter removes all traces of mercaptans (very light molecules containing sulphur atoms). Jet fuel is a white product, so-called because it is transparent. The quality of jet A1 is followed up after each manipulation until it reaches the aircraft. The oil must be free of water else it would be off-spec to fuel an aircraft. Some important specifications: Aromatics below 20% v/v, total sulphur below 0.25% mass, mercaptans sulphur below 0.002% mass, freezing point below - 47°C/-52.6°F and a flash point above 38°C/100.4°F. See also 'innerfloater' which is related to a jet petroleum storage tank. 'First foot sample' relates to the loading of a jet fuel cargo. Also 'kerosene' is related to jet fuel.

Jet/Kero 54

JP54 is US jet petroleum with a flash point of 42.2°C/108°F and sulphur of max 0.3%. There is also a JP55 which has its flash point at 50.6°C/123°F but lower sulphur at 0.04%.

Jetty

Place to berth a tanker for loading and discharging the cargo on board. At discharging it is the vessel pumping the oil and when loading it is the shore terminal which is pumping. A terminal will only approve vessels that are able to berth in a safe matter. Draft, LOA, and the vessel conditions are important as well as the information about ship's manifold. Operations are impossible when the loading-arm on the jetty cannot be connected to the ship's manifold.

Jetty Condition

Technical characteristics related to a jetty. It may also include the logistic possibilities and restriction.

Jetty Restriction

Maximum technical abilities at a terminal which would enable a vessel to berth at a jetty in a safe way. Can be based on draft, LOA or beam and vessel connection points. This is not the same as port restrictions as a port may have more terminals with different jetty restrictions. In Rotterdam there are terminals (Europoort and Maasvlakte) which can handle a VLCC while other terminals (Botlek and Pernis) are not able to handle vessels with a draft more than 38 feet. Same as berth restriction.

Jigged Out

A trader gets jigged out on a trade. That trader was working a trade, but suddenly the market turns around and before you know it the trader feels he got swindled into committing a trade.

Jobber

A trader who trades for small, short-term profits during the course of a trading session, rarely carrying a position overnight. Also called 'scalper' or 'day trader'.

Joint Venture, JV

A large-scale project in which two or more parties (in this book related to oil companies) cooperate. One supplies funds and the other actually carries out the project. Each participant retains control over his share, including liability and the right to sell. Two traders could share a cargo transport or vessel from Russia to Singapore. They would 'JV' freight. That is how they propose it to each other. Often the trader who chartered the vessel would propose a freight rate, sometimes just below market to make it attractive. The trader who chartered the vessel may have a cheap freight but is lacking product and finds another fellow trader who is in a position to fill up the vessel. In that way both companies can make money. Good network, relations and trust in the business is important.

Jokerbroker
In the oil trading world there is a lot of activity ongoing and a lot of money and active people are involved. There are a lot of brokers and agents related to the oil business. A lot of brokers are well established and well known to the market. Therefore they are reliable. However, there are a lot of people who would like to become a broker and act like they are a broker. These people send offers on email and use the internet to make various offers. Often the quantities are too big and unrealistic. The prices are not even close to real values. Terms like LOI, POP, RWA, IPCO, LOI, FCO etcetera are mentioned in the offer. The market has difficulty taking these offers seriously and never replies on this business. These types of brokers are therefore called 'jokerbrokers'.

JOM
Joint Operations Manual. You may find this term in contracts related to crude production. Usually a production field is shared by more than one shareholder. The biggest shareholder is normally the crude operator and has to act according to the JOM. The JOM is a manual as agreed by all equity holders of one field.

JP
Abbreviation used for jet fuel like JP 4 and JP54. JP means 'jet propellant'.

JP4
Military jet, army specification for jet fuel. In the past, a blend of gasoline with jet.

JP-5
Military jet fuel designed for use in aircraft stationed aboard aircraft carriers.

Juice

Crude oil or petroleum products to be traded, liquid hydrocarbons. A trader with a physical oil short position would be looking in the market, asking the brokers for some availabilities of juice. Or when he is long he has some juice to offer. Each trader is linked to a commodity so the brokers know which kind of juice they talk about.

Jumbo Pressure Car

Pressure train tank cars in excess of 30,000 gallons capacity.

Just in Time (JIT)

An organisation-wide practice that keeps the inventory to the minimum and provides customers with the right goods or service at the right time. Logistic risk of not getting product delivered is a big risk, especially as oil business is related to transport over sea where delays may happen due to all types of congestion. In a contango market the refinery tanks are preferred to be filled. The trader would prefer to supply to his customers just in time, based on his own production programme and keeping oil in own storage as long as possible. The receiver would like to have his tanks filled as well to take advantage of the contango situation. He would deviate from his 'just in time' concept. In backwardated markets the refinery wishes to push as much as possible into the receiver's tank. Here the receiver will be strict on his just in time concept. Market structure changes trading behaviour a lot.

K

K1/K2/K3

Old classification of oil based on flashpoints. Flashpoint below 28°C/82.4°F is and was classified as K1 product. Oil with a flashpoint over 55°C/131°F is and was classified as K3 product. And all between K1 and K3 is and was classified as K2. For HSE purposes terminals would treat K1 and K2 in the same way, tanks with floating roofs or in case of jet A1 a fixed roof with inner-floater. K3 is less flammable and a fixed roof is sufficient. K1 is gasoline, naphtha, K2 is jet fuel and K3 is fueloil and gasoil (heating and diesel). Crude oil is low flash oil and can be considered as class K1. Even though these are old classifications, the market still uses the terms related to oil logistics. That is the result of jargon in the business.

Kb

KiloBarrel. A trader talking about 800kb means to say 800,000 barrels. See also 'kt'.

Kero Merox Unit

Unit in the refining system which is washing out the acids and mercaptans in the kerosene with the use of caustics.

Kerosene

Lamp oil replacing whale oil in the 19th century until electricity came in place. Thereafter kerosene became fuel for aeroplanes. Middle distillate, heavier than naphtha and lighter than gasoil. Kerosene is called jet fuel when it meets the specification of fuel for aircrafts. Kerosene may be used for blending purposes with gasoil. The flash point often lies around 40° Celsius/104° Fahrenheit. In recent years demand has risen again as a result of kerosene's use in gas turbines and jet engines. In times of war and heavy NATO activity we see the price for jet petroleum rising.

Kerosene-Type Jet Fuel
A kerosene-based product having a maximum distillation temperature of 400°F/204°C at the 10-percent recovery point, and a final maximum boiling point of 572°F/300°C. It is used for commercial (normal passenger aircraft) and military turbojet and turboprop aircraft engines.

Key Points (Products)
These are the most important specifications of the different products:

- **Propane:** Temperature (refrigerated) methanol- sulphur-, ethane and propene content.
- **Butane:** Sulphur and oxygenates.
- **Naphtha:** Density, C4, piona-test, sulphur, mercury, methanol and RVP.
- **Gasoline:** Octane, RVP, olefins, aromatics, benzene, bio content, copper strip and sulphur.
- **Ethanol:** Purity.
- **Jet A1:** Density, flashpoint, smoke point, conductivity and water.
- **Kerosene:** Density, flash point and sulphur.
- **Diesel:** Density, sulphur, cetane index, flashpoint, aromatics, CFPP, cloud point, colour and bio content.
- **Heating Oil:** Sulphur, colour, viscosity, flash point, cloud point and cetane index.
- **VGO:** Sulphur and density.
- **Straight Run Fueloil:** Sulphur, P-value, sulphur, viscosity and density.
- **Cracked fueloil (Utility spec):** Density, sulphur, viscosity and flash point.
- **Bunkers Fueloil:** Density, sulphur, viscosity, metals and sediments.

Key Point Analyses
When a blend is ready the trader knows on which specification he blended close to the maximum requirements. He does that because he wants to avoid selling oil with giveaway of blending value. When the blend is ready, a sample will be taken. The qualities to test are the key points as those borderline

blended qualities can be just on-spec or off-spec. When the result of testing those key points show on-spec quality then a full quality report can be made. If one of the key points is off-spec then the trader needs to decide what action to take. Actions may be to homogenise a bit more and test a new sample or in the worst case re-blend by adding a bit more of a quality adjusting blending component.

Key Quality

When blenders are buying components they are looking for certain specifications. One may need low viscosity components, or there are special wishes for sulphur, density, octane, aromatics or whatever. For the blender these are specific qualities which he would look for. Specific qualities are of high importance to make a blend work. When the trader might find a seller of a good component then he would ask for guarantees on some key qualities. The trader would probably be prepared to pay a little bit up for the oil as long as he gets his component at the quality that he wishes. The seller may have to put in some extra effort to meet that specification. Giving guarantees involves also a risk, performance risk.

Kg/m³

Kilograms per cubic metre or ppm mass. Relates to density, see also 'G/mg'.

Kick in

When a deal is done the financial result makes a big move in the P&L. That can be positive or negative. "The result of that deal kicks in." I heard this jargon a couple of times.

Kinematic Viscosity

Absolute viscosity of a fluid divided by its density at the same temperature of measurement. It is the measure of a fluid's resistance to flow under gravity. To determine kinematic viscosity, a fixed volume of the test fluid is allowed to flow through a calibrated capillary tube (viscometer) that is held at a closely controlled temperature. The kinematic viscosity, in centistokes (Cst.), is the product of the measured flow time in seconds and the calibration constant of the viscometer. When product is heated the actual viscosity goes down and the oil floats better with the result that it speeds up the pumping rate. Nevertheless heating is very expensive. Viscosity is an important specification in bunker oil.

Knot

One nautical mile, 6,076 feet or 1,852 metres, per hour. The sailing speed of a tanker is measured in knots. Vessels try to sail in an economic way; if the logistics are challenging a vessel may speed up, but then the charterer might have to pay for the extra bunkers consumed. The average speed of crude oil tanker on open sea is approximately 12 to 16 nautical miles per hour depending on its size. In low draft areas the speed will come down, as at higher speed a vessel lies deeper in the water.

Knowledge Base

Very much based on experience within a trading team. In artificial intelligence, a given inventory of knowledge specific to a set of rules.

Known Loss

A loss discovered before or at the time of delivery of a shipment. It is not wise to let a vessel sale with a known loss. The commercial invoice is based on B/L figures. So the known loss will result in money loss.

kPa

Kilo Pascal. A unit used to report vapour pressure of gasoline or gasoline components. KPa is a measure of force per unit area. German gasoline has a summer spec with a max kPa of 60 and a winter spec with a max kPa of 90. 1 bar = 100 kPa. See also 'bar'.

KPI

Key Performance Indicator, like for a trader profit level, volumes, portfolio of customers, market share, etc. etc. Traders often get bonuses paid based on their performance.

Kt

Abbreviation for one thousand ton. It avoids writing many zeros. Products traders mention their volumes often in kt. Crude oil traders and product traders in USA use different measurement standards such as barrels and gallons (kb or kgal).

Kyoto Protocol

The Kyoto Protocol was agreed by all countries under the UN framework convention on climate change in Kyoto, Japan, in December 1997. The protocol requires industrialised countries to meet differentiated greenhouse gas emissions reduction targets relative to 1990 levels during the period 2008-12. The protocol establishes the framework for international emissions trading as well as the clean development mechanism which aims to incentivise clean investment in developing countries. The USA did not participate at the start, but finally the USA was also convinced about the protocol and it has participated as well.

L

L/15
Litres at 15°C/60°F. The oil market's standard quantity measurements are reported at this temperature. Initial measurements are done at actual temperature and then it is converted to the measurement at 15°C/60°F. Densities reported and discussed in the market are always based on this standard. But be aware that for logistic reasons you might need to convert your nominated quantities to actual temperatures. Fueloil often has a delivery temperature between 50°C/122°F and 60°C/140°F. It means that the real volume is bigger than the B/L. So make sure that your cargo fits in the tank. A mistake I have seen many times when the last 100 to 200 tons did not fit in the tank. Weight does not change when temperatures change.

Laden
Loaded aboard a vessel. A laden vessel.

Laden Speed
Speed of the vessel with cargo on board. The standard speed or can be arranged in the charter party also called 'tc-speed'. If higher speed is required the charterer can ask for maximum laden speed, but that will cost extra bunkers. If a vessel has plenty of time before it is allowed to discharge, can be part of a sales agreement, then the vessel get a lower laden speed or 'eco-speed'. Saving bunkers and money. In some cases it is the end receiver requesting an earlier arrival date. In that case the end receiver pays for the extra bunkers.

Lady

When we talk oil jargon related then a lady is a vessel. A vessel is female gendered and when it is named after a person then she carries the name of a woman or girl. When a new vessel is baptised then it should be done by a woman and that woman should get a pearl as a reward. So in logistics we ask when the lady is sailing or how much a lady is loading, the tanker. There may be countries where they would not use the name lady as substitute for vessel, maybe out of respect, religion or another reason. However, this book explains about oil business jargon, therefore a vessel is called a 'Lady'.

Land Locked Trading

Situation where traders sell oil production by supplies into pipelines only. Production of oil may not be loaded on board vessels because of the production location or because of the local market structure and availability to transport the oil through pipelines to those markets. A big example can be related to the Canadian sand oil production which finds a lot of outlet in the USA. Oil is supplied through pipelines in many batches. In Russia there is a big local market with many refineries processing Urals crude oil and some other light oils. That local trading activity is a land-locked activity with oil supplied through pipelines. It is therefore recommended to have a share in a pipeline system or at least have good access to pipeline capacity and storage linked to pipeline systems. It would give a company a great opportunity to trade and optimise. Being a major company but also being dependent on others controlling the systems does not always work in the long term. Trading land-locked is trading the logistics.

Landed Cost (of oil)

The cost of oil off-loaded at a port. Similar to CIF, but would also include any duties, fees, or taxes.

LASH

Lighter Aboard SHip. Lighter or barge taken on board a vessel to cross open seas from one area to another. Not each lighter or barge is able or allowed to sail on open sea. Basically you can consider the barge as being a big container on board of a barge carrier.

Last Look

Getting to see the last price offer. If the trader who got the last look is able to beat that offer, he will get the business. Giving someone a last look can be tricky and is not always the most popular way to trade; however, very efficient to ensure that you get the best price. Giving a last look to another company is often done because of good relations. However, as a trader you always prefer to have a last look. If you are not interested in the business you just let the deal go. You have at least the information about the latest agreed price in the market. See also 'first refusal'.

Last Minute Marker
The close of the business in Platts or Argus. The average price of the deals in the last minute will be the quoted price in the reports. See also 'window'.

Last Trading Day
The last day on which trading may occur in a given futures contract or option. A day where traders have the last chance to liquidate their futures positions before they get executed. A very busy day for most paper traders.

Latent Heat
Heat required for changing the state of a unit weight of a substance from solid to liquid or from liquid to vapour without change of temperature (0°C/32°F or 100°C/212°F for water).

Laycan
Laycan consists of two words which are lay-days and cancelling-days. If a vessel does not present within the dates as agreed in the charterparty, then the charterer is entitled the cancel the order.

Lay Days
The period of time described in the charter party during which the owner must tender his ship for loading. The charterer is not obliged to start loading before the commencement of lay days. The charterer may cancel the charter if the ship does not tender prior to the expiration of lay days. See 'laycan.'

Laytime
The allowable time specified in the charter party for a vessel's loading or discharging of a cargo. When more time is used than what has been agreed in the charter party the demurrage will be the consequence.

Layering
This occurs in tanks when a high density fuel is mixed with a low density fuel. But even if density in top-middle-bottom is equal a tank can still be layered on other specs. Then sometimes when the oil in tank is not on-spec it could be smart to homogenise the oil in tank for a few more additional hours. Often after retesting suddenly the blend tank is found to be on-spec.

LCFS
Low Carbon Fuel Standard.

LCIA
London Court of International Arbitration. A place to go to when parties cannot agree on a claim. See also 'AAA' and 'claim'.

LCO, Light Cycle Oil
Cutterstock for blending purposes in fueloil. It has a low density and a very low viscosity. Some grades are classified as dirty oil but on some occasions the LCO may be clean oil. In that case the clean grade may be used in gasoil blending. LCO as blendstock for fueloil is very expensive. The price of LCO is given in a percentage of gasoil. Depending on the quality and the availability in the market this percentage may vary between 70% and 90% of the gasoil quotations. That calculation would result in a fueloil price plus a premium.

Lead
Lead (TEL or Tetra Ethyl Lead) is a fatty high octane component which was allowed in gasoline until the end of the nineties. Gasoline was before the year 2000 classified as unleaded and leaded gasoline. Lead is extremely bad for healthiness. Lead was banned and was replaced by MTBE. MTBE was later replaced with ETBE and ethanol which are the used gasoline components today.

Learning Curve
How long would it take for a new trader to find out the learning curve where the learning curve stands for 'becoming a successful and profit making trader'. Some traders might say after a bad year that they made a learning curve. I hope they mean then that they learned how not to lose money.

Lease Condensate

A mixture consisting primarily of pentanes and heavier hydrocarbons which is recovered as a liquid from natural gas in lease separation facilities. This category excludes natural gas liquids, such as butane and propane, which are recovered at downstream natural gas processing plants or facilities. See 'natural gas liquids'.

Leg

Two prices which belong to each other could be a bid/offer price. If a price is missing then it is called 'off-leg'. In derivatives, a swap, there are also two legs. The fixed price for the swap is one leg and the average price of the covering month is the other leg, the floating leg. See also 'trading at settlement'.

Letter of Comfort, LOC

Statement from a mother company informing that they own a certain affiliate/ subsidiary. It is often credit related to certain activity, an oil trade, that open credit should be safe. The affiliate would like to make use of open credit but is not willing to issue a PCG. Such a letter could indeed give a feeling of comfort; however, it is not a 100% guarantee that the money is safe. It depends also on the good experience and the business relationship if after receipt of an LOC open credit can be given. It would maybe require some appetite for risk at the company's credit departments to make business possible. Maybe it works as an exception of the rule, a case by case decision.

Letter of Credit, L/C

A letter from a bank guaranteeing that a buyer's payment to a seller will be received on time and for the correct amount. In the event that the buyer is unable to make payment on the purchase the bank will be required to cover the full or remaining amount of the purchase.

Letter of Credit (LC) Terms and Types

- **Standby L/C**
  Guarantee that if the buyer fails to pay his invoice then the seller can go to the issuing bank and order for payment. (Guarantee against non-performance of payment by the buyer.)

- **Commercial L/C**

  L/C used as payment instrument. The seller can withdraw the payment direct from the bank. If it concerns a payment for one cargo only then it is a straight Letter of Credit and if it relates to a certain number of cargoes then the buyer can issue a revolving L/C.

- **Revolving L/C**

  A Letter of Credit that can cover a number of cargoes over a longer period where a maximum amount has been set. Could work with long term contracts where over a certain period of time oil cargoes are to be loaded. Can save a lot of administrative workload and supports a smooth operation between buyer and seller.

- **Straight L/C**

  A commercial Letter of Credit for payment of one cargo only. Opposite of revolving Letter of Credit.

- **Revocable L/C**

  L/C which can be changed or withdrawn without informing the beneficiary. Tricky way of doing business when using such an L/C. One can ask what the point of issuing such a document is. It does not protect anyone from risk.

- **Irrevocable L/C**

  L/C which cannot be changed or withdrawn without a written confirmation of all parties connected to this L/C. Very safe for the seller and therefore the best way to protect yourself from credit risk.

- **Back to Back L/C**

  A received irrevocable Letter of Credit which is used as cover to an issued L/C with the exact same terms for both L/Cs. If a trader sells a product he will require an L/C, but in order to cover that short he may need to buy the product as well and that purchase might need coverage by L/C as well.

- **Transferable L/C**

  A Letter of Credit which makes it possible to transfer all rights and terms from one party to another party. Similar to a back to back L/C.

- **Clean L/C**
A letter from the buyer's bank which confirms a commitment that payment will be executed at agreed date.

- **Confirmed L/C**
A 2nd confirmation or guarantee of an earlier issued irrevocable Letter of Credit. In case of doubt about the financial status of counterparty this document may be issued.

- **Unconfirmed L/C**
A Letter of Credit forwarded to the beneficiary by the advising bank without engagement on the part of the advising bank.

- **Deferred Payment L/C**
A Letter of Credit in which a fixed date is agreed for payment. Often just a couple of days after loading (B/L). Could be a seller's requirement for financing reasons.

Letter of Indemnity, LOI

A document which is issued if a Bill of Lading is not available but delivery and operation for discharge must be executed. At the same time it guarantees that the carrier will remain blameless for any losses, damages, costs etc. when discharging the cargo. The receiver indemnifies the carrier of the goods. As most often original Bills of Lading are not available in time when the vessel arrives at disport. Issuing of LOI became part of normal operations procedures.

Letter of Intent, LOI

Letter where one declares an intention to negotiate, buy, offer, show interest in business with a business partner. It is meant to show good will for doing business. Some LOIs may have a binding element, some don't. Investors prefer to receive a letter of intent to convince a financer or a seller of a project that they are ready and lined up to come into action and to show that there is business potential. A binding LOI involves financial risk, so be careful. A non-binding LOI may be given based on good relations but with a serious interest to make an attempt to do business. See also 'MoU'.

Letter of Protest
Written and signed document which describes the shortcomings in performance of a terminal or vessel. A captain or terminal will write these letters on behalf of the cargo owner. Basically they are writing notes when the non-performance is not caused by them. Slow pumping rate from a vessel or terminal is the main reason for writing a letter of protest. Apparently no one likes to pay demurrage or wants to be responsible.

Leverage Game
Activity in the oil market where a trader takes a huge paper position on a certain commodity (less liquid than the futures market). This can be diesel, gasoline or fueloil. The trader tries to buy up or sell down the physical market in order to gain on his paper position. If the trader is successful he might lose money on the physical activity, but gains much more on his paper position, as the paper position ought to be two or more times as big as the physical activity. This activity generates an awful lot of work in the back office and should be well organised before executing the strategy.

Liability
A company's legal debts or obligations which arise during the course of business operations. These are settled over time through the transfer of economic benefits including money, goods or services. Responsibility you have towards your counterparty as you have to perform according to the agreement you made with that counterparty. Being in breach of the contract could result in financial consequences such as claims which you might have to pay. You are liable for all costs and consequences as a result of bad performance. Although when you get a claim, first reject it on paper, then talk and find a commercial solution.

LIBOR (London Interbank Offered Rate)
The average interest rate which banks in London are charging to other banks when lending to each other. The LIBOR rate is used as benchmark for companies working with credit and to companies using lots of capital to run their business for external and internal purposes.

Licensed Warehouse
A warehouse approved by the exchange from which a commodity may be delivered on a futures contract. In oil business these are oil storage terminals.

Lift

A trader is said to be 'lifting' the offer when he initiates a trade that buys directly from the best offered price. This trader likely believes that the contract price will rise and is willing to give up the perceived edge to another trader by buying from his offer.

Lift Subject

Long term deals may be done subject to approvals, e.g. Management approval or vetting approval. When the approval is granted then the trader calls his counterparties and lifts subjects or subs. The deal is now official and ready to be signed and executed.

Lifting

Tankers and barges loading petroleum at a terminal or transfer point.

Lifting Programme

Overview of all cargoes of a certain quality or grade of crude oil to be loaded in the month to come at a certain producer, production country or production area, which involves the loading programme of various crudes. Traders are always looking for these overviews as it says a lot about the availabilities for the coming period. From the loading programme one can also see which companies are the producers or initial buyers/holders of the different cargoes. The market will follow each cargo which is a part of cargo tracking role in trading, e.g. Urals programme in Primorsk is showing each month roughly 60 cargoes of 100kt of REBCO to be loaded on FOB basis. On that list one can see the loading windows, the quantities and the suppliers or sellers of the cargoes. This information is also the first information used for cargo tracking. There are loading programmes in Iraq, WAF, USA etc. etc. Often the companies being commercially related to a certain producer will get the list first. After a few days these lists are pretty much shared in the market or available through wire reporters. Although each month it is a lot of work to get access to all those lists. If you do not ask for it, then it will not come automatically, so don't be passive.

Light Crude Oil

Has API gravity higher than 40. The higher the API number, the lighter the crude oil. For some refineries light oil is defined at a higher API level. But each refinery would classify crude according to their own technical set up.

See also 'classification crude (density)'. Production with an API over 50 is classified as condensate.

Light Gas Oils

Liquid petroleum distillates heavier than naphtha, with an approximate boiling range from 401°F/205°C to 653°F/345°C. Also called diesel No.2. Often also seen as light straight run gasoil which needs further processing at a refinery. Most often light refers to density, low density gasoil, flash point not less than 55°C /131°F.

Light Ends

Refers to light products naphtha and LPG (butane and propane). Also called gas liquids (G/L). Light condensate may also be accounted to light ends.

Lighter

General name for a broad, flat-bottomed boat used in transporting cargoes between a vessel and the shore. The distinction between a lighter and a barge is more in the manner of use than in equipment. The term 'lighter' refers to a short haul, generally in connection with loading and unloading operations of vessels in a harbour while the term 'barge' is more often used when the cargo is being carried to its destination or over a long distance over inland waterways. Like the barge market in ARA supplying oil to places in The Netherlands, Germany, Belgium or France over the river Rhine and Maas.

Lightering

Lightering is the process of transferring a cargo from one vessel to a number of smaller vessels or barges. Lightering is required as a result of port or jetty restrictions for bigger vessels. Lightering is costly and is part of a trader's calculation. Sometimes only half of the cargo needs to be lightered as draft challenges may be solved by then. Examples of lightering include VLCCs discharging oil cargoes into aframax size vessels in the US Gulf to allow cargoes to be taken to refineries through smaller waterways and Aframax oil supplies into barges in Northern Europe to deliver to inland terminals. Have a look also at 'STS'.

Light Naphtha

A category of naphtha that can be rich in paraffins and is used for ethylene cracking to make petrochemicals. However, if it is rich in aromatics and naphthenes it is used for reforming into gasoline or as blendstock for making gasoline. Light naphtha is classified as C5 and C6 (boiling range from 30-90°C/86-164°F and heavy naphtha is classified as C7-C12 (boiling range 90-200°C/164-392°F).

Light Products (Light Ends)

The group of petroleum products with low boiling temperatures, such as propane, butane and naphtha.

Line of Credit

An arrangement in which a bank or seller extends a specified amount of unsecured credit to a specified counterparty for a specified time period. Also called 'credit line' and often linked to open credit. This open credit is often given based on the credit rating of a company. Open credit is based on trust and given based on company rating, but can still be risky in times of economic crisis.

Line Displacement

Displacing the line content to a tank or into another storage unit. This may be done in order to transfer another quality through the earlier filled line. Line displacements may be done by use of a pig, push by water or a push by the product itself. Quantity measurement is important during such displacement, especially when it is a push with another product. You do not want to lose oil and you do not like contamination. Good procedures for such an operation must be in place. Terminals have a lot of pipeline systems and not all pipelines are empty. On a vessel's arrival it could well be that the pipeline to use is not empty. When discharging, the line content will be pushed to another tank with the vessel's cargo. When that is done, the line content is displaced and the cargo will be pumped into the nominated tank. After discharging it could well be that other oil is used again in order to push the cargo oil into the nominated tank. Oil in pipeline can be used to push oil. It is cheaper then pushing the oil with pigs by the use of nitrogen. Line displacement must be secure and can be a source of oil losses. How much of the cargo is pushed into the line displacement tank and is all cargo oil pushed in the tank where it should be? Inspectors must follow the procedures of the terminals and make their calculations. Line displacement with discharging and loading vessels has become common practice at terminals. Most terminals own their own oil for that purpose.

Line Section
A continuous run of pipe between locations. Sometimes called line-street.

Liquefied Petroleum Gases (LPG)
A group of hydrocarbon-based gases derived from crude oil refining or natural gas fractionation. They include: ethane, ethylene, propane, propylene, normal butane, butylene, iso-butane, and isobutylene. For convenience of transportation, these gases are liquefied through pressurisation. LPG in the Netherlands is used as a car fuelling system. It is cheap to drive on lpg. This lpg is a mixture of 60% butane and 40% propane during winter and vice versa during summer. Lpg is a seasonal product and one can see it in the prices. In the winter, more gas is used for gasoline blending and refineries consume more gas in their furnaces. Therefore, the refinery crack during winter season should be better than in summertime.

Liquefied Refinery Gases (LRG)
Liquefied petroleum gases fractionated from refinery or still gases. Through compression and/or refrigeration, they are retained in the liquid state. The reported categories are ethane/ethylene, propane/propylene, normal butane/butylenes, and isobutane/isobutylene. Excludes still gas.

Liquidate
To take a second futures or options position opposite to the initial or opening position. To sell (or purchase) futures contracts of the same delivery month purchased (or sold) during an earlier transaction or make (or take) delivery of the cash commodity represented by the futures market. Also referred as 'to offset'. Basically leaving all positions and balance the book to zero exposure. Or in trader's words: 'To flatten the book.'

Liquid and Illiquid Markets
The ability of a market to buy and sell at ease with no impact on price stability. A market is described as liquid if the spread between the bid and the offer is small. Another measure of liquidity is the presence of buyers and sellers, with more players creating tighter spreads. Liquid markets often trade standardised product qualities and are often transparent. Illiquid markets have fewer participants, the bid-offer range is often bigger and it trades very slowly. Easy in and easy out is impossible. Therefore having a speculative

position in such a market is risky. Price levels in illiquid markets may be easy to manipulate.

List, to
Announcing or communicating a deal done within the trading unit one works for. When a deal is listed it will create work for operators and back office people as action has to be taken to perform on the agreed business. A way of communicating deals committed within a trading unit and to back office functions.

Litre
A litre is 1,000th of a cubic metre. There are 3.78541 litres in a gallon. Densities are kilogrammes per litre at 15°C/60°F. There are about 159 litres in a barrel.

LLS
Light Louisiana Sweet traded in pipeline lots of 1,000 to 5,000 barrels for delivery between the 25th of one month and the 25th of the next month. API is 37 and sulphur content is 0.3 %. Basis loading port: St. James, La. A bit better quality than WTI and therefore higher priced, this oil can also be used as benchmark for pricing and valuation of other crudes, e.g. WTI – Maya spread, or LLS – Maya spread. Maya is heavy crude oil from Mexico used as benchmark for heavy crudes in USA.

LNG
Liquefied Natural Gas. Natural gas converted to a liquid state by pressure and severe cooling, and then returned to a gaseous state to be used as fuel. Natural gas will liquefy at a temperature of approximately -259° Fahrenheit/-160° Celsius at atmospheric pressure.

LNGC (LNG Carrier)
A tanker specially constructed to carry LNG in tanks. Sizes may differ from 500 Cbm up to 140,000 Cbm. Due to increased LNG production the fleet of LNGCs is still growing.

LOA
Length overall of the vessel. Important to know as next to draft restrictions some berths might be restricted based on the length of the vessel.

Load limit

The maximum weight of lading that can be loaded into a train tank car.

Load Temperature

Weighted average cargo temperature after loading. Important to consider in logistics as at hot temperatures the actual volume is bigger than the nominated volume. Nominated volumes are most often in tons calculated to litres at 15°C/60°F. When nominating a full vessel and the cargo's temperature (fueloil) is 60°C/140°F then there might be some logistic challenges; lack of ullage in the shore tank has happened many times.

Loadables

The potential quantities a vessel can take on board based on various draft levels. How much can be loaded based on arrival draft of 12.5, 13.0 or 13.5 metres. The master of the vessel will calculate this and inform how much oil can be taken on board at these draft levels. Not all ports have perfectly deep water. In one port, terminals can have various draft restrictions. Once the vessel is at loadport the master of the vessel will contact the agent at disport in order to get the latest arrival draft information. Only then, the master will decide how much oil he can take on board his tanker. Tides on arrival can have an influence on the cargo size as well. Otherwise, when the disport has good draft then the vessel will load her quantity as per voyage instruction. Getting loadables is just a matter of anticipating on operational expectations. The operator needs to direct the vessel in the right order at disport in case the vessel discharges in more than one terminal in the same port. The loadables indicate then what the vessel will take on board. That can be less than the contract in case of draft restrictions. That quantity needs to be adjusted in the P&L, as this will have an exposure effect.

Loaded Mileage

A train tank car travelling on the railroads with commodity.

Loading Arm

'Flexible' or hydraulic pipeline at the jetty which needs to be connected to the ship's manifold in order to load or discharge. Like an arm, the pipe can move. It can go up, down, left, right in order to get and stay connected to the ship. When a vessel empties it will lie higher in the water, as the shoreline connection is fixed to the manifold of the vessel; it is safe to think that such a connection is linked to the hydraulic system of a loading arm. The line will follow the height of the vessel which depends on the volume in the vessel and the water level, the tide.

Loading Programme

Weekly or monthly lifting plan for a commodity which is planned to be produced during a certain period. In crude oil production a monthly plan with different stems is published. A good start for 'cargo tracking'. See also 'lifting programme'.

Loading Tolerances

In nominations, to load an oil cargo, different loading tolerances are available. It is important to know whether the tolerance is in buyer's or seller's option. Most often, the one who controls the means of transport also has the option on the tolerance. However, in crude logistics we see for example in Russia that the producers/sellers control the tolerance. If a cargo loads too much or too little it could result in credit problems, as in such a case the B/L quantity is no longer within the range of the tolerance of the quantity as stated in the L/C. This can make an L/C invalid. I have listed the following 'tolerance' indications:

- **Approx.**
  - In the barge market in Rotterdam it would mean +/- 5% of the nominated quantity.
  - In the cargo market it would mean +/- 10% of the nominated quantity.

- **Plus/Minus a Percentage**
  Often indicated to avoid confusion which may happen from time to time when the interpretation of 'approx' is different between 2 different organisations, e.g. 1,000 tons +/-5% is minimum 950 tons and maximum 1,050 tons.

- **Max**
  Maximum nominated quantity but it includes also a non-mentioned minimum of 5% for barges or 10% for cargo below the nominated quantity.

- **Minimum Quantity and Maximum Quantity**
  The exact quantity tolerance is here given in absolute numbers.

- **Min/Max**

  As close to the exact nominated quantity. Good class terminals can load a 1,000 ton barge with a tolerance of only 200 litres or less.

- **Approx. WSG**

  Approx. 'wasserstand gemäss' or approx. according to water level. This is often used for barges going from Rotterdam to Germany. The buyer buys the loaded quantity with maximum 5% tolerance over the nominated quantity while the minimum quantity depends on the water level or draft at the disport in Germany. This is not L/C sensitive, this is about logistics.

- **BACTAP**

  But As Close To As Possible. This is more an added comment to the tolerance. By that the buyer or seller expresses the preferred quantity to be placed on board. Often combined as 'maxbactap'.

- **MOLCHOPT**

  More Or Less CHarterer's OPTion.

- **MOLOO**

  More Or Less Owner's Option.

Loading Weather

Weather circumstances can stop all possibilities of loading a cargo. A storm at sea makes big waves. A vessel cannot connect hoses when waves on the sea are too high, e.g. At 4.5 metre waves, a vessel cannot be connected. Once a vessel is connected to a loading hose at an offshore field, then loading can just commence. However, if the weather at sea is getting too rough, at e.g. 5.5 metres, the tanker may decide to disconnect from the hose and stop loading. It is, in most cases, the captain of the vessel who decides. Although in many cases, this can also be a standard in HSE rules of the vessel owner. Then the tanker has to wait until the weather at sea improves. Delays in winter can be severe. There is always a moment that the sea calms down; however, safe operations offshore always demands highest attention. So loading weather relates to wind and waves; a vessel can load when the sea is calm enough. The risk of bad weather is a tank top situation; see also 'tank top'.

Local

The trader in a pit of a commodity exchange who buys and sells for his or her account. A private trader/investor who stands in the inner circle of the pit. Banks, brokers or funds are standing on the outside of the pit. They need to be in contact with their colleagues who receive orders of what to buy or to sell. The local does not need those contacts, he makes his own decisions. This is based on the old system in the exchange called 'open outcry'.

Location Spread

Same as arbitrage. Difference in prices between different price-quoted geographic areas. As an example the difference between ARA quotations and the USGC quotations for gasoline. World economies and prices are changing all the time. With open arbs cargoes move Trans-Atlantic until prices change as a result of oversupply. Traders are always looking at any opportunity to export and lock in (hedge) the arb and move oil in order to take profits. With closed arbs the activity slows down rapidly. Shipping prices go down due to lack of transport demand, which could cause another open arb possibility because of cheap freight. Arbitrage trading is most often seen as an opportunistic trade. However, some flows will never stop due to long term obligations.

Logistic Optimisation

Organising the logistics in such a way that money (costs) can be saved or can be earned. Good cooperation between the trader and the operator is required. Competence is the key in this case. Interaction between traders of different commodities is also important to find opportunities to utilise logistics in the best manner. Gasoline to USA and distillate as backhaul cargo can be an example. Also topping up a cargo to avoid deadfreight is a good way of logistic optimisation.

LOI / Letter of Indemnity

A document which is issued if a Bill of Lading is not available but delivery and operation for discharge must be executed. At the same time it guarantees that the carrier will remain blameless for any losses, damages, costs etc. when discharging the cargo. The receiver indemnifies the carrier of the goods. As most often original Bill of Ladings are not available in time when the vessel arrives at disport. Issuing of LOI became part of normal operations procedures.

LOI / Letter of Intent

Letter where one declares an intention to negotiate, buy, offer, show interest in business with a business partner. It is meant to show good will for doing business. Some LOIs may have a binding element, some don't. Investors prefer to receive a letter of intent to convince a financer or a seller of a project that they are ready and lined up to come into action and to show that there is business potential. A binding LOI involves financial risk, so be careful. A non-binding LOI may be given based on good relations but with a serious interest to make an attempt to do business. See also 'MoU'.

Long

You own something. When you buy something you go long and you are immediately exposed to price changes. If you buy product and sell paper (a hedge) then you are flat. See also 'going long'. Traders talking bullish about the market are often having a long position. They base their position on a bullish sentiment in the market.

Long Freight

You are long freight when you have a ship (owner). If you are long physical freight. You sell the FFA.

Long Hedge

A hedge involving a long futures position.

Long Residue

Residue that is left over after atmospheric distillation. This goes up to 380°C and is called straight run fuel oil. Part of this oil may be further processed in the vacuum tower. The residue that is left over from that process is called 'short residue'. Often long residue is the sum of short residue plus residue from atmospheric distillation.

Long Ton

A unit of weight = 2,240 pounds or 1,106 kilos.

Look Back Opportunity

Opportunity where part of a cargo is already hedged and the seller has the opportunity to supply his cargo to another market at different quotations. If the hedge is in the money then the trader can cash in that paper position and decide to deliver a cargo to another geographic market. Due to pricing optionality this can be a very good way to make a decision. The trader can look back to the hedge of his earlier plan and then change supply location if there is profit on the table. A bit of allowed back trading I would call it.

Loose Emulsion
This consists of varying water droplet sizes with many droplets of a relatively large size, which separate readily upon settling.

LOP
Abbreviation of Letter Of Protest. A letter of protest can be issued by the vessel, the terminal, the agent, expeditor or the surveyor. The receiver of the lop will sign the letter for receipt only. No one would admit that something is wrong or have performed badly. It is often up to the claims departments in the offices to find out if there was a damage or demurrage. If there is nothing to claim then the lop is filed with the cargo documents. A claim can always be received at a later stage. The docs may be used as proof of innocence or by the other party as proof of right to claim. The lop is made for all matters which are different from the standards. So, one up to ten letters of protests from various parties involved in the cargo is very normal.

Loss Control
Focus on all operations of a cargo being loaded and discharged. It includes sampling before, during and after loading and discharging. It includes the tank inspection on the vessel before and after loading and discharging. It may include pipeline inspection on the supplying and receiving terminal and in some cases quantity control of tanks surrounding the tank in to which the oil should be pumped. Loss control is meant to minimise losses of a cargo travelling from a tank at loadport to a tank at disport. Some losses just cannot be avoided but they should never exceed standard allowances for losses. Every ton or barrel of oil lost costs money being deducted from the trader's P&L. Often the buyer suffers the loss unless the cargo is purchased based on quantity received. A term in DAP deliveries, the old DES.

Loss from Peak
Maximum allowed and accepted loss, in dollars per unit, during a trading session, a kind of own set mandate for a trading strategy. A loss from peak level is set based on a trading plan following trading discipline. A trader may

take a position with a plan to cut losses at 2 dollars loss from peak. When a trader would buy a futures position at 100 USD then he cuts losses when the price goes down to 98 Dollars. When the price moves up to 103 USD then he could take profit or keep holding the position, let profits ride. He would cut losses if the market would hit at 101 USD. So the level where to cut loss would follow the price level of the highs of quoted outright market prices. The market could go up to 107 and then fall back to 100 dollars again. If the trader would follow his loss from peak strategy he would have offset his position at 105 USD. The profit is 5 Dollars while his maximum allowed loss would have been 2 Dollars. Working with loss from peak is a typical strategy for spec traders. The loss from peak level depends on the volatility of the market, the financial strength of the speculator and risk appetite.

Loss (Sailing with a)
When the ship figures after loading are less than the B/L numbers then the vessel sails with a loss. Does not mean that there will be a guaranteed loss at disport, but rather you see it as a first indicator of trouble to come when the loss is significant. It shows a difference between shore and ship measurements.

Lot
Volumes traded on the exchange goes in 'lots'. 1 lot is equal to 1,000 barrels of crude oil, 100 tons of gasoil in Europe and 42,000 gallons of oil products on the Nymex. 42,000 gallons is equal to 1,000 barrels. 159,000 litres or roughly 120 to 140 tons of gasoline or gasoil on the Nymex.

Low
The lowest price of the day for a particular futures contract. Dip of the day.

Low-Emissions Diesel
From October 2005, 110 counties in East/Central Texas have required the use of low emissions diesel or LED in both on-road vehicles and in non-road agricultural and construction equipment. LED diesel must contain less than 10% by volume of aromatic hydrocarbons and must have a cetane number of 48 or greater.

Low Flash
Products with a flashpoint below 55° Celsius/131° Fahrenheit are called low flash products. Different rules for handling in logistics would apply

for this type of oil compared with 'high flash' oil. Low flash products are more flammable than high flash products. In the logistics with these oil products the combination of gas and air has to be avoided. This is because gas in combination with air is explosive. Low flash oil is stored in tanks with a floating roof as low flash products evaporate faster and could give a distinctive smell in the area therefore emissions must be avoided. Examples are crude, gasoline and naphtha.

Low Hanging Fruit
The easy, profitable deals where companies can make money with minimum effort, like a strong contango market situation. Probably such a company has a favourable position which creates that possibility; cheap storage may be within own systems. It is always nice to have certain base 'guaranteed' source of income. Often trading targets take more than harvesting low hanging fruit only. Further growth, long term business continuity and a stretch to maximise profit at minimum costs is being expected from traders.

Low-Sulphur No. 2 Diesel Fuel
No. 2 diesel fuel that has a sulphur level no higher than 0.05% by weight. Used primarily in motor vehicle diesel engines for on-highway use. Sometimes also called light gasoil.

Low-Sulphur Distillate Fueloil
Distillate fueloil having a sulphur content greater than 15 ppm up to max 500 ppm. Low sulphur distillate fueloil also includes product with sulphur content equal to or less than 15 ppm if the product is intended for pipeline shipment and the pipeline has a sulphur specification below 15 ppm. USA logistics related.

LPG
Liquefied Petroleum Gas, typically ethane, propane butane and iso-butane. Usually produced at refineries or natural gas processing plants, including plants that fractionate raw natural gas plant liquids. LPG can also occur naturally as a condensate. LPG can be used as car fuel or as fuel to use to heat barbecues etc. Often in wintertime refineries consume more propane and butane in order to heat the refinery furnace in the refinery process. Besides that, in wintertime the specification of gasoline allows more butane blending as a result of a higher RVP requirement in gasoline. LPG is then a

good gasoline component to boost octane as well. Change to wintertime is a good fundamental reason for higher prices of LPG in that season.

LRG
Liquefied petroleum gases fractionated from refinery or still gases. Through compression and/or refrigeration, they are retained in the liquid state. The reported categories are ethane/ethylene, propane/propylene, normal butane/butylenes, and isobutane/isobutylene. Excludes still gas.

LP Model
Refinery calculation model which advises how to run a refinery in the best economical and profitable way. This model requires a lot of input. Input can be crude prices, differentials, price forecast, qualities and quantities as a feedstock. Product prices, cracks, qualities, quantities, freight rates, etc. to know which products to sell at what price. Also components for blending optimisation or as additional feedstock are input for the LP model. Once all information is correct in the system, the LP model will calculate and it will advise which crude slates are preferred and what product the refinery wants to produce. A very precise job to control as markets change all the time. The refinery will give its purchase order for crude oil based on LP modelling. It is up to the traders to optimise as much as possible around that short to make some additional profits.

LS
Low Sulphur. Fueloil with a sulphur content which is less than 1.0% in volume.

LSFO
Low Sulphur FuelOil. This fueloil is mainly used in utilities such as electricity companies, steel companies or aluminium companies. LSFO is also a blending component connected to the low sulphur bunker market in the SECA and therefore the LSFO prices significant affect the low sulphur bunkers prices. When LSFO is used as burning fuel for bunkers or utilities then we can talk about cracked fueloil. There is also straight run fuel with sulphur levels from 0.3% up to 0.7 % and it has its own quotation, although it is not a really liquid market. Straight run low sulphur fueloil is used as feedstock in refineries. Straight run is higher priced and valued than cracked fueloil.

LTA
Lifting and Transportation Agreement. This is often related to a long-term contract. Nomination procedures, standard cargo sizes, flexibility, reporting of lifting schedules and many other logistic matters are written in this agreement. It can be between buyer and seller but also between a crude production operator and its equity holders. The more equity holders are involved the more challenging it is to make an agreement that makes all people happy. A change in the lta can only be made when all equity holders agree or at least have responded within a certain time after the proposal. The lta can also refer to transport of the oil, referring to a 'coa' which linked to the lta.

Lubricants
Substances used to reduce friction between bearing surfaces or as process materials, either incorporated into other materials used as processing aids in the manufacture of other products, or used as carriers of other materials. Petroleum lubricants may be produced either from distillates or from residues. Lubricants include all grades of lubricating oils from spindle oil to cylinder oil and those used in greases. Due to lower sulphur specifications in products, the lubricity of those products are worse. The market had to come with additives to solve the problem. Each company may use its own additive. Quality of fuel at petrol stations may differ due to that. Look at 'lubricity improver'.

Lubricity
Reduction of friction-level in a motor; this may depend on the use of certain petrol. Lubricity quality of oil is a requirement for protection purposes for the motor engine. Due to strong environmental requirements in diesel for maximum level of sulphur and aromatics the lubricity of diesel was reduced in the refinery processing system. Therefore different additives are blended into the diesel before it gets into the car. Adding of these additives is normally not a part of refining activity.

Lubricity-Improver
Environmental regulations have changed the characteristics of gasoil over the years. For example, the sulphur concentration in gasoil/diesel has been reduced significantly in order to protect the environment. However, because of sulphur spec changes in gasoil, the lubricating properties decreased a lot,

resulting in an excessive wear of diesel-engines. Lubricity improvers are nowadays applied in order to bring this characteristic to an acceptable level again. Each wholesaler or petrol station chain can add their own secret quality lubricity improver. From there the pump holder can market and advertise his best fuel.

Lucky Sample

Sometimes a tank is not well homogenised and is still a bit layered in qualities. After a first tank sample one of the parameters in the quality might be just a tiny little bit off-spec. After taking a new sample the quality is suddenly perfect – that is the lucky sample declaring that the tank is ready for supplies. Just imagine that a one litre sample represents a tank of up to 50 million litres. Based on the rules of reproducibility and repeatability the receiver of oil cannot claim. Taking a new sample should only be done after a new manipulation of the product in the tank. Sometimes 1 hour justifies taking another sample.

Lumpsum

Agreed sum to be paid for a service. Could be a sum for a pumpover. But also chartering a vessel may be done at a lumpsum. A VLCC from Europe to Singapore could be at a lumpsum of 4 million Dollars. One has to check what service is included in the lumpsum. What is agreed upon will be noted in the charter party. Opposite of a certain rate per unit like cents per barrel or worldscale based. The trader would convert the lumpsum to the freight costs per ton or barrel. By that he can calculate a price to be offered or bid for a cargo to be delivered.

LVN

Light Virgin Naphtha, straight run naphtha, can be used as gasoline component or can be further processed and upgraded. It can also be used as feedstock for the petrochemical industry. Light virgin naphtha comes from atmospheric distillation.

M

M/L

Mooring Line. Shipping related. You may see it in a time sheet, the date and time when the mooring line is on board.

MACD, Moving Average Convergence Divergence (Technical trading)

A trend following momentum indicator that maps the difference between two exponential moving averages, the 26 and 12-day. A nine-day exponential moving average is plotted on top of this as a 'signal' line to show buy/sell opportunities. MACD graphs are easy to find on 'the screen' on the trader's desk.

Maiden Trip

First loaded voyage of a tanker after delivery from new building. A first trip with heavy oil might lead to a voyage loss due to first clingage.

Mainline Pipeline (MLP)

Multiproduct pipeline in UK from the refineries at Milford Haven supplying oil North up to Manchester and Nottingham.

Major

The bigger oil producing companies established when first oil got drilled, i.e. Shell, BP, ExxonMobil, Chevron, Conoco. Originally formed by the seven sisters. The seven sisters consisted of three companies formed by the break up forced by the U.S. government of Standard Oil, along with four other major oil companies. With their dominance of oil production, refinement and distribution, they were able to take advantage of the rapidly increasing demand for oil and turn immense profits. Standard Oil was later abbreviated to S.O., which sounds like 'ESSO'. See also 'seven sisters'.

Maintenance Margin

A set minimum margin (per outstanding futures contract) that a customer must maintain in his margin account to retain the futures position. When that minimum required margin is not covered then the account holder gets a margin call.

Make Bulk

Storage companies are often used for break-bulk, blending, trading and make bulk. Cargoes from different locations are collected into one terminal. Once a planned cargo is collected (make bulk) then it can be loaded for export to its final destination. Russian fueloil is often exported to Singapore by VLCC which can load up to 300kt. It is impossible to load a VLCC at the Russian loadports due to draft restrictions at the 'Big Belt', maximum 15 metres, while a full VLCC measures a draft of roughly 22 metres. Therefore traders collect their oil in Rotterdam by buying Russian cargoes and by collecting barges with fueloil and components in the local market. Once the tanks are filled and the Arb to Singapore is open, a VLCC will be chartered for export. The tanks will be empty after loading and new bulk can be created. Maybe the trader will play a 'leverage game'.

Mandate

Authorisation to trade a certain commodity on behalf of a company at a maximum risk position level. This mandate is to be followed by the company's controller. When a position is out of mandate it is the controller's role to warn the trader and report the breach of mandate to management. The trader has to take action in order to position himself within mandate within a certain time. Mandates may be given as outright trading mandate and spread mandate which is what traders most look at when taking positions. Other mandate is VaR mandate which says more about the activity and money at risk. I used to call it: "A stakeholder's P&L". Even though a VaR mandate controls the size of the book and its activity, it may affect the trading power when oil prices and volatility are high. A trader can also request permission to rent a tank at a certain price. Granted permission will become the mandate to conclude a storage deal at a given price.

Mandateship

Someone who claims that he represents a major company and has mandate to buy or sell on behalf of that company. Many brokers or consultants may be used to find new markets or source new crude on behalf of another company, but it happens rarely that an oil company gives full mandate to trade, buy or sell, to someone who is not employed by that company. Be careful here: there are many middle-men claiming that they have a mandate to buy or sell. If it is real then this must be proven by proper documentation, but honestly speaking, which oil company would allow a third party to play with their millions of Dollars?

Manifest

Document that lists in detail all the Bills of Lading issued by a carrier or its agent or master for a specific voyage. A detailed summary of the total cargo of a vessel. Used principally for customs purposes. Same as 'cargo manifest'.

Manifold

Place on the vessel featuring pipes and valves used to load and discharge oil vessels. The manifold is the connection to the loading arm of the terminal for that operation. The flange at the manifold is the exact place where title and risk passes from seller to buyer at load or disport depending on the type of delivery as agreed in the physical oil contract, CIF/CFR/DAP/FOB.

Manual Tank Measurement

Most shore tanks are well equipped concerning measurement requirements. One can read the levels in tank from a screen and there are calibration tables available of each tank in order to calculate the cubic metres in tank. Such measurement can also be done in the old fashioned, manual way. Each tank roof has gauge hatches which are situated North, East, South and West on the tank (3, 6, 9 and 12 o'clock). If you measure the oil level in tank on those 4 points and you take the average then you have the first number. Then if you measure the oil level in the middle of the tank you have a second observation. The average of the two results is the official level in tank. Then by use of the calibration table the quantity in tank can be determined. Probably the volume needs to be adjusted to the temperature at 15°C/60°F. ([North + South + East

+ West/4] + Middle)/2 = level in millimetres. Millimetres multiplied with the number on the calibration table is volume in tank. See also 'calibration table'.

Marginal Barrel
The last few percentage points of supply that can make the difference between shortage and comfort. The marginal barrel affects the price of oil (Dated Brent).

Margin (Futures Account)
An amount of money deposited by both buyers and sellers of futures contracts and by sellers of options contracts to ensure performance of the terms of the contracts (the making or taking delivery of the commodity or the cancellation of the positions by a subsequent offsetting trade). Margin in commodities is not down payment, as in securities, but rather a performance bond.

Margin
Sales price minus purchase price minus all costs related to the trade plus a premium if available. Time value is part of the whole deal but not of the margin as such. It can happen that margin is given away on purpose when more money is to be made on time value.

Margin Call
A call from a clearinghouse to a clearing member or from a broker or firm to a customer, to bring margin deposits up to a required minimum level. If you get a margin call then you are losing money on your position. So either cut loss and liquidate your position or put more money on your account and wait for the next margin call, but it is better to make money. See also 'discipline'.

Marine Bunker Oil Classification
Vessels/Barges burn different type of bunkers. It means that there are different requirements for density, viscosity, sulphur and a few other small specifications. For sulphur I would refer to the SECA area, where 0.1% is the maximum. Also barges used for inland shipping are using other type of engines compared with the big sea going vessels. Different naming of oil in the trading environment has to be understood, as each quality of oil has its own value. Look at the qualities here under:

· **MGO** (Marine gas oil), made from distillate only.

- **MDO** (Marine diesel oil), a blend of heavy gasoil that may contain very small amounts of black refinery feedstock, but has a low viscosity up to 12 Cst. so it does not need be heated for use in internal combustion engines. MDO may also be red dyed for tax purposes.
- **IFO** (Intermediate fueloil), a blend of gasoil and heavy fueloil, with less gasoil than marine diesel oil.
- **MFO** (Marine fueloil), same as HFO, just another name.
- **HFO** (Heavy fueloil), pure or nearly pure residual oil.

Marine Residual Fuels							
Parameter	Unit	Limit	RMA 30	RMB 30	RMD 80	RME 80	RMF 180
Density	kg/m^3	Max	960.0	975.0	980.0	991.0	991.0
Visc @ 50dc	mm²/s	Max	30	30	80	180	180
Sulphur %	% (m/m)	Max	3,50	3,50	4,00	4,50	4,50
In Seca Area the max Sulphur is 0,1%							
Parameter	Unit	Limit	RMG 380	RMH 380	RMK 380	RMH 700	RMK 700
Density	kg/m^3	Max	991.0	991.0	1010.0	991.0	1010.0
Visc @ 50dc	mm²/s	Max	380	380	380	700	700
Sulphur %	% (m/m)	Max	4,50	4,50	4,50	4,50	4,50
In Seca Area the max Sulphur is 0,1%							

Marine distillate fuels						
Parameter	Unit	Limit	DMX	DMA	DMB	DMC
Density	kg/m^3	Max		890	900	980.0
Visc @ 40dc	mm²/s	Min	1,4	1,5	-	-
Visc @ 40dc	mm²/s	Max	5,5	6	11	14
Sulphur %	% (m/m)	Max	1,00	1,50	2,00	2,00
In Seca Area the Max Sulphur is 0,1%						

Marine Cargo Insurance

Insurance covering loss of or damage to goods in the course of international transportation. But losses in oil have to be above a certain level before the insurance starts paying out. Normal operational losses are part of the risk when working in the oil business. Often river barges are insured for losses which are higher than 0.3% and losses from tankers are paid back when they are higher than 0.5%. Both percentages are, according to me, the most common percentage levels at insurance companies. It does not mean that smaller losses are acceptable. Oil is expensive, a 0.2% loss on 1,000 kb costs at 100 Dollars per barrel 200kUsd (20 cents per barrel).

Marine Diesel Oil (MDO)

Marine diesel oil is a middle distillate fueloil which can contain traces of fueloil, often 10% or more residual fueloil from transportation contamination and/or heavy fueloil blending. The MDO does not require heated storage. MDO can be red-dyed.

Mark to Market

To debit or credit on a daily basis a margin account based on the close of that day's trading sessions. In this way, buyers and sellers are protected against the possibility of contract default. In physical oil it is important that different commodities in a P&L are priced against the correct quotation related to the correct geographical area. It will show the correct result and the correct position of the trader, who can make his hedges.

Marketable Coke

Those grades of coke produced in delayed or fluid cokers that may be recovered as relatively pure carbon. This 'green' coke may be sold as-is or further purified by calcining. See also 'calcined cokes'.

Market-Based Rate

A price for a commodity that is usually mutually determined by the buyer and seller based on prevailing conditions in a competitive marketplace. Occasionally used interchangeably with free-market price. In the oil industry, the market on which this type of price is based is usually the oil spot market.

Marketers

Traders/marketers who are only interested in selling the produced volumes of oil at the highest possible price. In oil producing companies the production does not stop, meaning waiting to sell is not an option. Therefore selling on a constant and timely basis at the highest price possible is the task of a crude oil (marketing) trader. So a marketer (oil producer) has no choice; he always has a position to sell. Opposite is a margin trader who can choose to buy, sell or do nothing. A trader would try to sell at highest margin, which is not always the same as highest price because of time elements in a trade. Time is money. Taking no position is also a decision which can be taken by a trader. The marketer has no choice. He always has a position.

Market Maker
A trader who is willing and able to either buy or sell at the stated bid and ask prices at a specific moment. Hedge funds and banks are good market makers and by that they supply good liquidity and capital in the paper market.

Market Making
Constant willingness and ability to buy or sell a commodity at a price. This constant availability or liquidity is convenient for other market participants and can be essential to the proper functioning of many markets. The market-maker earns a thin margin (bid/offer spread) and assumes limited risk by providing liquidity to a market.

Market Order
An order to buy or sell a futures- or option- contract at a price which is obtainable when the order reaches the trading floor. The order to buy or sell is given to a broker or bank who will execute on your behalf.

Market Participant
Any party involved as a buyer or seller of oil in the oil market; it includes brokers. But also potential buyers or sellers making their bids and offers are very much participants in the market. In Platts/Argus window sessions it happens that bids and offers are done in the cargo market but no trade is committed. Also that activity gives direction to price levels in the oil market.

Market Power
A given party's ability to influence some or all aspects of a market's behaviour. Market power can consist of ability to control price, demand, supply and/ or delivery, and can be exerted through ownership of a critical level of any portion of the supply chain or through the ability to purchase or consume a critical level of supply. See also 'leverage', where companies try to use their power to control prices in order to make money on their paper positions. High oil prices can limit credit facilities. As a result of that a company may lose its market power. Also VaR mandates are reaching their limits faster. High oil prices multiplied with percentages in VaR mandates produce higher amounts at risk. It can affect the buying power if the set up around VaR mandates is not organised in a good way.

Market Price

Market price is the transparent price of a commodity concluded between buyer and seller at the moment of the conclusion. At this set market price it should in principle be possible to repeat the deal price one or more times. Repeatable numbers are more common in liquid markets. The more liquid the market, the more the set market prices of such a commodity becomes the benchmark commodity price. In principle the market value is the price of a commodity where buyers and sellers meet each other. Where bids and offers come together and a deal is agreed, the market price is set. Even when something is very cheap or expensive, buyers and sellers create the market value of commodities by committing deals.

Market Risk

The risk of loss from being on the wrong position as a result of a potential change in market prices. Markets are changing all the time, a matter of question and demand. Besides that, the world economy and other fundamental issues make the oil market a volatile environment. One can lose a lot of money when being uncontrolled in that market. Market Risk can be avoided by taking no positions, good hedging and good discipline in trading. Risk appetite is needed to be able to make money and grow the business. One cannot make money without taking risk.

Market Sentiment

Crowd psychology, typically a measurement of bullish or bearish attitudes among investors and traders. Discussions in the market are the same everywhere and as a result traders take a position based on that sentiment. As long as that sentiment lasts the traders can make some Dollars. Sentiments may change suddenly resulting in some volatility. Traders would then say: "The market is everywhere", meaning they have no clue what is happening. The market trend is often the indication of the market sentiment.

Market View

The opinion of a trader about how the market moves. To create a market view the trader must get information about the activities in the market. Based on the market view a trader will take a position. Once having a position the trader will need to check if his market view is still the same and if the market movement is going as anticipated. At the moment that the trader has no opinion about the market then it is wise to leave all positions and flatten the book. If the trader makes money then he had a good market view. If the trader loses money he would say that the market is wrong.

MARPOL
The protocol of 1978 relating to the International convention for the prevention of pollution from ships, 1973. It includes dumping, oil and exhaust pollution.

Material Safety Data Sheet (MSDS)
Document which describes the properties of a certain oil, how to treat the oil operationally in a safe way and what to do when accidents happen. It is an important document in the light of health, safety and environment. People have to know what they are working with and what safety rules apply. People working in oil operation outside on the terminal must have easy access to an MSDS. Producers should present their MSDS on request from a terminal working with the oil. If there is something special in a specification related to mercaptans or other specs which cause toxic emission then that must be mentioned as well. It is people working with the oil and it is the terminal holder's and the oil holder's responsibility to secure HSE. But also the person working with the oil on the terminal has the obligation to access the MSDS and read it thoroughly before executing his task. See also 'REACH'.

Maturity Date
The end of the life of a contract.

Maxbactap
Maximum But As Close To As Possible. See also 'loading tolerances'.

Max Capacity
Gross size of a tank. At that capacity per barrels or per Cbm a tank is often rented out. See also 'work capacity'.

Max Intake
The maximum a vessel can load according to her capacity related to the nomination. If there is no draft restriction at load and disport then the vessel can load a full cargo. The max contractual or nominated cargo size is then the max intake. However, if a vessel sails to a port with draft restriction then the vessel cannot load a full cargo; the max intake will be based on safe arrival draft at disport. If a vessel can load more than the contractual quantity then

the buyer and seller can agree to increase the cargo to be loaded. There will be a freight benefit that is normally shared by the vessel owner, the buyer and the seller. See also 'overage' and 'loadables'.

Maya

Maya is heavy crude oil from Mexico used as benchmark for heavy crudes in USA. It has an API of 21 and sulphur of 3.4%. Heavy crude has to be processed at the so called complex refineries.

Mazut M100

Russian fueloil for export. 100% mazut or M100. M100 is available as cracked and straight run fueloil. Cracked grade is linked to the ARA barge market and bunker oil. M100 is loaded in lots of 80 to 120 kt in the Baltic ports like Tallinn, Klaipeda, Ventspils or Ust Luga. This grade is also linked to STS activity at Skaw for fueloil arbitrage business to Singapore. The other grade of M100 is the straight run quality. The straight run oil is linked to arbitrage business to the US Gulf coast or China and is sold to refineries as feedstock for further processing. Straight run is more expensive then cracked M100. Most cargoes are typically pricing on Rotterdam high sulphur quotations. See also 'mean of the mean'. Due to tax reforming in Russia on export of oil products, the Russian refineries had good reason for getting upgraded. Due to increased cracking capacity the export of volumes of straight run fueloil M100 is expected to decrease significantly.

Mean of the Mean

This term refers to the Platts or Argus quotation when it concerns the average to different price quotations. In fueloil we see Russian M100 straight run and cracked being offered at mean of the mean. The quotations are not mentioned when traders talk about it. But in this case it is the average of 1) the mean of Rotterdam FOB barge quotations for high sulphur fueloil and 2) the mean of the NWE CIF cargo quotation for high sulphur fueloil. Straight run fueloil is sold at mean of the mean quotations with a higher differential than cracked fueloil.

Mean Reversion

The tendency of a market variable (interest rate) to revert back to some long-run average level.

Med.
Mediterranean Area. Trading area with attached price quotations in the lists of price quotation, reported as in Platts or Argus. Often CIF prices may be related to Augusta, Sicily. Oil loaded in Caspian area and Black Sea is also traded on Med. quotations. Deliveries to other places than Augusta will be price corrected based on actual freight differential as per charter party.

Mediation
A voluntary process in which the parties to a futures-related dispute work with a neutral third party to find a mutually acceptable solution.

Medium Sulphur Crude
Crude oil with a sulphur-content between 0.5% and 1.0%. Most often this crude is traded by the low sulphur crude oil traders. But that depends also on the way a trading unit in a company is organised.

Melting
A trader melting his mandate or account is a trader who lost so much money in a short time that he is not able to trade further as he lost mandate or his account is short cash.

MEO (Month End Option)
Flat price optimisation on purchases from producers (National Oil Companies) where at month end the pricing period may change due to the option to change from month end to a 5 day pricing range, or by delaying the B/L the pricing month may change if it is related to month of loading where B/L date sets the loading (pricing) month. If a hedge is in the money the buyer would cash in the profit from the paper position and load delayed. Structure of the forward market and volatility is of importance to make it a profitable way of trading. Traders might be willing to pay a bit higher differential if a month end option is available. There is added value in such an option. It should not matter much to the seller of the oil. The seller does not hedge and is interested in getting best differential on top of the benchmark crude.

MEOH
Relates to the methanol content in crude oil. When new crude production fields start up there may be traces of methanol in the crude. Refineries do not want methanol in the crude oil. With distillation the traces may be absorbed

into the naphtha stream. The first buyer of new crude would therefore buy or bid on such a cargo at a discounted price. In the first place because it is a new crude-quality and specifications are always a bit uncertain, but also MEOH (methanol traces in ppm) and water/sediment percentages are higher in the start of production. Methanol is something to keep in mind when loading from new oil fields. It reduces the value for the refinery. After a few cargoes, the methanol should not be an issue anymore. Methanol traces are more often detected in crude from onshore facilities, rather than offshore facilities. One can also agree on a methanol de-escalator – the more methanol the more discounted the oil will be.

Merc
See Nymex (New York Mercantile Exchange).

Mercaptans
Acid gas giving a bad smell to oil and so a bad image to the refinery running it. Therefore mercaptans are removed in a process called 'sweetening'. Cargoes with H_2S challenges can also be treated on board the vessel at disport. Each refinery and company has set their own rules about the acceptance of cargoes that are rich in mercaptans. It is a serious HSE issue to keep in mind. Refineries which are closely located to communities where people live are often required to set strict limits on mercaptans contents in feedstock. Their neighbours would not support refinery activity when the emissions are too big and smell bad. Vapour recovery units (VRU) may absorb the emissions and the bad smell that would have been released is then avoided. A VRU would therefore speed up operations in an environmently friendly manner.

Mercaptan-scavengers
Oil can contain relatively high levels of mercaptan. Mercaptan can be a cause for metal-corrosion, and create, because of its readiness to evaporate, a very offensive stench even in small concentrations. Mercaptan-scavengers are used to reduce the mercaptan concentration in the liquid phase. The cargo needs to be treated before it can enter the discharge port. It is just a standard HSE rules per company. The closer a refinery is situated to cities and civilisation the stricter a receiver's requirement may be. People living close to a refinery would complain when bad smell is observed in their back garden. Local authorities may have set maximum limits in the licence of a terminal. It is to protect civilians from exposure to bad smells and poison exhaust. A terminal

can be fined or can even lose its licence. With some use of a small addition of chemicals, the oil can be treated before entering the harbour. It happens a lot that a small barrel of mercaptan scavengers is taken on board the vessel at sea. After adding and mixing the scavenger in the cargo the H_2S level should have been reduced enough to enter the harbour. The time used for treatment is at the cost of the buyer or seller depending on what has been agreed when the product was sold. Here some product and quality understanding can save a lot of money. When the buyer forgets to make a quality requirement in his contract the demurrage can be the consequence. Refineries may dislike oil qualities that are treated with chemicals for H_2S reduction. The chemicals may affect the production, towers and catalysts. Some chemical reaction may be found back in the final product. A refinery would rather buy feedstock that does not cause problems.

Merox Unit

Refinery process in which various impurities are being removed from refined products. This removal is done by a caustic wash of the oil.

Merchant Oxygenate Plants

Oxygenate production facilities that are not associated with a petroleum refinery. Production from these facilities is sold under contract or on the spot market to refiners or other gasoline blenders.

Metals Content

A measure of the content of nickel, vanadium, aluminium, silicon, iron or other metals. High metals content can affect the fuel burning or upgrading characteristics of a crude oil or residue. Also bunker fuel has maximum metal specification requirements.

Methanol (CH_3OH)

A light, volatile alcohol intended for gasoline blending as described in oxygenate definition. Blends of methanol and gasoline-grade tertiary butyl alcohol (GTBA) such that the total oxygen content does not exceed 3.5 percent by weight and the ratio of methanol to GTBA is less than or equal to 1.

Metric Ton

A unit of 1,000 kilograms, also 1kt, usually it is expressed in 'Vac.' (Vacuum) but some may report in 'air'. In density the differential between tons in vacuum and in air is 11 points (0.0011). Metric tons say nothing about volume. Metric tons divided by density is litres. There are more litres in one ton of gasoline than in one ton of fueloil. A metric ton of feathers or a metric ton of lead implies 1,000 kilograms of product, for both, regardless of the volumetric or area being covered.

Mg/L

Milligrams per litre = PPM (parts per million). These abbreviations PPM and mg/l are very much used in specifications of oil. It is also used when blending with additives such as flow improvers. A cargo can easily be off-spec based on impurities in the oil, which are often reported in ppm and mg/l. Mg/l is volume based. Mg/wt is ppm and is mass based.

Micron

A unit of length. One millionth of a metre or one thousandth of a millimetre. One micron equals 0.00004 of an inch. The hole of a diesel filter is said to be 4 micron.

Middle Distillate

Term applied to hydrocarbons in the so-called 'middle range' of refinery distillation. Examples: heating oil, diesel fuels, and kerosene. Traded by the distillate traders.

Middle Office

Department in a company in charge of market analysis, forecasts and the valuation of trades at current market prices. Neither an administrative support function nor a marketing or sales function.

Midline Pipeline

Multiproduct pipeline connecting a refinery from Fawley up North. This line is also connected to the 'Mainline Pipeline'. Look at that one as well.

Midstream

A term sometimes used to refer to those industry activities that fall between exploration and production (upstream) and marketing (downstream). The term is most often applied to pipeline transportation of crude oil or natural gas and oil refining.

Midstream or Middle Distillates

Refinery products in the middle of the distillation range of crude oil, including kerosene, kerosene-based jet fuel, home-heating fuel, range and diesel fuel.

Mineral Oil

Oil derived from mineral sources, notably petroleum, crude oil and petroleum products. Ethanol and MTBE have to be considered as chemicals and require different treatment in storage and other logistics than mineral oil. Such treatment will be different once they are used as part of a gasoline blend. Chemicals consist of one type of molecule only and are more sensitive to contamination than any mineral oil which is built up from many different molecules.

Minimise Risk

The use of techniques to expose one's capital to as little downside fluctuation as possible. This can include being patient, waiting for excellent entries (fat pitches), using stop-loss orders and exiting positions after a short period of time if they are not showing immediate profitability. To reduce risk in the physical oil market one would buy or sell paper as hedging tool. Without a market view the trader better reduces his risk position so that money cannot roll uncontrolled out of his P&L. A physical trading position is never 100% free of risk. The perfect hedge does not exist.

Minimum Price Fluctuation

The smallest allowable increment of price movement for a futures contract. Also called 'tick'.

MM

Millimetres.

Mmtpa

Million metric tonnes per annum. Often an abbreviation used when presenting statistics about oil consumption. Can also give an indication of the size of a refinery. A trader should know this number when talking business that is related to his refinery. It says something about the trader's position in the market. A trader may brag about it, although should not do that too much.

MOC (Platts)

Market On Close; during the Platts window at the very end of the day, buyers and sellers in the oil market can bid and offer their cargoes in a 30 or 45 minute session. The prices traded in that time are used to create the Platts quotations as according to Platts rules. See also 'Platts Window'.

MOGAS

Abbreviation for motor gasoline. Can be premium unleaded, euro-grade or regular gasoline (98, 95 or 91 octane).

Molecule

The smallest division of a compound that still retains or exhibits all the properties of the substance. When a tank contains low density material and one discharges high density oil on top of it then litres of oil will get lost as the molecules of the blend are shuffling into each other. A kilo plus a kilo of different grades is 2 kilos of new grade. But 1 litre plus 1 litre of two different grades is not necessarily 2 litres of the new grade. To illustrate: Take a bucket of tennis balls and throw a kilo of sugar on it, the volume in the bucket does not change as the sugar finds the empty spaces, just like molecules would behave in oil. Only the quality might change. A trader saying that he wants to load his molecules means that he needs his cargo.

MOM

Mean Of Month. This is related to month average pricing. May be confused with mean of the mean, so make sure what you are talking about.

Momentum (Technical Trading)

The relative change in price over a specific time interval. Often equated with speed or velocity and considered in terms of relative strength.

MON

Motor Octane Number. Gasoline octane is reported in MON and RON rates but also as octane index. The average octane or PON, pump octane number. RON number is an important rate for the slow and relaxed style of driving a car, while the MON number is an important rate for the more speedy and aggressive style of driving a car. MON requirements in gasoline (reg, eurograde and premium) are 81-85-87. The RON is usually 10 points above the MON, as according to European gasoline specification requirements. More information is available at 'octane number' and 'octane rating'.

Mont Belvieu
Mont Belvieu, Texas. The main propane trading hub along the United States Gulf Coast.

Month End Option
See 'MEO'.

MOPAG
Mean Of Platts AG. The mean of the high and low components of a Platts assessment for oil cargoes loading from the Persian Gulf (Arab Gulf). Often used as a component in floating price deals.

MOPJ
Mean Of Platts Japan. Japan is here the price quotation area which one can read in the Platts report. Often used as a component in floating price deals.

MOPS
Mean Of Platts Singapore. Singapore is here the price quotation area which one can read in the Platts report. Often used as a component in floating price deals.

Morning Star (Technical Trading)
Another observation in technical trading which indicates how prices in the futures market would develop during the next days to come. It is based on the candle stick graph which shows a certain shape of sticks (trading days) in a row. E.g. Just a pattern of 3 days seen as a bullish indicator. The first day is a day (a stick) with prices going down (high opening with lower close), the second day opens lower than the close of day one but prices that day go up a little and on the third day the market opens a bit higher than the close of day two and due to increasing prices the close of that day is equal or higher than the opening of day (stick) one. Technical traders observe these three sticks and see that as a signal for prices to increase further. They would take a trading based position on that.

Motor Gasoline
Petrol, low flash car fuel. A complex mixture of relatively volatile hydrocarbons with or without small quantities of additives, which have been blended to form a fuel suitable for use in spark-ignition engines. See also gasoline and gasoline components.

Motor Gasoline Blending
Mechanical mixing of motor gasoline blending components, and oxygenates when required, to produce finished motor gasoline. Finished motor gasoline may be further mixed with other motor gasoline blending components or oxygenates, resulting in increased volumes of finished motor gasoline and/or changes in the formulation of finished motor gasoline. E.g. Conventional motor gasoline mixed with MTBE to produce oxygenated motor gasoline.

Motor Gasoline Blending Components
Naphtha (i.e. Straight-run gasoline, alkylate, reformate, benzene, toluene, xylenes) used for blending to make a certain required finished gasoline quality. These components include unfinished gasoline. One could blend RBOB (reformulated gasoline blendstock for oxygenate blending) and add oxygenates later to make RFG (reformulated gasoline). So in addition to the qualities above which were produced in a refinery one can import oxygenates as components as well. One can conclude that gasoline as such is not coming direct from distillation or from a cracking process. Each unit in the refinery is basically producing a blending component. Only after import of the missing components and after blending it all in good ratios the gasoline is ready to be commercialised.

MoU
Memorandum of Understanding. Often to be used with long term negotiation where one of the party might need to invest in infra-structure but prefers to have a kind of guarantee or understanding that they will get access to a certain oil delivery or outlet for sales purposes. See also 'LOI, letter of intention'.

Moving Average (Technical Trading)
A technical analysis term meaning the average price of a security over a specified time period (the most common being 20, 30, 50, 100 and 200 days), used in order to spot pricing trends by flattening out large fluctuations. This is perhaps the most commonly used variable in technical analysis. Moving

average data is used to create charts that show whether a futures price is trending up or down. They can be used to track daily, weekly, or monthly patterns. Each new day's (or week's or month's) numbers are added to the average and the oldest numbers are dropped. Thus, the average 'moves' over time. In general, the shorter the time frame used, the more volatile the prices will appear, so, for example, 20 day moving average lines tend to move up and down more than 200 day moving average lines.

Moving-Average Charts (Technical Trading)
A statistical price analysis method of recognising different price trends. A moving average is calculated by adding the prices for a predetermined number of days and then dividing by the number of days.

Moving Average Crossover (Technical Trading)
The point where a short-moving average crosses a longer-moving average. These are often taken as buy or sell signals. When the shorter MA crosses the longer from below and both are turning upwards, it is called a 'golden cross', a strong buy signal.

MSDS
See 'material safety data sheet'.

MT
Metric ton, 1,000 kilos. The European market for oil products nominates the order in metric tons and report in tons and litres at 15°C/60°F. In USA logistics calculates its volumes in barrels and gallons. See the conversion calculations at the back of this book.

MTBE
Octane boost in gasoline that blends up to max 15.0 percent by volume. When lead was banned from gasoline, in the late nineties, MTBE came in as a replacement. MTBE is an octane booster. Now MTBE has been replaced by ETBE or ethanol. In the old days Finland had a minimum requirement of oxygenates in their gasoline. Finnish gasoline always contained about 15% of MTBE. Finland was a big MTBE producer; apparently, they were good in lobbying and advertising the use of MTBE. Finland was the only country that had such minimum requirement in Europe.

Multiphase Flow

Flow in a pipeline of gas and liquid oil simultaneously. Even though these two products are mixed in the pipeline they will not be completely dissolved with each other. This flow comes from oil and gas production. Gas production is on some occasions often transported direct from the production field into long distance pipelines to its final point of supply. The gas and liquid will be separated at point of arrival.

N

N+A

Naphthenic and Aromatics. Related to N+A naphtha being rich in naphthenes and aromatics. This naphtha is very much used in USA for blending purposes as high aromatic content causes a higher octane number. Due to a high naphthenic content the naphtha is in demand in the petrochemical industry as feedstock (e.g. Ethylene production). This naphtha may also be of use for further processing in a reformer which produces the gasoline blending component reformate.

N-Grade

Regular USA unleaded gasoline, conventional. A pipeline designation for unleaded gasoline.

NA

Not available or not applicable. However, in the context of the message it could also mean North America or normal paraffins and aromatics n+a-naphtha.

Naked Position

A long or short position in the market that has not been hedged or covered. Gains and losses are greater when a position is unhedged. Also called 'outright position', a position with a high risk profile.

Naked Physical Short Position

Position where physical deliveries have been sold to be delivered at a certain time period in future. The sourcing of the oil has not been covered yet to make the supply possible. The trader is having a physical oil short position. "Buy what you don't need and sell what you don't have." The way to create a strategic position to enter a new market and let business grow or just based on an opportunistic market view. A 'flexible short' is a good example.

Naphtha

Straight-run gasoline fractions. Used as a feedstock for reforming and as a petrochemical feedstock.

Naphtha (N+A)

Naphtha with a certain quality that may be used as gasoline blending component due to its high octane rating. Often N+A-naphtha finds its way to USA for such blending activity. The naphthenic content is more of an interest to the petrochemical industry or for further processing to produce reformate. It is important to follow the gasoline-naphtha spread and sell it to the end-user paying the best price.

Naphtha Cracker

A unit that cracks naphtha into ethylene molecules for use in the manufacture of higher-value plastics and petrochemicals. Using naphtha as feedstock. In bad economic times we see a fall in demand for end products which affects the petrochemical industry followed up by bad refinery margins in the oil industry. Naphtha could end up in the gasoline market. That creates bigger challenges for the refinery related to the refinery margins as gasoline will become cheaper due to oversupply. For the oil industry it is important to understand the petrochemical market and the capacity of how the naphtha crackers are running. Bad naphtha economics might lower prices in Europe which may lead to an open arbitrage for gasoline into the USA or West Africa.

Naphtha-Type Jet Fuel

A fuel in the heavy naphtha boiling range having an average gravity of 52.8° API, 20 to 90 percent distillation temperatures of 143°C / 290°F to 243°C / 470°F, and meeting military specifications for grade JP-4. It is used primarily for military turbojet and turboprop aircraft engines because it has a lower freeze point than other aviation fuels and meets engine requirements at high altitudes and speeds.

Naphthenes
Hydrocarbon found naturally in crude oil and we see it back in N+A naphtha. Naphthenic naphtha is preferred as petrochemical feedstock in competition with the reformers for making a gasoline component.

Naphthenic Naphtha
Favoured form of reformer feedstock naphtha.

NATO Oil Codes
The codes I heard earlier in the market but I had to check these on the NATO website, so it is publicly available. NATO has its own codes for oil for movement on sea, land and in the air. For aviation purposes you could see spec requirements for F-18, F-34, F-35, F40 and F44. I would say all the same type of jet fuel but with different additives. Jet F35 is also known as fuel for civil operators. For road transport specs as F-46, F-57 and F-67 are used which refers basically to Unleaded 91-95-98 grades. Diesel grades have spec F-54, F65 and F75. (F-75 is also used for marine vessels.) For marine purposes they would use specs as F-75, F-76 and F-77. These qualities are closer to middle distillates or light viscosity residue. These qualities are of course required due to the fact that marine vessels have different engines compared with a tanker, even though F-77 is meant for 'slow' speed diesel engines, but still faster than normal vessels. Besides that a marine vessel sailing at 12 knots on RMG380 would not be so impressive. You might see these specifications being required in the market. Now you know to which consumer these oils are to be delivered.

NATO Pipeline (The Netherlands and Jet related)
NATO pipeline in Europe is used for jet A1 supplies from Rotterdam to Amsterdam, Antwerp, France and Germany. As the specification for jet A1 is a standard quality this system works as a kind of banking system where an authorised terminal can pump or let its customers pump the accepted qualities in the pipe to supply jet A1 to the different connected airports. In The Netherlands this is controlled by the organisation DPO in Noordwijk. From experience I can report that a lot of testing is done before the oil is allowed into the pipeline. Pumped through filters at perfect spec. As the

system works as a kind of banking system, the oil that is pumped into the line is not the same molecules which arrive at the final destination. But as all quality in the system is all the same, it is a well-accepted way of transportation of Jet-A1 which best secures the quality. This oil is basically not exposed to any contamination with other oil until it arrives on a terminal. But then only terminals that are certified by this system are allowed to pump into the system or can receive from that system. A very thoroughly inspected and controlled terminal. Also referred to as the CEPS pipeline. See 'CEPS'.

Natural
Unblended oil, original oil. Can be processed oil by normal distillation, surely not cracked or special treated.

Natural Gas
Naturally occurring gas, predominantly methane, but usually containing some proportions of ethane, propane and butane. Natural gas can either be associated gas or non-associated. Natural gas produced in association with crude oil. The condensed gas is also called gas-condensate or just condensate. So for the condensate traders it is of interest to see where natural gas is produced as condensate cargoes may be produced as well and is not always available at crude oil departments. However, check also 'multi-flow'.

Natural Gas Condensate or Condensate
A mixture of hydrocarbon liquids that is present as gaseous components in the raw natural gas. Due to pressure and warm temperatures underground these hydrocarbons are gaseous. A naturally occurring gaseous hydrocarbon that liquefies when cooled to surface temperature. Once this gas is pumped up and the heavy molecules cool down it becomes wet. Condensate is considered to be a part of crude oil production. This definition is contested by some OPEC members who want to produce large quantities of this product outside official OPEC quotas. Condensate might on some occasions be considered as NGL. The naphtha content in condensate is about 75% or more. Some condensate cargoes are directly sold as feedstock to the chemical industry. Where gas is produced one will often find condensate as well. See also 'dew point'.

Natural Gas Field Facility
A field facility designed to process natural gas produced from more than one lease for the purpose of recovering condensate from a stream of natural gas;

however, some field facilities are designed to recover propane, normal butane, pentanes plus, etc., and to control the quality of natural gas to be marketed.

Natural Gas Liquids

Those hydrocarbons in natural gas that are separated from the gas as liquids through the process of absorption, condensation, adsorption, or other methods in gas processing or cycling plants. Generally, such liquids consist of propane and heavier hydrocarbons and are commonly referred to as lease condensate, natural gasoline, and liquefied petroleum gases. Natural gas liquids include natural gas plant liquids (primarily ethane, propane, butane, and iso-butane; see Natural Gas Plant Liquids) and lease condensate (primarily pentanes produced from natural gas at lease separators and field facilities. See also 'lease condensate'.

Natural Gas Processing Plant

Facilities designed to recover natural gas liquids from a stream of natural gas that may or may not have passed through lease separators and/or field separation facilities. These facilities control the quality of the natural gas to be marketed. Cycling plants are classified as gas processing plants.

Natural Gasoline

Naphtha from atmospheric or primary distillation. Naphtha is the basis for gasoline but needs further processing before it can be used as gasoline. Gasoline therefore does not come directly from distillation. It is a matter of blending the different components that were produced from cracking, reforming and many other activities at a refinery. Untreated naphtha can be used as feedstock for the petrochemical industry.

Natural Hedge

Some oil companies buy and sell oil all the time. Often they buy feedstock for a refinery and sell products to the market. When they buy to go long one grade and when they sell to go short the other grade, the book stays in balance and no paper hedge is needed. Purely on quantity exposure the purchase and sales are balancing each other. The basis exposure is then linked to the refinery margins. So due to market changes a company would lose money on crude positions but simultaneously make money on product positions. The result of such a situation is no result (loss/gain) on the total position of the book. The P&L consists of all grades. But of course those companies follow crude and products activity as well, as the trading margins are highly focussed. Due to this balance by natural hedging some companies do not need to trade in the paper market for hedging purposes, they would rather see a paper hedge as a risk position due to the nature of their organisation of trading a global book. In such companies they would say that the hedge is losing money while the paper position gives a negative result even though the price for physical oil gave a positive result. A hedge is to lock in a result or to minimise risk resulting from price fluctuation. A hedge should never be considered as a risk position.

NCS (Norwegian Continental Shelf)

Crude oil produced on the Norwegian continental shelf. Norwegians mention the NCS a lot when talking about the oil. The NCS consists of three areas: The North Sea, the Norwegian Sea and the Barents Sea. The Barents Sea is linked to Arctic activity. An area that will get lots of attention today and in the near future. The North Sea and the Norwegian Sea are areas where active oil production is happening on a daily basis, but still there are enough fields to discover. I call it Norwegian oil jargon, the Norwegians like talking in abbreviations, 'NCS'.

Neat Customers

Customers who need the oil. The consumer of the oil, wholesalers, and the processor of the oil, the refineries. Just in the business, not only oil business, the popular way of writing 'need' is in phonetic writing 'neat'. Call it language development or jargon.

Needle Coke

Coke produced from feedstocks without asphaltenes present, normally FCCU decant oils, and named for its needle-like structure. Needle coke is the premier coke, used in graphite electrode manufacturing (used in steel arc furnaces) and commands a high price, but needle coke requires special feedstocks, special coking, and special calcination to obtain the optimum properties that it requires.

Negotiable or To order

A Bill of Lading in which the merchandise is consigned directly 'to order' or 'to the order of' a designated party, usually the shipper or a bank. The phrase 'to order' or 'to the order of (a designated party)' signifies negotiability permitting the title of the merchandise to be transferred many times by means of appropriate endorsements.

Nelson Complexity Index

The Nelson complexity index is a rating which indicates the complexity of an oil refinery. The higher the index number, the greater the refining costs, but those are also extracting the highest value from producing a bigger volume of light oil products. Each unit in the refinery gets a value based on the Nelson complexity index with values scaled on the basis of the capacity of the unit. Just some examples: A CDU with a capacity of 100 kbd gets a rating of 1; an FCCU with a capacity of 50 kbd gets a rating of 3; a hydro-cracker with a capacity of 30 kbd gets a rating of 1.8; a VDU with a capacity of 60 kbd gets a rating 1.2 and so on. The sum of the rating of each unit at the refinery becomes the Nelson complexity index of the refinery. Therefore a high score in the Nelson complexity index means that the refinery is very sophisticated and able to process high value products. Those refineries with a low score are the simple refineries. They have lower costs and export the straight run fueloil, VGO and lighter blending components.

Netback

Price calculated back till a certain basis level in order to compare different offers and to make a decision to trade. Calculating the FOB netback value or price of an oil cargo from prices or values at delivery points by subtracting various costs such as freight, handling, interest, duties, transit losses and commissions from reports or estimates of outlet-market levels. Calculation of netback values are important to make as they might be needed to make decisions by traders when they want to sell a cargo to the buyer who bids the best netback value.

Netback Differential

The difference between the spot and rack prices for refined petroleum products. Calculation of all cost between bid price and basis price (often FOB price).

Netback Pricing or Agreements

A contractual crude oil arrangement very prevalent during the mid-80s which set the sales price of crude oil on the value of the derivative petroleum products. Those sales agreements came from the producers in the Middle East and were basically guaranteeing a fixed refinery margin to the refineries. This way of pricing was done as futures prices for crude oil did not exist. Today Brent, WTI are used as benchmark and priced with differential including an OSP set by the producing countries in the Middle East.

Net Capacity

The number of tons or cubic metres of a cargo which a vessel can carry when loaded in salt water to her summer freeboard marks. Also called 'cargo carrying capacity', 'cargo deadweight', and 'useful deadweight'.

Net Loser

A trader who loses a lot of money because he does not cut losses in time which results in big losses. At the same time he does not let profits run and takes profits too early. That trader might look great if he takes 10 times a small gain and celebrates that, but the one loss which he is quiet about wipes out all the 10 small gains and results in a net loss. Not following trading discipline makes this trader a net loser.

Net Observed Volume (NOV)

The total volume of all petroleum products but excluding free water and BS&W at observed temperature. Expressed in cubic metre and/or barrels. Related to cargo/ship measurement and inspection reports. In crude business the contract and invoice is based on net barrels. Gross volume would include water. A refinery does not want to pay for the water in the oil. 0.2% water in a million barrel cargo is 2000 barrels of water. That would be part of the gross barrels. If a refinery pays for gross barrels then they would pay 2,000 barrels of water at an oil price. That does not work. The oil market is therefore always related to net barrels. Oil losses are related to water; check BS&W in load and disport.

Net Position

The difference between total open long and total open short positions in any one or all combined futures contract months held by an individual or entity. The outright exposure and spread in the P&L.

Net Production Crude

Production over a certain period of time of crude oil reported in barrels from a designated area or reservoir. These are reported numbers based on supplies for transport and are therefore measured at the transfer point.

Net Production Rate in BOPD
The net production for a certain period of time divided by the number of calendar days in that period of time. Average day production in barrels.

Net Receipts
The difference between total movements into and total movements out of a terminal, refinery or controlled area by pipeline, tanker, and barge. There is always an operational loss or refinery loss resulting from the calculation. However, in a refinery, the size of the molecules can change and then there is potential for a refinery gain, but just very small volumes only.

Net Specific Energy
Measures the energy available from a fuel or distillate, taking the density and sulphur-, water-, and ash contents into account. Expressed in MJ/kg. Also known as 'calorific value'.

Net Standard Volume (NSV)
The total volume of all petroleum products excluding BS&W and free water corrected by the appropriate volume correction factor (VCF) for observed temperature and density to a standard temperature. Expressed in cubic metre and/or barrels.

Net Standard Weight (NSW)
The total weight of all petroleum liquids, excluding sediment and water and free water, determined by deducting the S&W weight from the gross standard weight.

Net Tons
Gross tons minus BS&W are net tons. In crude trading the gross tons are important for the shipping and other logistics. The net tons are the tons which are priced on the commercial invoice.

Net Weight (Train)
The weight of only the contents of a rail car. See also 'GRL – gross rail load'.

New York Banking Day

A day other than a Saturday, Sunday or public holiday in New York when banks are open for business in all regions necessary to make payment pursuant to an agreement.

New York Mercantile Exchange (NYMEX)

WTI crude, heating oil and gasoline futures are traded on the Nymex. Prices can be followed on the screen, which may also be used for technical analyses. The futures market for oil is a liquid market. Oil is traded in lots and one lot is equal to 1,000 barrels of crude oil. Crude on the Nymex is therefore priced in Dollars per barrel, while products are priced in Dollars per gallon. 42,000 gallons is equal to 1,000 barrels. See also 'Cushing' as crude oil prices in the Nymex are related to the delivery place.

NGL

Portions of natural gas that are liquefied at the surface in lease separators, field facilities, or gas processing plants, leaving dry natural gas. They include, but are not limited to, ethane, propane, butane, naphtha, and condensate.

Nm

Nautical miles, often used for distance calculations at sea, e.g. The distance between Rotterdam and Hamburg over sea. Nautical miles is used for distance calculations and knots relates to the speed of a vessel. See also ' 'knot'.

NNPC

Nigerian National Petroleum Corporation. Very much related to the famous crude production of Bonny Light Crude Oil (BLCO).

No. 1 Oil Kero

Refers to ultra-low kerosene as reported in USA, Midwest and Chicago markets.

No. 1 Diesel Fuel

A light distillate fueloil that has a distillation temperature of 288°C / 550°F at the 90-percent recovery point and meets the specifications defined in ASTM Specification D 975. It is used in high speed diesel engines generally operated under frequent speed and load changes, such as those in city buses and similar vehicles. It is used in high speed diesel engines. These qualities and quotations are available in the US market.

No. 1 Distillate
A light petroleum distillate that can be used as either a diesel fuel or a fueloil.

No. 1 Fueloil (Heating Oil)
A light distillate and low sulphur fueloil. 10% is distilled at 400°F/204°C and 90% of its volume is distilled at 550°F/288°C and meets the specifications defined in ASTM specification D396. It is used primarily as fuel for heating purposes. These qualities and quotations are available in the US market. But be sure what one means as many people say fueloil, but they mean gasoil, clean oil, for heating purposes. Fueloil as heavy fueloil is merely the No. 5 and No. 6 oil.

No. 1 Low-Sulphur
Ultra low diesel max 15 ppm sulphur used for 'blending' on-road fuels. These qualities and quotations are available in the US market.

No. 1 High-Sulphur
Clear high sulphur diesel is used for various off road agricultural and industrial purposes. These qualities and quotations are available in the US market.

No. 2 Diesel Fuel
A distillate and low sulphur diesel. 10% of its volume is distilled at 500°F/260°C and 90% of its volume is distilled at 640°F/338°C and meets the specifications defined in ASTM specification D-975. It is used in high speed diesel engines generally operated under uniform speed and load conditions, such as those in railroad locomotives, trucks and automobiles. These qualities and quotations are available in the US market.

No. 2 Fueloil (Heating Oil)
A distillate and low sulphur fueloil. 10% is distilled at 500°F/260°C and 90% of its volume is distilled at 640°F/338°C and meets the specifications defined in ASTM Specification D 396. It is used for industrial burning. These qualities and quotations are available in the US market.

No. 2 Low-Sulphur

Clear low-sulphur (LS No. 2) diesel has a sulphur-content up to 500 ppm and can be used for up to 20% of the USA on road diesel fuel sold at the retail level. In addition to clear No. 2 low sulphur, OPIS also provides pricing for red dye, premium, winter, low-emissions diesel and lubricity grades of low-sulphur diesel fuels. These qualities and quotations are available in the US market.

No. 2 High-Sulphur

Clear high-sulphur No. 2 diesel is used as an off-road fuel for equipment such as farm machinery or as home heating oil. These qualities and quotations are available in the US market.

No. 2 Ultra Low-Sulphur

No. 2 ultra-low-sulphur diesel has a sulphur content of less than 15 ppm and must be used to supply at least 80% of the USA on road diesel fuel sold at the retail level since 2006. In addition to clear No. 2 low sulphur, OPIS also provides pricing for red dye, premium, low emissions and winter grades of ultra-low-sulphur diesel fuels. All of the OPIS ultra-low-sulphur diesel products are understood to include lubricity. These qualities and quotations are available in the US market. See also 'OPIS.'

No. 3 Fueloil

Low viscosity fueloil for burning purposes. Not much used in the market, may be the bunkers spec in future. These qualities and quotations are available in the US market. No. 3 oil is named as fueloil, distillates or diesel – the higher the number the heavier the oil.

No. 4 Fueloil

A distillate fueloil made by blending distillate fueloil and residual fueloil stocks. It conforms to ASTM Specification D-396 and is used extensively in industrial plants and in commercial burner installations that are not equipped with preheating facilities. These qualities and quotations are available in the US market. No. 4 fueloil is named as fueloil, residual fueloil or distillates. The higher the number the heavier the oil.

No. 5 Fueloil

Industrial heating oil. This is not heavy oil. These qualities and quotations are available in the US market. No. 5 fueloil is named as residual fueloil, heavy fueloil or residuals. The higher the number the heavier the oil.

No. 6 Fueloil

Heavy fueloil may be of use for bunkers. No. 6 oil is classified in different sulphur levels. These qualities and quotations are available in the US market. No. 6 fueloil is named as residual fueloil, heavy fueloil or residuals. The higher the number the heavier the oil.

No Brainer

A trading opportunity which is, according to the trader, guaranteed to be a good and profitable deal. It is just a matter of making the commitment and cash in. Traders call these easy deals a 'no brainer'. You must be crazy to not take advantage of such an opportunity. It would not be a problem to commit if the counterparty is approved including the understanding or expectation that the oil is of acceptable and good quality and one can count on good performance. Just be careful when a deal is 'too good to be true'. Sometimes as a result of enthusiasm a trader might call an opportunity for a long-term commitment a 'no brainer' when trying to convince his manager to get a mandate. Risk, credit, financials, HSE, IDD and potential market changes are enough reasons for using brains when taking decisions. See also 'low hanging fruit'.

NOC

National Oil Companies. Often these companies are linked to crude oil producing countries in the Middle East, South America, Russia, Asia and Africa but also in Europe like in Norway. Some shares of NOCs are available on the stock exchanges, but the market would still see them as a NOC. Just some well-known company names: SOMO – Iraq; NIOC – Iran; KNOC – South Korea; Rosneft – Russia; PDVSA – Venezuela; ENI – Italy; PEMEX – Mexico; Aramco – Saudi Arabia; Sinopec – China; PetroChina – China; Sonangol – Angola; ADNOC – Abu Dhabi; EGPC – Egypt; Gazprom – Russia; KazMunayGas – Kazakhstan; KPC – Kuwait; ONGC – India; Pertimina – Indonesia; Petrobras – Brazil; Petronas – Malaysia; PKN Orlen – Poland; Sonatrach – Algeria; Statoil – Norway; and many more.

Noise

Price and volume fluctuations which do not provide meaningful information about the market's direction.

Noise (Report)

Uncontrolled elements or errors in a report, such as a P&L, which affect the final outcome of the reported result. If noise leads to exposure errors, then that needs full attention as this can cause unpleasant and unexpected resultant effects in the P&L, which is unacceptable in trading.

Nomenclature Products

- **Gaseous products**

  Propane
  - 27.11.12.11 = For use as power or heating.
  - 27.11.12.19 = Other purposes.

  Butane
  - 27.11.13.10 = For undergoing a specific process.
  - 27.11.13.30 = For undergoing a chemical transformation.

- **Light oil**

  Naphtha
  - 27.10.12.15 = For undergoing a chemical transformation.

  Gasoline
  - Unleaded Gasoline 27.10.12.41 with Ethyl alcohol content of more than 10% (v/v)
  - Unleaded Gasoline 27.10.12.45 with RON >95 -<98
  - Unleaded Gasoline 27.10.12.49 with RON >98
  - Leaded Gasoline 27.10.12.51 <98
  - Leaded Gasoline 27.10.12.51.11 with Ethyl alcohol content of more than 10% (v/v)
  - Leaded Gasoline 27.10.12.59 >98

- **Medium Heavy oil**

  Jet/kerosene
  · 27.10.19.21 = Jet fuel and kerosene.

- **Heavy oil**

  Diesel
  · 27.10.19.46 = Sulphur content >0.001% - <0.002% weight
  · 27.10.19.47 = Sulphur content >0.002% - <0.1% weight
  · 27.10.19.48 = Sulphur content >0.1% weight

  Fueloil
  · Fueloil Straight Run Feedstock 27.10.19.51
  · Fueloil 27.10.19.62 sulphur <0.1% weight
  · Fueloil 27.10.19.64 sulphur >0.1% - < 1.0% weight
  · Fueloil 27.10.19.68 sulphur >1.0% weight

Nomenclature Determination Codes of Oil

Customs has classified the taxation number of oil products based on the distillation curve sulphur content, lead content and the use of the product. Hereunder a simplified overview:

- **Gaseous products**
  They are classified in Chapter 27.11.

- **Light oils**
  Product from which at least 90% would evaporate (distillate) at a temperature of 210° Celsius/410° Fahrenheit. (Classified in 27.10.11…)

- **Medium heavy oil**
  Product from which less than 90% evaporates at 210° Celsius/410° Fahrenheit and from which minimum 65% evaporates (distillates) at 250° Celsius/482° Fahrenheit. (Classified in 27.10.19.21)

- **Heavy oil**
  Product from which less than 65% Evaporates at 250° Celsius/482° Fahrenheit. (Classified in 2710 19 31 till 2710 19 99.)

- **Gasoil**

  Gasoil is a heavy oil product from which at least 85% evaporates at 350°
  Celsius/662° Fahrenheit (Classified in 2710 19 31 till 2710 19 49).

- **Heavy fueloil**

  Heavier oil than gasoil and less than 85% would evaporate at 350°
  Celsius/662° Fahrenheit. (Classified in 2710 19 61 till 2710 19 69.)

Nomenclature of the Customs Cooperation Council

The customs tariff system used by most countries worldwide. It was formerly
known as the Brussels tariff nomenclature and is the basis of the commodity
coding system known as the harmonised system. It is organised into 99
chapters arranged in 22 sections. The basic code contains four-digit headings
and six-digit subheadings. Many countries add digits for customs tariff and
statistical purposes. Find codes in Europe. For oil use section V: Mineral
products and go to chapter 27.10. Most oil products can be found there.

Nomenclature Website

EU taxation-website for import duties:

http://ec.europa.eu/taxation_customs/dds2/taric.

Nomination

Supply or loading instruction and information sent from buyer to seller and
vice versa in order to arrange the logistics for the oil cargo as agreed in a physical
oil contract. Traders buy and sell, the agreed business will be confirmed in
a contract and the operator or operations department will make sure that
logistics are taken care of according to contract. The operations department
is responsible for sending the nomination, also called 'loading' or 'discharge
instruction'. When a trader sells FOB then often the buyer, who charters the
means of transport, will send the nomination or the loading instructions to
the seller. It is also the seller's duty to ask for a nomination. When a trader
sells a CIF or DAP cargo then the seller has to charter transport. The operator
will then send the nominations and the planned supply information, timing
etc. At a storage terminal it is only the customer of the terminal who can send
instructions to load or discharge. Also when taking samples etc. it is the one
who rents the tanks and is assumed to be the owner of the oil in tank, who
can give the orders.

Non-Associated Gas
Natural gas, which is found in a reservoir that does not contain significant quantities of crude oil.

Non-Negotiable or Straight
A Bill of Lading in which the merchandise is consigned directly to a designated party, generally the buyer, but not to his 'order'. Delivery of the merchandise is made only to the designated party, usually without surrendering the Bill of Lading.

NOPEC
A group of independent crude oil producing nations that are not members of OPEC, but have collectively restricted production levels in support of OPEC. That includes Malaysia, Mexico, Oman, Egypt, Angola, China and Columbia.

NOR
Notice Of Readiness. Time and date that a vessel arrives at the pilot station of the harbour of destination. Upon arrival the vessel makes contact with the authorities at the pilot station and registers that the vessel has arrived and is ready to enter the harbour as soon as the jetty is available. The NOR is now tendered. The first 6 hours waiting or part thereof at pilot station are for the account of the owner of the vessel. Thereafter time starts ticking for the charterer. Too long waiting can cause demurrage. The sailing time used from pilot station to the berth until mooring completed is for the account of the owner of the vessel. Pay attention also to 'pilot station'.

NOR Date
Official date and time that the notice of readiness is tendered. Logistic time starts ticking. The NOR date can also be important related to the pricing of cargo. Payment terms are in many cases also related to the NOR date. In the case of ice formation on sea it might be that the vessels have to wait for ice breakers. In that case it can be arranged that the NOR is tendered at ice-edge. The NOR acceptance at ice-edge is to be agreed between the buyer and the seller during the negotiations of the trade.

Normal Butane (C4)
A normally gaseous straight-chain H10 hydrocarbon that is a colourless

paraffinic gas that boils at a temperature of -0.5 °C / 31.1 °F and is extracted from natural gas or refinery gas streams.

Normal Paraffin

Hydrocarbon consisting of un-branched molecules in which any carbon atom is attached to no more than two other carbon atoms. Also called 'straight chain paraffin' and 'linear paraffin'.

Normal Weather

Any weather conditions which are between calm weather and adverse weather. Perfect weather for offshore loading. Light gaseous crude is safe to load as there would be some wind. Calm weather can be a challenge for fields supplying high vapour pressure oil. You prefer to avoid gas clouds on the offshore unit and on board the vessel. A good vapour recovery unit could work. See both definitions in this book. See 'calm and adverse weather'.

Norm Price

Tax reference price. Production from a well is sold at certain prices during a month. Based on the sales number governments calculate a monthly price (average) or shorter period price average of the crude value of that export month which is used for tax purposes. Pretty much the opposite compared with the Middle East where the OSP is announced prior to the month of loading, or in Russia where export tax is announced prior to the month of loading.

NOR Pricing

Agreed pricing period after the NOR date. 'NOR + 5' means that the oil price is the average of the 5 price quotations of a certain benchmark after the NOR date. NOR date does not count as quotation in the price.

Northern Sea Route

Look for the explanation at 'NSR'.

NOS

Abbreviation for 'not otherwise specified'.

No–Show

Cargo which has been booked but the vessel does not arrive in time to be loaded or a loaded vessel does not arrive in time at the discharge window. Based on lay-can the charterer has the opportunity to cancel the trip or refuse the cargo. However, refusal of a cargo is often only possible if it is based on non-performance. A storm or a small damage is not always a legal reason to refuse a cargo. A no-show could lead to product shortage at receiver's side or production limitations at producer's side. This could cause financial damage which is a reason to send a claim.

Notice

To put one on notice. Holding someone responsible by sending a formal message on paper and in order to retain the opportunity to claim at a later stage. Always keep the right to revert on your matter. If someone puts you on notice, then reject all responsibility and leave the case to the experts in your claims department, the lawyer. See also 'liability'.

Notice Day

Any day on which a clearinghouse issues notices of intent to deliver on futures contracts.

NOx

Oxide of nitrogen. Related to exhaust of cars. NOx reacts in sunlight and ground level ozone is formed. The famous problem in summertime in big cities as a result of car emissions, smog (smoke-fog). One of the main reasons why reformulated gasoline is required in certain crowded and heavy traffic states in the USA. VOC emissions coming from RFG are at low level. Due to RFG the VOC exhaust has been decreased significantly.

NPRA

The National Petrochemical & Refiners Association is a national trade association based in Washington, D.C. Like IP week in London or APEC in Singapore there is also an NRPA week in the USA held in Texas – Houston or San Antonio. Held in March each year.

NSR

Northern Sea Route. The route through the Arctic from Europe to Asia. Draft of 17 metres, 55 feet is possible. The route is not without risk and is only open during summertime as there is too much ice during the winter. This route requires some preparations as it sails through an area without any infra-structure nearby. Vessels have to sail in convoy guided by a nuclear ice breaker. Closer to 2025 it is expected that the route will be open during summer and winter as a consequence of global warming. Compared with the traditional route from Europe to Asia it would save roughly 10 days of sailing. Not many vessels have done the voyage yet. LNG and condensate production from the Arctic will find its way first. Crude will follow and the biggest drivers for that are time saving and avoidance of problems with piracy close to the Suez Chanel. The money saved on a trip is significant – less sailing time also means less bunkers consumption.

NSV
Net Standard Volume on the Bill of Lading. The total volume of all petroleum liquids, excluding sediment and water and free water. See also 'crude oil voyage loss calculations' in the back of the book.

Nut
A nut is the total cost of broker fees on the trades. On a bad day a trader could say that his trades were not even good enough to earn back a nut.

NWE
North West Europe. A price setting area as quoted in Platts/Argus and other price quotation reports. The cargo market and the barge market quotations are here set basis Rotterdam and/or ARA. The other quotations in South of Europe are based in the 'Med.', the hub which takes Augusta as point of reference.

NWML
National Weights and Measures Laboratory (United Kingdom). UK governmental authorities, controlling arm.

NYH, New York Harbour
The delivery point for the Nymex gasoline and heating oil contracts.

NYMEX
WTI crude, heating oil and gasoline futures are traded on the Nymex. Prices can be followed on the screen, which may also be used for technical analyses. The futures market for oil is a liquid market. Oil is traded in lots and one lot is equal to 1,000 barrels of crude oil. Crude on the Nymex is therefore priced

in Dollars per barrel, while products are priced in Dollars per gallon. 42,000 gallons is equal to 1,000 barrels. See also 'Cushing' as crude oil prices in the Nymex are related to the delivery place.

O

OBQ TCV

On Board Quantity. Sum of measured liquid volume, including free water and measured non-liquid volume but excluding any vapours, in cargo tanks prior to loading. On-board quantity includes water, oil, slops, oil residue, oil/water emulsions, sludge, and sediment. See also 'crude oil voyage loss calculations' in the back of the book. Opposite of OBQ is ROB, remains on board. See also 'ROB'.

OBQ Water

On-board quantity of all free water measured in cargo and slop tanks before loading. See also 'crude oil voyage loss calculations' in the back of the book.

Octane Index

Octane index is the average of RON and MON, (R+M)/2. The use of the octane index as specification requirement is typically used in the American gasoline requirements. Although often there is also a minimum requirement on the MON number included in the gasoline specifications. At petrol stations in the USA you may see the PON number, pump octane number. PON is the same as octane index. RON number is an important rate for the slow and relaxed style of driving a car, while the MON number is an important rate for the more speedy and aggressive style of driving a car. RON is the 91-95-98 as we see at European petrol stations. The MON is usually 10 points below the RON, as according to European gasoline specification requirements.

Octane Number

A performance rating used to classify motor fuels by grading the relative antiknock properties of various grades of gasoline. A high-octane fuel has better antiknock properties than one with a low number. See also 'RON and MON'.

Octane Rating

A quality specification for gasoline that measures its tendency to ignite spontaneously, creating engine knock and causing the engine to operate less efficiently. Two basic rating systems exist. The research octane number, or RON, and the motor octane number, or MON. In both cases a higher number means better performance. Lead has traditionally been used as a low-cost additive to raise the octane number of gasoline, but it has been banned for health reasons. MTBE replaced lead and now ETBE and ethanol are replacing MTBE due to the change in gasoline as a result of biofuel requirements.

OECD

Organisation for Economic Co-operation and Development. The mission of the OECD is to promote policies that will improve the economic and social well-being of people around the world. Economic growth is followed by trading analysts to see how markets develop. With that growth we also see oil consumption increasing which makes some fast growing countries like China and India important countries for investment, although the BRIC countries are not a member of the OECD yet. The OECD website is www.oacd.org.

Offer

An expression indicating one's desire to sell a commodity at a given price and/or quality. Opposite of bid. Or, the price at which a given product can be purchased immediately with no dispute or negotiation. Lifting the offer means accepting the offer, deal done. Now you are long on cargo or paper position.

Official Selling Price (OSP)

NOC declared price for each export oil blend. OSP is most often used by the Middle East crude oil producers. Often the OSP is mentioned as a fixed differential to a benchmark. Depending on the quality and the market circumstances this can be a premium or a discount of 10 cents up to some Dollars. The moment when such price is announced is very important for traders as the price level makes the trader decide to supply the oil to different locations in the world, pretty much arbitrage based. Related to OSP you might also spend time reading about 'netback pricing or agreements'.

Off-Loaded
Discharged in shore tanks ex vessel.

Off-Road Diesel
High-sulphur No. 2 oil. This fuel can be used for off-road purposes such as powering diesel construction equipment. It is often red-dyed because of tax reasons. Tax is at a lower level compared with on-road diesel.

Offset
To take a second futures or options position opposite to the initial or opening position. To sell (or purchase) future contracts of the same delivery month purchased (or sold) during an earlier transaction or make (or take) delivery of the cash commodity represented by the futures market. Also referred as 'to offset'. Basically leaving all positions and balance the book to zero exposure. Or in trader's words: "To flatten the book." Also called 'liquidate'.

Offshore
Crude oil production at sea, waterborne oil production. Opposite of onshore production. See also 'waterborne' and 'landlocked'. Brent is waterborne oil production and requires transhipment by tankers. WTI is landlocked oil production and is pumped through pipelines. In the US Gulf/Gulf of Mexico a lot of crude oil is produced offshore. Most crude is transported through underwater pipeline to the shore. Waterborne becomes landlocked business.

Offshore-Loader
Vessel loading crude oil or condensate from the oil platforms at sea. This type of vessel receives the oil at the very front of the vessel, at the bow. Often these vessels are owned by the oil companies but one can also take them on time charter. These vessels load offshore and may have fixed discharge ports. In that case they are also called 'shuttle tankers'. An offshore loader is not often used for arbitrage cargoes. The charterer needs his vessel to off-load the production from the platform on sea. These vessels are preferred for loading from the production fields and supply to the nearest market. For arbitrage business the vessel may do a ship to ship operation or the oil

must be collected at a storage terminal first. Offshore loaders are also called 'bow-loaders'. Scheduling offshore tankers is very important. When a vessel is too late production might have to stop temporarily; that would cost a lot of money and it would be seen as non-performance at trading and operations.

Offshore Loading Systems (OLS)
Many crude oil-fields on open sea have different designs and a different system to load an off-shore tanker. You need be aware of the technical capability of a tanker related to the OLS.

- **Tandem Loading**
  A kind of ship-to-ship loading, from the FPSO to the tanker. Both vessels are lying opposite to each other as the oil flows from bow to bow. Oil loading direct from the production unit.

- **Single Point Mooring (SPM)**
  Load point is a buoy or rigid tower in the sea where the tanker (bow loader) connects the loading hose to her system. The buoy system is also called CALM, catenary anchor leg mooring. The oil is transported from the production unit in a pipe to the buoy or rigid tower.

- **Dynamic Positioning**
  Also loading from a buoy. This buoy is below sea level, sometimes up to 55 metres down. When a vessel arrives, the buoy will come up to the surface so the vessel can start her loading procedure. After loading, the buoy will sink again. There is not really a mooring point. The vessel loading must have good dynamic positioning system. See also 'dps'.

- **Submerged Turret Loading (STL)**
  A buoy that is connected to another buoy which needs to be lifted up to create a connection to the tanker. The buoy will be anchored with the vessel. There may be strong requirements related to the DPS of the vessel, see also 'dps'.

- **Single Anchor Loading (SAL)**
  Assistant mooring system. It has a mooring line to the vessel. This system allows the tanker to freely rotate. This system is also designed for a vessel with a good dynamic positioning mooring system.

Off-Spec Crude

Crude oil with an obtained specification that deviates too much from the assay. A bad quality which is not acceptable by the buyer or refiner. Off-spec crude can ruin the economics of a refinery and the buyer would claim for a discount. Also crude with a too high BS&W level is often seen as off-spec. Normal crude would have a max BS&W of roughly 0.5% which may go to max 1% but not more than that. The buyer bought oil, not water.

Off-Specification Product/Cargo

Refined products or other cargoes which do not meet the nominated quality requirements. A receiver of an off-spec cargo may have the right to reject the cargo or in some cases the receiver has the opportunity to ask for compensation on the price. He will ask for that in case he is able to fix the problem himself at a low cost unknown to the seller. Quality is in most cases checked at loadport so the problem can be avoided in the most optimal way. In some cases when the product on arrival is off-spec, the seller may disregard the situation based on allowed 'repeatability' and 'reproducibility' differential of the specification of the sample taken. Spend time also on 're-tested sample'.

OGUK

Oil & Gas UK, the association of offshore operators on the UK continental shelf. See also 'NCS'.

Oil

A liquid hydrocarbon which can have many different specifications. From light oil to heavy, from sour to sweet, from high TAN to low TAN. Just take a quick look at 'petroleum'.

Oil Consumption Efficiency

Efficient behaviour related to the consumption rate of oil, saving energy. In the 1980s we started to become aware that oil is bad for the environment and that at a certain time in future the world would run out of oil. As a result of that conclusion car producers started to make car engines that used less fuel and that development is still on-going. If in the USA all SUVs were replaced by more standard cars which consume less gasoline per mile, the gasoline market would collapse immediately as a result of lower demand. Refineries struggle to make good results due to oversupplied markets. Also the 'new' driving style gets more focus. Drivers can anticipate earlier on situations where they might have to stop because of a red traffic light or so. Letting the car roll out when approaching a red traffic light is an energy saving behaviour. Or the new cars with 'intelligent engines' are also changing petrol consumption. Engines switch off when standing in a stationary position. Efficient behaviour saves energy and is good for the environment.

Oil Equivalent
A unit of energy equivalent to that contained in a barrel of oil. Production units' capacity is often reported in oil equivalents. It says something about the size and expectation of a field. A sum of the potential production of oil, gas and condensate of the field.

Oil Gravity
The most widely used indicator of a crude oil value to the producer is its API gravity. Normally, the price which a producer receives for his oil depends on its gravity. The lower density oil (higher API gravity) is most valuable. This price schedule is based on the premise that the lighter oil contains higher percentages of the more valuable products such as gasoline. API Gravity (degrees) = (141.5/Density in kilos per litre/15) - 131.5. See 'API gravity'.

Oil in Kind
Oil at value. It can be that a huge investment related to oil production is not paid back in Dollars or other currency, but is paid back as supplies of crude oil coming from the investments, such as drilling, etc. You get paid back in barrels of crude at oil in kind. The higher the oil prices the faster payback obligations are fulfilled. The value of the oil may be Brent, WTI or another benchmark related. Often it is a formula based on market value.

Oil Loss
Loss of oil caused by operations, evaporation or errors in measurement. But one can also suffer losses from overstated Bills of Lading – the reason why inspectors and expeditors are so important. Oil is expensive so losses should not be seen as common part of the business and therefore become generally accepted. In the past when oil was cheap an oil loss did not have much financial consequences. Today a loss of 2,500 barrels on a vessel of 1 million barrels is 0.25 per cent, but the cost or financial loss is around 125 kUsd, based on an oil price of roughly 50 US Dollar per barrel. See also 'apparent loss', 'physical loss' and 'voyage loss'.

Oil Losses

- **Storage loss**

Oil sticks on walls, goes through pipelines, oil evaporates, and samples are taken. These are considered to be operational losses that must be accepted. Very good operations can limit losses. In order to minimise a loss one should look at the type of tank to use, vapour recovery systems, heating planning, cow when discharging, line displacements and line flushing.

- **Voyage loss**

Loss that occurs during the voyage; evaporation and other operational losses that occur during transport. Voyage loss is the difference between ship measurement at loadport and disport. The difference can also be caused by measurement methods or stability of the vessel when it is measured in the port. Bad weather at sea can affect the ship measurement. However, if the difference is significant then it could indicate a problem. The final outturn is then very important to be compared with B/L numbers.

- **B/L versus ship figures**

Measurement systems from a supplier will always show different figures compared with the vessel. On land everything is standing still and is well calibrated. Vessels are moving all the time and use experience factors for quantity corrections. It is important to look at the differentials, as it should not be too big. It is an important indicator that something with the quantity is right or wrong. You can be sure that a master of a vessel and inspector will make a letter of protest, just to cover themselves. The final outturn in disport will show if a possible error was made in loadport. When ship figures at loadport are higher than the B/L then the vessel sails with a plus, and vice versa the vessel sails with a loss.

- **Ship figures at loadport versus ship figures at disport**

Call it the ocean loss. But even then the measurement of ship figures may differ as result of weather circumstances. A vessel at sea versus a vessel in a harbour. It has an effect on measurements and the result of that.

- **Ocean loss**

Other word used for voyage loss.

- **Outturn loss**
  The B/L compared with the terminal received quantity. When buying CIF or FOB the loading figures at loadport are the invoiced numbers, the B/L number. The receiver will have an outturn loss in disport. When buying on DAP-terms it is the outturn figure that counts as the commercial number. The receiver has no risk on outturn losses. The seller is running that risk. Most often the DAP price is therefore a bit higher than the CIF price.

- **Loss from blending**
  When blending oil with different densities, molecules from different sizes will move into each other. Simplified example: A bucket full of tennis balls gets a kilo of sugar on top of it. The sugar finds its way between the spaces. The volume is still the same; it is just the weight that becomes more. This is in blending called a shrinkage effect. A blender can find an API shrinkage table for this, so he can calculate the potential volume loss from blending.

- **Losses from human mistakes**
  People make mistakes and a wrong calculation can cost a lot of money. An operator should read the inspection reports or terminal reports when a big loss is observed. Most companies have specialists working for them to capture the mistake and get the oil back. A big mistake that may cause a loss is the use of the wrong measurement system. The specialist being able to see such errors is worth a lot of money for a company, which has to be acknowledged. Often a vessel, inspector and terminal compare their numbers before they are final. By that, a mistake can be quickly observed and adjustments can be made. However, in some terminals they refuse to compare. They just report that their number is correct – a headache for claims people. When it concerns big losses and the oil prices are high then the use of an expeditor is really worth the money.

- **Losses as result of fraud**
  Oil has a lot of value. Overstating a B/L on purpose can give a lot of money to the criminal. A person committing a fraud is to me a criminal. To protect your company against that it is important to use an inspector and in some cases an expeditor. The requirement towards the seller should be that the surveyor and expeditor get complete access to tanks and other infrastructure to check if everything is done in a proper way and no oil can be stolen. In some places this is not possible. Some places guarantee a

maximum loss in their contract. In such cases, you often see that the loss is always that maximum. Are you protected here or does this agreement give the right to the seller to steal some until the maximum contractual guaranteed loss is reached. How to prove it? Accept it with adjusted prices or stay away from this business. When your inspector has no access to the terminal facilities then consider the terms to use when you buy. Use the CIF, FOB and DAP terms to protect yourself from potential fraud in that case.

Oil Pollution Fund

The international oil pollution compensation funds (IOPC Funds) are three intergovernmental organisations (the 1971 Fund, the 1992 Fund and the Supplementary Fund) which provide compensation for oil pollution damage resulting from spills of persistent oil from tankers. The IOPC funds are financed by levies on certain types of oil carried over sea. The levies are paid by entities which receive oil after sea transport, and normally not by states. The amount to pay depends on the number of spills and the use of the fund. If lots of money is spent in a year the levy goes up. The more volume of crude is received the higher amount one has to pay. Storage companies are officially the receivers of the oil, but in their GT&C they announce that those levies are forwarded to their customers. So years after a big oil spill in the world an invoice related to the oil pollution fund may follow, often as an unwanted surprise invoice. It is part of the responsibility when participating in the oil business. This is related to crude oil transportation only.

Oil Products

Refined products such as propane, butane, naphtha, gasoline, jet A1, kerosene, diesel, gasoil, heating oil, straight run fueloil, cracked fueloil. Also called 'petroleum products'. This oil is commercialised by the so-called 'product traders'.

Oil Reserves

Total amount of oil per registered field which has not yet been produced. All registered oil and oil equivalents which has not been produced. It also includes fields which are registered but not yet brought into production. Basically these are estimates as one never knows exactly how much oil is really producible.

Oil Sands

Mixtures of oil and sand. Very heavy oil which needs to be processed to separate the sand from the oil. This oil needs to be blended with diluent to make it transportable through pipelines to reach the refineries or shipping logistic points. This crude is expensive to produce and as it is a heavy crude rich in bitumen it also has a low sales price, discounted versus the benchmark crude. Also known as 'tar sands' or 'bitumen crude'. Canada and Venezuela are famous for oil sands. See also 'synthetic crude'. Canadian sand oil is sold through pipelines into the USA. A landlocked type of business. It requires a lot of planning to get access to time-slots on the pipelines. See also 'landlocked'.

Oil Spill

An oil spill is an unplanned release of liquid oil on the surface of water or oil vapour in the atmosphere as a result of an error due to human activity. The risk of an oil spill is high when vessels load or discharge an oil cargo or when they are bunkering oil. Other spills – or more usually called 'environmental disasters' – happen at accidents with oil tankers, but also container vessels, ferries etc. which are carrying bunker oil for their engines. Bunker tanks on most vessels are single hull tanks. Oil companies pay premiums to an international oil fund. That premium depends on the activity per company and on the number and consequences of oil disasters per year. The oil spills in the shape of vapour are often caused by too high a pressure in refinery systems not being flared off or a leakage in trucks or trains during transport of dangerous goods. A vapour cloud can be extremely dangerous. For the record: "A planned oil spill, dumping oil, is a heavy crime."

Oil Stocks

Oil stocks include crude oil (including strategic reserves), unfinished oils, natural gas plant liquids, and refined petroleum products.

OIW

Oil In Water. Slops on board a vessel need to be analysed. The percentage oil in water is important. If it might be as high as 10% then lots of money can be thrown away. One could at disport discharge the water that was settled in the slops. The oil in the slops has a value and can be reprocessed in a refinery. Free oil. It is important of course that the slops do not contain chemical compounds. If that is the case, the slops would be better taken off board. Just a reminder, slops and water should always be checked on H_2S. One never knows how long the slops have been on storage. I have seen H_2S values up to 2,000 ppm. It is a deadly level for people. When supplying slops in order to get rid of it, the OIW is important to mention when offering it to the receiver. The more oil in water the better, lower priced, the offer will be. The receiver will separate the oil from the water. The gained oil generates an income. Therefore, the receiver is willing to give a better price for slop water higher content of IOW. It is obvious that a low percentage of IOW is more expensive, and as mentioned, H_2S levels can make it even very expensive. Otherwise, one needs to think volumes as well. Not every company can take relatively high volumes in storage. In some cases the water being offered is so much, that floating storage has to be used by the water treatment company to be able the process the slops. Water cleaning can be time consuming. A receiver of slops would also like to serve his local smaller customers. Big volumes of slops have therefore a negative effect on the price as well. It will increase the costs due to extra storage-requirement as well.

Olefins

A group of petrochemicals characterised by their straight or branched structure. Includes ethylene, the largest volume petrochemical, propylene and butadiene.

OLPT

Offshore Loading Procedures for Tankers. No chance to do things differently with any dispensation. This is company HSE rule related and here every company sets their own standard for this, and all are very strict.

On Board Quantity (OBQ)

Sum of measured liquid volume, including free water and measured non-liquid volume but excluding any vapours, in cargo tanks prior to loading.

On-Spec

Finished oil, or oil which meets the minimum requirements as agreed in a trade. Oil products ready for consumption.

On-stream

An oil field is on-stream when it is producing oil or gas. After a shutdown the production starts up again. We say that the field is on stream again.

OPEC

The Organisation of Petroleum Exporting Countries (OPEC) is an oil cartel. It was founded at the Baghdad Conference on September 10–14, 1960. Current members (with years of membership) include Algeria (1969-present), Angola (2007-present), Ecuador (1973-1992 and 2007-present), Iran (1960-present), Iraq (1960-present), Kuwait (1960-present), Libya (1962-present), Nigeria (1971-present), Qatar (1961-present), Saudi Arabia (1960-present), United Arab Emirates (1967-present), and Venezuela (1960-present). Countries no longer members of OPEC include Gabon (1975-1994) and Indonesia (1962-2008). Its principal aim is 'the coordination and unification of the petroleum policies of its member countries and the determination of the best means for safeguarding their interests, individually and collectively; devising ways and means of ensuring the stabilization of prices in international oil markets with a view to eliminating harmful and unnecessary fluctuations; giving due regard at all times to the interests of the producing nations and to the necessity of securing a steady income to the producing countries; an efficient, economic and regular supply of petroleum to consuming nations, and a fair return on their capital to those investing in the petroleum industry'. (Chap 1, Art. 2; Statute of OPEC.)

OPEC Basket

The new OPEC reference basket (ORB), introduced on 16 June 2005, is currently made up of the following: Saharan Blend (Algeria), Girassol (Angola), Oriente (Ecuador), Minas (Indonesia), Iran Heavy (Islamic Republic of Iran), Basra Light (Iraq), Kuwait Export (Kuwait), Es Sider (Libya), Bonny Light (Nigeria), Qatar Marine (Qatar), Arab Light (Saudi Arabia), Murban (UAE) and BCF 17 (Venezuela).

OPEC Quota

Periodically, OPEC sets a production limit or quota for each of its member countries, in an attempt to manage the supply and hence price of oil. The OPEC quota applies to black oil only, and does not apply to condensates or natural gas. OPEC is not as strong as it used to be. It has started to lose control on the oil price. More oil is produced by countries that are not connected to the OPEC. Russia, South America and West Africa have become huge producers. Furthermore, today (2015) we see so many troubles in the mid-east area. Iran's embargo has reached its end. Many oil producing countries in the mid-east need money and will go for full production and other mid-east oil producing countries are still not well organised due to geo-political issues, but eventually they will come back in production as well. All prices are under big pressure. A heavy task for OPEC to re-arrange the oil quota in a good manner.

Open

The period at the beginning of a trading session officially designated by the exchange during which all transactions are considered to be made 'at the open'. The opening price of the market. When looking at candle sticks in graphs you can see the opening price, the high, the low and the close. See also 'candlestick'.

Open Account

A trade arrangement in which goods are shipped to a foreign buyer without guarantee of payment.

Open Credit

Financial uncovered debt given to big companies often triple 'A' rated, but also lower rated to single B for example. The amount of open credit depends on the rating and risk willingness per company. A company would get open credit according to the credit rating as registered by Standard & Poor's, S&P. Based on that rating a company can choose to give a certain amount of open credit. For products trading the cargoes are not that big and a cargo may easily be covered by the open credit availability. In crude trading it can be different. A cargo of crude can have a value of 70 up to 120 million Dollars. Credit monitoring is very important in the oil business. Look also at 'credit rating'. Buyers prefer open credit as opening an L/C can cost roughly between 4 and 8 cents per barrel depending on the strength of the company or even worse with a bad country rating. When a company buys oil and the open credit level is already used by that company then this company may buy its next cargo from another party that can give open credit. So open credit attracts business until it is used. Not giving enough open credit will result in missing orders as the buyers also want to keep their costs low. With oil prices at a high level the open credit availability is quickly used. Also getting new business in can be a challenge when limited credit is available. More credit, more business, but also more risk.

Open Interest

The total number of long positions outstanding in a futures contract (equals the total number of short positions), which have not been settled.

Open Outcry

A method of public auction for making bids and offers in the trading pits of futures exchanges. Unfortunately most exchanges have switched over to an electronic system. For old fashioned 'open outcry' I would recommend having a look at the movie 'Trading places' with Eddie Murphy. Very funny movie ending with an extreme 'open outcry' scene. The brokers with the loudest voice got served first and perhaps get the best deals fulfilled.

Open Trade Equity

The unrealised gain or loss on open positions. The best moment to take profit or cut losses depending on the rules of trading discipline.

Opening Range

The range of prices at which buy and sell transactions took place during the opening of the market. At opening such a range can be rather big and after some time there will be a smaller gap between bid and offer.

Operable Capacity

The amount of capacity that, at the beginning of the period, is in operation; not in operation and not under active repair, but capable of being placed in operation within 30 days; or not in operation but under active repair that can be completed within 90 days. Operable capacity is the sum of the operating and idle capacity and is measured in barrels per calendar day or barrels per stream day.

Operable Utilisation Rate

Represents the utilisation of the atmospheric crude oil distillation units. The rate is calculated by dividing the gross input to these units by the operable refining capacity of the units.

Operational Loss

Physical loss of oil as result of logistic operations of a cargo. Losses are caused by evaporation, voyage losses, line fill losses and/or shrinkage. See also 'apparent loss', a loss caused by errors. Loss control is very important here as due to high oil prices any loss will be very expensive and goes straight into the P&L. I would strongly advise the use of inspection during loading and discharging. There is good value in minimising losses. For the same case even the use of expeditors is an option.

Operational Stock

The oil in a terminal or refinery which cannot be commercialised as it needs to be retained to keep processes and operations running. A refinery is never empty. There is always oil in the processing units and pipelines. In storage tanks there may be fixed heels in the tank; it is undesirable in some cases to completely empty a tank as one might want to avoid pumping tank bottoms. In most cases operational stock is not part of the P&L and therefore it does not need to be hedged. A pity in contango days but good news when the market is backwardated.

Operator (Crude Production)

The individual or company responsible for the drilling, completion and production operations of a well, and the physical maintenance of the leased property. Often the biggest shareholder of a production field becomes the operator. Some NOCs may have the biggest share but leave the operatorship to the biggest investor.

Operator (Trading Related)

Also called 'commercial operator'. In a trading department the operator is a person who takes care of the execution of the oil contract by supplying and receiving the relevant information and instructions between the counterparties. A good operator can add value by optimising logistics. The more business there is the more possibilities there are to create benefits from good optimisation. An operator must have good knowledge about every activity related to logistics. They also nominate inspection and follow up quantities, qualities and the timing of the activities. They are in contact with the operator of the counterparty, storage terminal and refineries. They anticipate on challenges related to shipping and all other activity related to logistics. An operator has to be a proactive person. Solve challenges before they become a problem. A good operator can make a good deal from a bad deal. But he can also make a bad deal from a good deal. The cooperation between a trader and an operator is very important. Operations in oil is a

24/7 activity; most operators are on call and many are day and night available in case something happens. Traders and operators are to be teammates.

Opex
Operational expenses. Costs made for continuous running operations. See also 'capex'.

OPIS
Oil Price Information Service. The leading U.S. provider of retail fuel price information.

Opportunistic Trading Decision
Trading decision taken when it is very certain that a margin can be made. Arbitrage business, bringing oil from one geographic to another geographic trading area is done when it is profitable; even if it is not part of the main strategy the trader would not leave money on the table when the opportunity arises. Many traders make use of the opportunity when they have oil in hand. Less experienced traders would sell their oil on a FOB basis and let others do the arbitrage. Nevertheless they still get a reasonable price for their oil, but the potential to make more is then lost. A lot of opportunistic arbitrage cargoes may be sold to traders in the supplied geographic area as those traders may have a much better network which helps selling the cargoes to the end receivers. If arbitrage business becomes a strategy then it is better to create a local network or have an office available in different places. That makes oil trading a 24 hours activity around the world. Do not leave money on the table.

OPRG
'Oxygenated fuels Programme Reformulated Gasoline' is reformulated gasoline which is intended for use in an oxygenated fuels programme control area.

Optimisation
Organising supplies, sales and logistics in the best way in order to keep the processes running in a smooth way to maximum financial benefit and minimum costs. This with open mind-set and a maximum flow of information and communication between the refineries, traders and marketing departments. Good communication and exchange of knowledge

can be a basis for cutting logistic costs and to achieve the best prices in the market. 'Knowledge is power.' Optimisation requires from both the trader and the operators a creative mind-set and dedication to their job.

Option
Contract that gives the holder the right, but not the obligation, to buy (Call option) or to sell (Put option) the underlying product or futures contract, at a certain price, for a limited period of time.

Origin
Place, country or producer where crude or an oil product is coming from. The Chamber of Commerce is able to issue a 'Certificate of Origin' officially stating the origin of the oil. The certificate of origin is needed by most importers as part of customs regulations. Sometimes a Form-A document or EUR1 document is seen as a certificate of origin. But those are signed by Customs and are both stating the origin and can in addition be used as preferential certificates to receive a tax release when importing.

Original
A document marked as original is allowed to be accepted as an original by banks, even though it is a copy of the original documents. Important factor for intermediaries and presentation of documents. Opposite of copy.

Original Bill of Lading (OBL)
A document which requires proper signatures for consummating carriage of contract. Must be marked as 'original' by the issuing carrier. See also 'B/L Types'.

OSC
Oil Service Companies. Companies related to the oil business and supplying mainly logistic service, like storage terminals and shipping.

OSP
NOC declared price for each export oil blend. OSP is most often used by producers (NOC) in the Middle East. See also 'official selling price'.

OT Equalisation
Outturn equalisation. When one cargo is sold to two different customers

both in their own terminal then both receivers should equally share the outturn loss and gain at disport. This is calculated from the accumulated received oil quantities at both receivers. As an example; when a total cargo of 800,000 barrels is sold 50/50 to two customers then both customer will get a Bill of Lading of 400,000 bbls. At discharging it could be that at one terminal 405,000 bbls is discharged and at the other terminal 394,000 bbls. (The accumulated loss in disport is 1,000 bbls.) For one customer this looks like a gain of 5,000 barrels versus his 400 kb B/L while the other customer would have a 6,000 barrels loss versus his 400 kb B/L. This is not fair and therefore it is standard practice to have an OT equalisation clause in the contract. The sum of the total discharged figure is 799,000 bbls. One customer received 405,000/7,990 = 50.688% and the other customer received 394,000/7,990= 49.312%. Both 400 kb B/Ls need to be adjusted: One B/L becomes 50.688% of 800kb = 405,504 barrels and the other B/L becomes 49.312% of 800 kb = 394,496 Barrels. Now the outturn loss and the B/L have been adjusted on pro rata basis. Customer 1 pays for 405,504 barrels and had an outturn loss of 504 barrels and customer 2 pays for 394,496 barrels and had an outturn loss of 496 barrels. Seller happy and buyer happy, business as usual. Receivers of the oil will require the discharge report from each other in order to check the calculation.

OTS
Offer To Sell. A pre-advice issued before an official offer is issued. A buyer/seller who specifically solicits goods from a supplier should not ask for an OTS but a quote or offer. OTS is an invitation to buy goods based on information provided by a supplier to the buyer/seller at will without solicitation. Traders are testing the market to see if there is any willingness in the market to buy.

Outage
Space left in a product tank to allow for expansion during the temperature changes it may undergo during shipments and storage. Often the difference between gross and net capacity of a unit used for logistics.

Outright Long
Long means you have something or you bought something. If you have something you are exposed, you have the risk that prices are going up or down. The value of your product is changing. If that trading position is unhedged then you have an outright long position.

Outright Short

Short means you are lacking something or you sold something. If you lack something you are exposed, you have the risk that prices are going up or down. The value of your product which you are lacking is changing. If that trading position is unhedged then you have an outright short position.

Outturn

The measured oil quantity as received in a terminal. A trader could sell on DAP- or DES-Terms. This means that the seller runs the risk of oil losses at disport. It is normal to buy oil based on B/L figures that are made at the loadport. There are always operational losses. Selling on outturn figures can be done but in that case, the traders want a slightly better price when selling based on outturn figures. In some cases a trader knows that at a certain loading terminal the B/L is always too low. In that case selling on outturn figures can be smart, as more oil will be measured after discharging. Good experience and terminal knowledge can help a lot. Some terminals always have losses; in that case selling on outturn numbers is better to be avoided for sure when such a terminal does not cooperate when a claims department is not allowed to investigate the loss at that terminal. Losses over 0.5% are insurance cases. Only the insurance companies will pay out the value of the loss over 0.5%. Therefore, a good loss controller would rather investigate what causes the loss. Good knowledge and experience is required. All inspection reports are checked on calculations and on the fact that the correct measurement methods have been used. The loss controller will look at both loadport and disport. It happens from time to time that losses can be reduced to a percentage well below 0.5%. This is often more money gained back rather than waiting for an insurance company to pay out. With DES and DAP the title and risk on board the vessel is with the seller of the oil. Often sales are done on DAP or DES basis, but loaded B/L quantity to be used as commercial numbers. Here the customer just avoids risk and title while the cargo is sailing.

Outturn TCV

The total calculated volume of all oil, water and sediments from the vessel as measured at the receiving terminal. See also 'crude oil voyage loss calculations' in the back of the book.

Outturn GSV

Gross standard volume as measured at the receiving terminal. See also 'crude oil voyage loss calculations' in the back of the book. The logistic volume which arrives in tank. The commercial volume is the real crude volume which is gross tons minus BS&W.

Outturn NSV

Net standard volume as measured at the receiving terminal. See also 'crude oil voyage loss calculations' in the back of the book. The real volume that can be processed at a refinery. The gross volume is pumped to the refinery but in the coalescer the BS&W is removed before crude enters the column.

Out Trade

A trade which cannot be cleared by a clearinghouse because the data submitted by the two clearing members involved in the trade differs in some respect. All out trades must be resolved before the market opens the next day. My recommendation here is to read the book from Nick Leeson, 'Rogue Trader', which describes how some out trade was booked in a special account. That was not the correct way when dealing with out trades.

Ouwe

Dutch word translated as 'elderly' = Captain or commander or boss.

Over the Counter (OTC)

OTC trade is a direct trade with a counterparty which means that the buyer and seller know each other. When you go to the butcher, the butcher stands behind the counter. You order your meat and he hands it over the counter to you and you give the money over the counter to the butcher. Oil is traded on the phone but the concept is the same. The buyer and seller know each other. On the exchange buyers and sellers do not meet. A physical broker or a paper broker in the swap market may be involved in the OTC market. OTC markets are often very transparent markets. Participants get easy access to the trading activity and traded prices. Based on that the market knows how to bid or offer on the next deal and a good trader knows when the market goes empty or when it is oversupplied. One may benefit from the situation.

Overage

Surplus. When a vessel is chartered to load 100kt then the freight price is based on that quantity. In some circumstances there may be opportunities to load some extra volume. If the vessel is able to take more than 100kt on board then the extra utilised ullage is called overage. Most often it is agreed in the charter party that the extra freight, when overage capacity is used, will be split 50/50 between the charterer and the owner. Those freight savings of 50% are often shared again by the buyer of the CIF cargo and the charterer if the total loaded cargo is more than the contractual agreed cargo size. Making use of the overage option is another way of optimising freight. See also 'topping up'.

Overbought

A technical opinion that the market price has risen too steeply and too fast in relation to underlying fundamental factors. Typical situation which makes traders nervous. The fundamentals say that price should go down but some forces in the market may be due to a leverage game and are pushing the price up. Short positions lose money because of that. Difficult for a trader to step in and take a position. You can go long because prices are in an uptrend or you may go short because the overbought situation is about to reach its highest level. Fundamentals say the market is overbought and prices should fall.

Overlift

Loading more oil than the available entitlement. In crude production, the monthly availability of oil can be calculated. The equity holder then knows how much he can lift in that month. If more is loaded than the available volume, the stock at the end of the month will show a negative figure. The equity holder overlifted on his entitlement. Often this is caused due to the standard cargo size related to the crude oil. If the availability is smaller than the standard cargo size, then overlifting cannot be avoided. When the negative stock gets too much then the equity hold has to load one cargo less resulting in underlift.

Overnight Limit

The maximum amount of a net long or short position that a trader can carry over into the next dealing day. The limit is equal to the maximum mandate a trader has got from his trading management.

Overnight Position

The trader's long or short position of his trading book at close of business until next day opening. One can be long or short overnight. Day traders would always close their position before the end of the day. Fundamental changes overnight or in a weekend could create big surprises which may affect the trading result in a significant way. Trend traders think longer term and will have overnight positions. In physical oil trading there are always positions open and so overnight positions cannot be avoided. A trader might be able to minimise risk and secure his position by proper hedging. But in physical oil trading most positions are spread positions, they just stay as they are. It is the outright positions that a trader can control.

Overriding Prices
Trades at prices which are higher than the offered price or lower than the bid price. Either a wrong trade or the levels indicate tremendous urgency to either buy or sell the futures. Also called 'printing the O'.

Oversold
A technical opinion that the market price has declined too steeply and too fast in relation to underlying fundamental factors. See also 'overbought'.

Overstated B/L
Bill of Lading on which too much volume is noted. At discharge port a big oil loss will be noticed which has a significant negative resultant effect. The B/L figures are representing the commercial invoice. The involved traders of the two or more companies, buyer, seller and eventual trader between both, have lots of discussions. Claims departments have to come into action and in some cases new B/Ls will be issued if the supplier agrees that a huge mistake has been made at loadport. To avoid such problems as much as possible an inspector has to be used to guard the volumes. 1,000 barrels on a crude cargo may be 0.1% of a total cargo and looks like an operational loss. It has a value of more than 100kUsd, so even a small overstated B/L has financial consequences. B/L figures have to be precise and the measurements or calculation have to be closely monitored by an independent inspector with good ethical standards.

Oxidation
Combining elemental compounds with oxygen to form a new compound. A part of the metabolic reaction.

Oxygenate

Substances which, when added to gasoline, increase the amount of oxygen in that gasoline blend. Fuel ethanol, methyl tertiary butyl ether (MTBE), ethyl tertiary butyl ether (ETBE), and methanol are common oxygenates. Keep the cargo free from water. Water will absorb the oxygenates and this will have an immediate effect on the quality of oil. Gasoline would in such a case lose some octane value. The product can become off spec.

Oxygenated Gasoline

'Oxygenated gasoline' is a mixture of conventional gasoline and one or more combustible liquids which contain oxygen ('oxygenates'). At present, the most common oxygenates are ethanol and MTBE (methyl tertiary-butyl ether). ETBE (ethyl tertiary-butyl ether) and TAME (tertiary-amyl methyl ether) have seen some use and the use may increase in USA. In Europe there is in gasoline specs a maximum allowable content when it concerns the use of oxygenates. Only Finland in Europe has a minimum requirement of oxygenates in gasoline.

P

P&C

Private and Confidential. Used by commodities traders to describe non-public transactions. Often business in the physical oil market is done P&C, but nevertheless in a short time brokers or traders have mentioned the business in the market. Therefore alternatively P&C means in some cases 'public and confirmed'.

P&I Insurance

Protection and Indemnity Insurance. A club in native insurance. 'P&I' is most often used in the shipping industry.

P&L

Profit and Loss overview of the trader. The trading book of a specified commodity. Each trader enters his trades into the P&L. The sum of all the deals together gives an overview of the overall trading position of the trader. Day by day market prices are updated in the P&L and each morning the trader can see the financial result based on the actual position. The P&L is extremely important for the trader and has to be accurate. A P&L reporting wrong positions could cause huge uncontrolled results in the P&L. Especially when markets are extremely volatile, even the smallest updates on operational level can have huge effects on the results. Each person with a job linked to a P&L has to take that job very seriously and contribute to quality input. Controllers are checking the input of the P&L and are following results which are to be reported to management as well. The P&L is also used by controllers to see to it that the trader stays within his mandate. The controller's role should be to contribute to the quality of the P&L and to report the results. Traders like to receive their daily P&L in time in the morning before markets open. The P&L confirms the position of the trader and is needed to start a new day's trading. Without knowing his position the trader cannot do his work.

P-Value
The P-value (ASTM D 7112) is a standard test method for determining stability and compatibility of heavy fuel oils and crude oils, and therefore it isn't intended for VGO. Vacuum gasoil would in most cases be used as a boost for improving poor stability in heavy fuel oil. Trying to measure stability on a stability booster will give problems mostly in the case of too high intensity on the instrument or instrument errors. P-Value testing on fuel straight run fueloil only.

PADD
Petroleum Allocation for Defence District. A group of five geographic areas in the USA used in reference to petroleum distribution. PADDs are organised as follows:

- **PADD I (East Coast)**
- **PADD IA** (New England): Connecticut, Maine, Massachusetts, New Hampshire, Rhode Island, and Vermont.
- **PADD IB** (Central Atlantic): Delaware, District of Columbia, Maryland, New Jersey, New York, and Pennsylvania.
- **PADD IC** (Lower Atlantic): Florida, Georgia, North Carolina, South Carolina, Virginia, and West Virginia.

- **PADD II (Midwest)**
  Illinois, Indiana, Iowa, Kansas, Kentucky, Michigan, Minnesota, Missouri, Nebraska, North Dakota, Ohio, Oklahoma, South Dakota, Tennessee, and Wisconsin.

- **PADD III (Gulf Coast)**
  Alabama, Arkansas, Louisiana, Mississippi, New Mexico, and Texas.

- **PADD IV (Rocky Mountain)**
  Colorado, Idaho, Montana, Utah, and Wyoming.

- **PADD V (West Coast)**
  Alaska, Arizona, California, Hawaii, Nevada, Oregon, and Washington.

Panamax

The maximum size ship that can fit through the Panama Canal in terms of width, length and draft, generally about 80,000dwt. Such size is normally used for crude oil cargoes. Panamax vessels are therefore 'dirty' vessels and freight quotations may be found on price reports under dirty tanker rates.

Paper Barrels

A generic term for oil that is bought and sold in the forward or futures markets. Thus, it involves commitments to make future deliveries rather than exchange of actual physical supplies. Oil prices are set by 'paper barrel' (futures contracts) trading in futures exchanges of New York (Nymex) and London (ICE, former IPE).

Paper Deal

Deal without any oil movement. Can be a futures contract, option, CFD or swap. Traders buy and sell oil on paper at a quoted price. They do that for hedging purposes or speculation only.

Paper Market

A market for contracts where delivery is settled in cash, rather than by delivery of the physical product on which the contract is based. The paper market refers to futures, swaps and options.

Paper Trader

Trader who is responsible for buying and selling derivatives. The trader can have a function to hedge the trading book only, to speculate with paper or both hedging combined with a mandate to speculate. The paper trader is basically risk managing the book. Physical oil trading is done to make margins, but also the pricing element in physical trades is based on margins. The physical trader may buy a cargo on a month average and sell the same cargo with B/L related pricing (3 days after). The time value for such a deal can be locked in by the paper trader. The sum of the margin and the time value is the result of that cargo trade. The physical trader and the paper trader have to communicate and understand each other well. It is a matter of team work. The paper trader gives information about the time values in the paper market to the physical traders. And the physical trader informs about the hedges he needs.

Paper Trading

Trading derivatives such as futures, options and swaps. Paper trading is done because of hedging purposes and for speculation reasons. One can go outright long or short and one can take spreads based on time, location, products or refinery cracks (product versus crude).

Paraffinic

A high content of paraffin. A white, odourless, tasteless, chemically inert, waxy substance derived from distilling petroleum. A crystalline, flammable substance composed of saturated hydrocarbons.

Parallel Body Length

The straight side of the tanker at the berth. When the tanker empties and lies higher in the water the shape of the side of the vessel looks different compared with the higher side of the vessel. It is important for HSE that a moored vessel is still in touch with the berth and mooring poles when it becomes empty. Each port or berth is different and has different mooring poles. When clearing the vessel the technical fit is important. A vessel should stay stable at the mooring points or dolphins. Vetting departments often look at the HSE approvals, while terminals also have to look at the technical requirements.

Paraffinic Naphtha

Favoured quality of naphtha for ethylene plant feedstock.

Parent Company

An affiliated company that exercises ultimate control over a business entity, either directly or indirectly, through one or more intermediaries. The parent is the mother company, headquarters. The company which makes the yearly financial reports.

Parent Company Guarantee (PCG)

A parent company guarantee (PCG) is a guarantee by a parent company of a contractor's financial performance under its contract with its client, where the contractor is a subsidiary of the parent company. Most companies consist of the mother company which may be listed; trading units, refineries, marketing affiliates are registered as daughter company. For these affiliates a PCG might be required to receive open credit. A PCG is very important when managing credit risk. If a subsidiary has no coverage by a PCG then a Letter of Credit would be required. When a mother company withdraws their hands from a subsidiary and you have given open credit without a PCG, then you might be in trouble. Some companies would try a Letter of Comfort. It may work but it does not guarantee anything.

Part Cargo (P/C)

A part cargo is often indicated when a vessel or barge is loading different qualities of oil or when the collected total cargo comes from different suppliers which results in more than one B/L for the same quality of oil in the vessel. When qualities of oil are different then often the nomination is to load the 'part cargo segregated' on board the vessel. When the quality is the same for each cargo or when different qualities are blended on board the vessel, the nomination would say: "Part cargo non segregated". The product will then be commingled on board the vessel.

Particulates or Particular Matter

Particulates are small matters of soot exhausted by diesel engines, which are often linked to cancer and respiratory problems. Diesel exhaust causes significantly fewer particulates than they did just a few years ago, due to strict fuel quality standards and new features such as particulate filters. The image of diesel has much improved. The car industry has done great work in further improving the diesel engine to make it suitable for cleaner diesel. Due to the pressure on the car industry the diesel engines became cleaner and the refineries had to change their qualities as well. Sulphur levels have come down drastically and now bio diesel is well used and produced. See also 'dieselisation'.

Payment Term

Term in which buyer and seller agree to pay the commercial invoice at an agreed due date. In oil products payment is often due 5 days after B/L and in crude oil payment is often due 30 days after B/L. Focus on supply of credit is important here. Some deals may be agreed with delayed payment terms. In that case the trader has to make sure that he gets a slightly higher price to cover the financing costs. See also '3/5 days payment term' and '30 days payment term'.

PBA
Pilot Boarding Area. Related to shipping when a vessel arrives at her final destination. NOR is tendered and a pilot has to come on board in order to sail safely to the berth. Pilot comes on board by helicopter or small boat. With extreme weather the pilot will not be able to come on board. Pilots are striking in that case and the vessel will have to wait for improvements. It will delay logistics, but that is part of the risk. Pilots services are part of the port costs.

PBL
Abbreviation for parallel body length of a vessel. See 'parallel body length'.

PDPR
Demurrage related: e.g. 17,000 USD PDPR, per day pro rata. Extra lay-time (more than as agreed) will cost 17,000 USD per 24 hours. Apr. 708 USD per hour.

Peak production
Max production. A new crude oil field builds up production rates per day. At a certain moment a field gets to its maximum production level. At a certain moment production per day will come down and will decrease. The field has reached its peak production. New techniques or connections to other new fields may increase the production again. A new peak may be reached. Nevertheless each field will become empty and production will decrease until the well is completely empty or dry. Often peak production is used in the context of worldwide production for crude oil. Peak oil has already been reached.

Pegged Price
The price at which a commodity has been fixed by agreement.

Pennants (Technical Trading)
A price chart pattern that looks like a vertical line with a small triangle at the top. It is seen as a sign that a trend will continue after a brief consolidation, e.g. A 'bullish flag'.

Pensky-Martens
A closed-cup test for flash points of oil.

Pentanes Plus

A mixture of hydrocarbons, mostly pentanes and heavier, extracted from natural gas. Includes iso-pentane, natural gasoline, and plant condensate.

Performance

The results of activities of an organisation or investment over a given period of time. Based on performance good trades business may be repeated and long term business relations may be concluded if two companies can make money together. Before trading with a new company business references may be required. It is important to know how a new company will perform. Does a company perform on supply of oil and is it available in time; what about quality? And also important to know is how a company performs on payment. Of course a Letter of Credit gives good coverage against risk, but it is better and safer to stay away from trouble. Some risk with new companies and new relations is always applicable. Over time a good relationship can generate long term business. Next to performance of companies we can also look in the mirror. Performance can be measured per individual based on the trader's competence, trading behaviour and other important KPIs. Performance for a trader is most often measured on financial results.

Performance Risk

Risk that the counterparty does not deliver the cargo or does not deliver the correct quality or quantity of oil as agreed. This leads to claims and frustration. The commercial damage is often much bigger than the final claim. Before entering long term commitments with new partners it is best to check business references or maybe start with a spot cargo. IDD is very important is well. Take a look at 'IDD'.

Persian Gulf

The countries that comprise the Persian Gulf are: Bahrain, Iran, Iraq, Kuwait, Qatar, Saudi Arabia, and the United Arab Emirates.

Pet. Chems

Popular abbreviation for 'petro chemical feedstock', but also for the chemicals derived from naphtha cracking, i.e. Ethylene, propylene, butadiene, benzene, toluene and p-xylene.

Petrochemical Feedstocks

Chemical feedstocks derived from petroleum principally for the manufacture of chemicals, synthetic rubber, and a variety of plastics. The categories reported are 'naphtha less than 205°C/401°F' and 'other oils equal to or greater than 205°C/401°F'. Products which come from the processing in the chemical industry are plastics. Naphtha is therefore a very important feedstock for the petrochemical industry. In good and growing economies the demand for luxury products is big. As a result of that the demand for plastics, to make those luxury goods, is huge. As a result of the acceleration effect the demand for naphtha may even be bigger and the price for naphtha will rise to levels higher than gasoline values. The refineries will make great financial results in that case as they will produce less gasoline, read less cracking and other processing required. The refineries will cash in very good refinery margins, like the years 2005 to 2008. So the economy is very important for the refining industry.

Petrochemicals

Chemicals derived from petroleum, such as naphtha. Feedstock for the manufacture of plastics and synthetic rubber. Petrochemicals include benzene, toluene, xylene, styrene, and methanol.

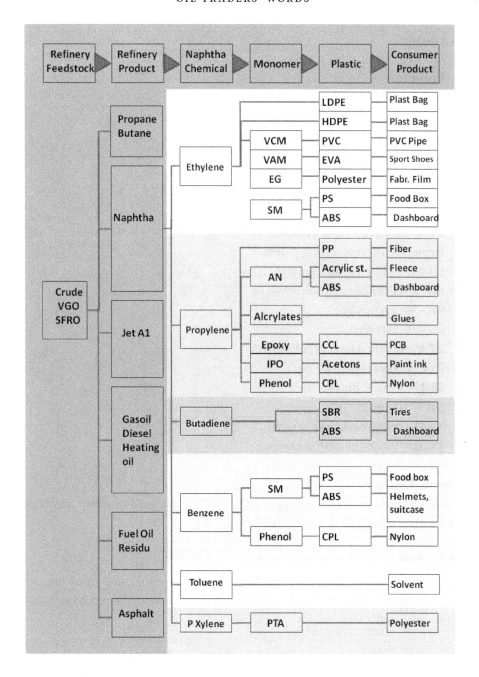

Abbreviations from the Petrochemicals to plastic scheme:

- **Monomer**
  Small molecule that may bind chemically to other monomers to form a

polymer.

- **Polymer**
  Plastics.

  · **ABS** – Acrylonitrile butadiene styrene.
  · **AN** – Acrylonitrile.
  · **CCL** – Copper-clad laminates.
  · **CPL** – Polymer to make nylon.
  · **EG** – Ethylene glycol.
  · **EVA** – Ethylene-vinyl acetate.
  · **Expoxy** – Thermosetting polymer.
  · **HDPE** – High density polyethylene.
  · **LDPE** – Low density polyethylene.
  · **PP** – Polypropylene.
  · **PS** – Polystyrene.
  · **PTA** – Purified terephthalic acid.
  · **PVC** – Polyvinyl chloride.
  · **SBR** – Styrene Butadiene.
  · **SM** – Samarium.
  · **VAM** – Vinyl acetate monomer.
  · **VCM** – Vinyl chloride monomer.

Petro-Dollars

Popular way in USA for naming the Dollars that are paid to other countries when oil is imported to the United States.

Petroleum

From Latin 'petra' (rock) and 'oleum' (oil) therefore meaning 'rock oil, the term is applied to crude oil and commonly used to describe products made from 'crude oil'.

Petroleum Administration for Defence (PAD)

Districts. Geographic aggregations of the 50 States and the District of Columbia into five districts by the Petroleum Administration for Defence in 1950. These districts were originally defined during World War II for purposes of administering oil allocation.

Petroleum Coke

A residue, the final product of the condensation process in cracking. This product is reported as marketable coke or catalyst coke. The conversion factor is 5 barrels per short ton.

- **Marketable coke**
  Those grades of coke produced in delayed or fluid cokers which may be recovered as relatively pure carbon. This 'green' coke may be sold as is or further purified by calcining. See also 'needle coke', 'sponge coke' and 'shot coke'.

- **Catalyst coke**
  In many catalytic operations (e.g. Catalytic cracking) carbon is deposited on the catalyst, thus deactivating the catalyst. The catalyst is reactivated by burning off the carbon, which is used as a fuel in the refining process. This carbon or coke is not recoverable in a concentrated form.

Petroleum Products

Petroleum products are obtained from the processing of crude oil (including lease condensate), natural gas, and other hydrocarbon compounds. Petroleum products include unfinished oils, liquefied petroleum gases, pentanes plus, aviation gasoline, motor gasoline, naphtha-type jet fuel, kerosene-type jet fuel, kerosene, distillate fueloil, residual fueloil, petrochemical feedstock, special naphthas, lubricants, waxes, petroleum coke, asphalt, road oil, still gas, and miscellaneous products.

PG

Persian Gulf (same as Arab Gulf, AG).

Physical Delivery

Execution of a physical oil trade. The oil may be delivered on a FOB basis. The seller has oil in tank and has sold the oil based on quality in tank. The buyer needs to present a barge or vessel to load the cargo. When delivering CIF or CFR the seller supplies the oil to the agreed location. The seller charters the vessel in this case. For FOB, CIF, CFR risk and title is transferred from buyer to seller when the products arrive on board the vessel. With DAP (old DES) deliveries risk and title are transferred when the oil is leaving the vessel. The seller charters the vessel and has risk and title on board the vessel.

The quantity supplied is based on out-turn figures. It means that the seller is risking the voyage loss. Therefore it should be allowed to ask for a little better premium for DAP deliveries. With FOB, CIF and CFR it is the buyer who receives the oil who takes the voyage loss. With physical deliveries it is therefore important to use good inspection to get the correct volumes on the B/L. At high oil price levels an overstated B/L can become expensive and the loss is realised in the trader's P&L. Those come as a surprise as that loss is realised after discharging and measurement, weeks after the deal was committed in the first place. A good operator would notice a shortage first and will start asking questions to all parties involved. With big losses claims departments should be involved at an early stage when the case is still fresh.

Physical Delivery (Expiry of Futures)
The transfer of ownership of an underlying commodity between a buyer and seller. Real oil supplied, based on one holding a futures contract which has expired and where delivery is prioritised over a cash settlement.

Physical Loss
Loss of products as a result of operations, also called operational loss. Due to manipulation of the oil, losses cannot be avoided. One cannot often count on a gain. Only when B/L figures are understated a gain will appear but that would not be an operational gain rather an error at loadport. Physical losses are most often caused by evaporation, voyage losses (ROB), line fill losses and shrinkage. With current high oil prices losses can turn out to be very expensive. Loss control by the use of inspection at loadport and disport is important. In some cases the use of an expeditor would be helpful.

Physical Trader
Trader who is responsible for buying, selling and optimising the oil molecules. He can trade from a refinery or marketing system, but it can also be a trader who is in the market to buy and sell and cash in margins or quality values. He takes positions by buying and selling by using different pricing methods; often this job is combined with paper trading or if the activity in the book is too much he may be assisted by a paper trader. A physical oil trader has to be competent. He must know all about the different qualities and he must be able to set values on qualities. Also logistics connected to his commodity are important. The physical oil trader has to be a team player. His trading decisions are to be shared with the people around him. Making a profitable

trade is only possible when the operations are well executed and when the hedging activity is arranged well. Some traders have a very important role in the value chain within the company they work for. Sharing information within the value chain between different roles creates better value and more opportunities for optimisation within the value chain. It also affects the behaviour related to the trades of oil cargoes which are done in addition to value chain trading.

Pig

Huge plug (size is the diameter of a pipeline) which is pushed through a pipeline by nitrogen or air with the purpose of emptying the pipeline. An intelligent pig is a more sophisticated pig with measurement equipment to inspect the pipeline on damages and leakages. See also 'smart pig'.

PIIRA

Petroleum Industry Information and Reporting Act. Well used and acknowledged in the oil market as source for information. Analysts may use the reports from Piira.

Pilot Station

Official harbour authority where a ship should be registered when it arrives at the port of destination. Registration on arrival is required before the vessel or tanker is allowed to enter the port. The pilot station is in contact with the ship's agent to find out if the jetty of destination is available. If the jetty is available the vessel is allowed to enter the port. In most cases a local pilot will guide the oil tanker into the harbour until arrival at the jetty. It is important to know as well that as soon as registration at pilot station is done, the NOR is tendered and time starts ticking. The first 6 hours after tendering of the NOR are for the account of the owner. See also 'NOR'. Also sailing time from pilot station to the berth is for account of the owner of the vessel. Used laytime starts ticking again when the vessel is at the berth in status 'mooring completed'.

PIONA Test

Naphtha quality test on Paraffin, Iso-paraffin, Olefins, Naphthenes and Aromatics. All contents are measured in volume percentage. Important test for the petrochemical industry. The purchase of the chemical plant would allocate value to the naphtha when looking at the outcome of the PIONA test.

He would also look at the C4 content, the part which may evaporate in the cracking process.

Pipeline
A tube or system of tubes used for the transportation of oil or gas.

Pipeline (USA Petroleum)
Crude oil and product pipelines used to transport crude oil and petroleum products respectively (including interstate, intrastate, and intra-company pipelines) within the 50 States refinery input, crude oil. This is also called landlocked business. The big competitor of pipeline is the train system.

Pipeline Capacity
The quantity of oil which can be pumped through a pipeline per hour. On some occasions a tanker has more pumping capacity than a shore pipeline can handle. Pipeline size is very important in logistics. Pipelines that are too small are often the bottleneck on old terminals. Also the available pipelines say something about pipeline capacity. Russia invested in the BPS2 and ESPO. Since then there is more pipeline capacity than crude oil production in Russia. Pipeline capacity means here total quantity of oil they can pump per day to the different receiving terminals.

Pipelines
A network that allows crude oil, refined products and gas liquids to move across the country, usually from either refineries to terminals or from coastal (import) locations to terminals and refineries further inland. See also 'CEPS'.

Pipeline Systems (Just a few)

- **Baku-Supsa Pipeline**
  Pipeline which connects Sangachal terminal in Baku with the Supsa terminal in Georgia at the Black Sea. It is meant for transporting oil from the Azeri-Chirag-Gunshli field. Length 833 km or 518 miles.

- **Baku-Novorossiysk Pipeline**
  This pipeline is also called the Northern route export pipeline and it is connecting the Sangachal terminal in Baku with the loading facilities in Novorossiysk, Black Sea. Operated by SOCAR (State Oil Company of

Azerbaijan Republic) and Russian Transneft. The pipeline is operating Azeri crude. Length 1330 km or 830 miles.

- **Big Inch**
A pipeline built during second world war to avoid German problems with tankers. The pipeline connects Texas with New Jersey and was later extended to Phoenixville, Pennsylvania. From there other connections have been added.

- **BTC Pipeline Baku, Tbilisi, Ceyhan**
Crude oil pipeline starting at Caspian Sea in Azerbaijan Baku to Tbilisi in Georgia until Ceyhan in Turkey, Mediterranean Sea. Length of 1100 miles or 1768 kilometres.

- **BPS**
First Baltic Pipeline System, transporting Urals crude oil, REBCO, from the production fields to Primorsk. The pipeline is operated by Transneft and the lot sizes in Primorsk are 100kt per cargo, roughly 725 kb. Since 2006 the maximum capacity of this pipe has been utilised and roughly 60 to 66 cargoes per month are loaded. With BPS2 coming up there will be more capacity available to the ports at the Gulf of Finland. Primorsk volume might come down a bit due to re-routing of Urals crude oil to BPS2. Both BPS and BPS2 crude will be loaded at the Gulf of Finland, North West Europe trades, Primorsk and Ust Luga.

- **BPS2 (Crude Pipeline)**
Baltic Pipeline System 2nd project. A new pipeline connected to the Druzhba pipeline meant to bypass former Soviet transit countries. Russia does not want to be dependent on other countries when supplying crude oil. This pipeline will end in Ust Luga seaport in the Gulf of Finland. BPS1 supplies to Primorsk in the Gulf of Finland. First crude through BPS2 started loading in 2012.

- **Brent System Pipeline**
System where close to 20 North Sea oilfields are connected to Sullom Voe terminal in Shetland, Scotland.

- **Calnev Pipeline**
Oil products pipeline connecting Los Angeles with Las Vegas. Length 890km or 550 miles.

- **Caspian Pipeline Consortium.**
A pipeline connecting the Tengiz field to Novorossiysk terminal at Black Sea. Transport of CPC. Length 1510 km or 940 miles.

- **Chad-Cameroon Pipeline**
Pipeline from Doba, Southern Chad to the oil facilities at the coast of Cameroon. Length 1070 km or 660 miles.

- **Colonial Pipeline**
Organisation with headquarters in Alpharetta Georgia which supplies oil products originated in Houston, Texas through their pipeline to states such as Louisiana, Mississippi, Alabama, Georgia, South Carolina, North Carolina, Virginia, Maryland, Pennsylvania, New Jersey until final destination New York.

- **Buckeye Pipeline**
Buckeye Partners is an organisation in Houston and it is managing oil distribution through a pipeline network of roughly 10,000 kilometres (6,200 miles) in the USA.

- **Druzhba Pipeline**
Also called 'friendship pipeline'. Pipeline network in Russia. Connecting Russian oil streams by pipeline to Belarus, Czech Republic, Germany, Hungary, Kazakhstan, Poland, Slovakia and Ukraine.

- **Enbridge Pipeline System**
A crude oil connection from Canada to USA with length of 5000 km or 3100 miles, including multiple connections.

- **Forties Pipeline**
A pipeline network in the North Sea connected to Hound Point terminal in UK. It covers roughly 30% of UK's crude oil production.

- **Grozny Tuapse Oil Pipeline**
  Connecting the Grozny Area oilfields in Russia, Tetsjenia to Tuapse terminal at Black Sea.

- **Kazakhstan-China Oil Pipeline**
  Connection for crude supply from Kazakhstan Caspian shore to Ainjiangin China. Cooperation between KazMunaigaz and CNCP. Length 2228 km or 1384 miles.

- **Keystone Pipeline**
  A pipeline meant to transport oil sands from Alberta, Canada to Illinois and Oklahoma and then further to U.S. gulf coast.

- **Kirkuk-Banias Pipeline**
  This pipeline connects the Iraqi Kirkuk field with the Syrian port of Banias. Length 800 km or 500 miles.

- **Kirkuk-Ceyhan Oil Pipeline**
  These are two pipelines coming from Kirkuk which find their way to Ceyhan in Turkey. Length 970 km or 600 miles.

- **Minnesota Pipeline**
  Crude oil pipeline connecting Clearbrook, Minnesota with the twin cities Minneapolis and Saint Paul.

- **Odessa Brody Pipeline**
  A connection from Odessa at the Black Sea to Brody in Ukraine. Plans are to extend the line to Polish Plock refinery and Gdansk, Northern harbour of Poland.

- **Portland-Montreal Pipeline**
  Crude oil connection from Portand, Maine to Montreal.

- **RAPL**
  Rotterdam-Antwerp Pipeline. From Rotterdam there is a crude oil pipeline going to Antwerp. Mainly used to pump crude oil to the refineries Totsa and Exxon who together are the owners of the pipeline.

- **RRP**

  Rotterdam Rhine Pipeline. Pipeline for crude oil from Rotterdam storage and refineries to Germany owned by Shell Petroleum, BP, Ruhr Petroleum and Shell Germany.

- **Samsun-Ceyhan pipeline**

  This is a planned pipeline connecting Black Sea Harbour, North of Turkey Samsun to Ceyhan terminal in the Med. South of Turkey. Target is to make this an alternative route for Kazakhstan crude. Currently all crude is transported through the Bosporus which often causes big delays due to bad weather.

- **SPSE Société du Pipeline Sud Européen**

  Pipeline connecting FOS Southern harbour in France with refineries in France, Switzerland and Germany, Karlsruhe.

- **Sumed Pipeline**

  Suez-Med. Pipeline, length 320 km. Pipeline in Egypt connecting Gulf of Suez, Ain Sukhna terminal to Sidi Kerir in the Med. A VLCC discharges a part of her cargo into the pipeline enabling he to sail without draft problems through the Suez Canal. In Sidi Kirir she can re-load her cargo and sail to her final destination. By this capping can be avoided. Money and time is saved.

- **Trans Israel Pipeline, TIP Line**

  Also called Eilat-Ashkelon pipeline, built in 1968 and has been used for transporting crude from Iran to Israel. At this stage it is used to supply crude in revised direction but then from Ashkelon to Eilat. Unsure if the pipeline connection to Israel is still in place and operational, but whether it is being used today would be the big guess.

- **Transalpine Pipeline (TAL)**

  A pipeline connecting Trieste in Italy with Austria and Southern Germany.

- **Transnet Pipeline, Petronet**

  South African pipeline network for crude and petroleum products connecting two Durban refineries, a refinery at Coalbrook and two Sasoil plants at Secunda.

- **TAPS (Crude Pipeline)**
  Trans Alaska Pipeline System transports crude oil produced in Northern part of Alaska to the South where it is shipped in vessels for supplies in US West Coast. Pipeline above surface and therefore most seen on photos.

There are too many pipelines to mention in this book. This is just a small selection to give an impression of oil pipeline networks. In areas with many refineries one can assume that these refineries are also connected by pipelines. Most pipelines can be seen as 'common carriers'. That does not mean it is for free and that it is easy to get access to the pipeline. See also 'landlocked' and 'Cushing,' the price base of WTI at the Nymex.

Pit
The area on the trading floor where trading in futures and options contracts is conducted by open outcry. Since exchanges are more and more replaced by electronic exchange systems, the pit or the open outcry will soon become history.

PL
Pipeline (not P&L).

Plain Vanilla
A term used to describe a standard deal.

Platformer
Unit that produces high-octane blendstock for the manufacture of gasoline. The blending component would be called platformate. A component with good octane value between 95 and 100 RON.

Platts
Platts is a provider of energy information around the world that has been in business in various forms for more than a century and is now a division of The McGraw-Hill Companies. Products include Platts Energy Economist, industry news and price benchmarks for the oil, natural gas, electricity, nuclear power, coal, petrochemical and metals markets. Platts uses bids, offers and trades to set the price for hundreds of non-transparent, over-the-counter physical oil and energy products every day. Platts pricing has been

the benchmark for oil trading for generations. Oil prices are generated in the Platts window. The other oil price reporter in the market is Argus.

Platts/Argus Quotation
Platts/Argus quotes the market in the prices. A low price and a high price. The average of the high and low quotation is the mean quotation. The difference between the high and low often depends on the commodity. LPG difference between high and low is often 5 or 10 Dollars per ton; in oil products the difference can be 50 cents per ton. In crude oil we see a high low difference of 4-5 cents per barrel. The Platts/Argus quotation is used as the benchmark; sometimes a price plus or minus a differential is based on a Platts/Argus high quotation or on the mean quotation.

Plus (sailing with a)
When the ship figures after loading are higher than the B/L numbers then the vessel sails with a plus. Does not mean that there will be a gain at disport. It shows at least a difference between shore and ship measurements.

POD
Port of discharge or port of destination.

Point
1/100th of a cent (0.0001). In density 1 point is 0.0001. A tank is declared homogeneous when the difference between top and bottom is below 11 points. E.g. Gasoline 0.7550 top versus 0.7561 bottom would be a homogeneous tank of gasoline. Or fueloil bottom 0.9785 (M100) versus top 1.0012 (slurry) is not homogenous. After homogenation the blend may turn out to become a bunker grade when the average of top, middle and bottom is max 0.991 density. Provided that other specs are within requirements as well.

POL
Port Of Loading.

Polar Low
Unannounced heavy storm in the Arctic. Weather conditions in the Arctic can change in a short and unexpected time. Polar lows are weather conditions which are not easy to predict. Polar lows are one of the biggest challenges when drilling, producing and transporting oil in the Arctic. Think heavy

storm, rain, snow, more wind, darkness and temperatures far below zero. More oil is to be explored in the Arctic in the near future, a real challenge. These challenges are related to HSE.

Political Risk

Risk of a sale of goods where it may happen that the government in the buyer's country may take some action that prevents the buyer from paying. This covers possibilities such as foreign exchange controls and non-payment due to war or insurrection.

Pollution

The reduction of clean quality of land, air and water as a consequence of the industry, use of energy, car traffic etc. etc. Pollution gets a lot of attention from many authorities, action groups and the public. Terms like 'greenhouse effect', 'CO_2 emissions' and 'climate change' are common discussions due to the pollution caused by human activity. Requirements on exhaust from transport vehicles and industry are getting tighter all the time. Looking at the environmental changes in the world, setting these rules cannot be strict enough and not be executed fast enough. In the meantime the oil industry is driving the economy a lot. All involved in the oil business can contribute and limit part of pollution a bit by following HSE rules in a strict manner. Understanding the business and understanding the commodity including logistics makes people aware of what they are working with. Maybe this book contributes a bit.

Polymers

Polymers can be used as flocculation agents to clarify the various industrial oil-in-water emulsions in different processes, like filtration, flotation, sedimentation or API-separation. They can also be used in sludge thickening treatment as aids in a mechanical separation process.

Polypropylene (PP)

This is polymer, a plastic made by the chemical industry. In the nineties many fueloil M100 cargoes coming from Russia were contaminated with polypropylene. As a result of this, bunker fueloil got this chemical as well with the result that vessels who received bunker oil in Rotterdam had big problems. Filters of the vessel engines were soon filled up with plastics and some vessels got into trouble on open sea. Since this was discovered a lot of fueloil became worthless. Luckily in that time the spec for fueloil burning in utilities was still allowing for high sulphur content. The utility spec is now max 1.0% sulphur while most bunker oil has an allowance of max 3.5% sulphur. In today's contracts in the fueloil business the specifications include the remark that the fueloil to be delivered must be free of any chemical compounds and free of polypropylene. One cannot be sure enough.

PON
Pump Octane Number, the average in gasoline of RON and MON (R+M)/2, see also 'octane index'.

POP
Proof Of Product. Unfortunately, in my opinion, one has to be careful when seeing terms like this in oil offers as this term has been used a lot in fake offers from 'jokerbrokers' and there are a lot of those in the market. POP is often used then in combination with many other abbreviations such as LOI, IPCO, TTT, RWA, SPA or TTO etc. plus price levels which are way off real market levels. Also the quantities in the offers are basically impossible and do not make any sense.

Port Charges
General term which includes charges and dues of every nature assessed against the vessel or its cargo in a port. It usually includes harbour dues, tug boat charges, pilotage fees, custom house fees, consular fees, etc.

Port Cargo
This is a cargo which is or will be discharged in more than one discharge port or received by more than one receiver at the discharge port. Rotterdam has many places to discharge oil cargoes. You can discharge in that port at 5 refineries, storage companies and pipeline connections to Antwerp and Germany.

Port Log
Timetable in which activities related to the cargo to be loaded or discharged of the vessel are described. This includes all kind of stops, inspections and bunker activities. If a demurrage claim is due, this port log proves the real time used for account of the charterer. Basically a timesheet. The agent, the ship, the inspector and the receiving terminal issue a timesheet. All parties

related to the cargo communicate with each other about each stop and change or readiness. The overview shows NOR, Pilot on Board, Entering sea passage, first line ashore, mooring commenced, completed mooring, all fast, inspector on board, inspection off board, ready for discharge hoses connected, start pumping, stop pumping, bunkers receiving, inspection on board again, hose disconnected, unmooring, time of sailing, end of sea passage and so on. The more facts happen during a stay in port, the more will be noted on the timesheet. See also 'sof'.

Portfolio

Collection of traded commodities in a trading book. Or collection of counterparties in a trading book, a customer portfolio. It may be important for companies to have a variation of different counterparties to trade with. Being dependent on one or two contacts is not always wise. Refineries which are extremely big, as they can be in many Asian countries, prefer a wider portfolio of different crude slates. Also being dependent on one supplier only would be very risky. Economy of scale works well for such a refinery with so much buying power, but good portfolio management is important. Governments may even give tax releases on import of crude from certain production countries. They have to do that otherwise those exporting countries would not see an open arbitrage opportunity to supply the oil and that would again make the import country too much dependent on too little a number of suppliers.

Port Restrictions

Port restrictions are referred to as the maximum technical abilities of a port which allows a vessel to enter. Often this is related to the maximum draft at the port and at berth as well as the maximum beam and length overall (LOA) and eventual other technical or HSE requirements as set by the authorities. A charterer, a vessel owner and the captain must know these restrictions. Port restrictions are not the same as jetty restrictions. Jetty restrictions are caused by the technical set up of the terminal receiving the vessels. A port often has more than one terminal with different possibilities and restrictions. Port restrictions are set by the port authorities and count for all the terminal and jetties. Terminals may have additional challenges at their jetties.

POS
Point Of Sale. Where title and risk moves from seller to buyer. The location disport or loadport depends on the sales terms, CIF, FOB, DAP and DES.

Position
Trading position is the position as reported according to the P&L. The P&L reports the risk level of the trading book. Length, shorts and spreads get the main focus. The trader has the responsibility to hedge or not to hedge. It depends on the market view of the trader, his risk appetite and the mandate to trade. Based on that the trader is positioning himself and is right when money is made. If no money is made often the traders say: "The market was wrong."

Position Limit
The maximum position (mandate) a trader can be long or short. But also when having a futures account there is a maximum position one can take as the amount available on the account sets the limit. See also 'VaR'.

Posted Price
A statement of the price requested by a seller of crude oil or oil products. The 'list price'.

Posting
A bid or offer during the Platts/Argus window is advertised on the pages on the screen. A posting on the screen.

Pour Point
The lowest temperature at which oil will readily flow without disturbance when chilled. Pour point has a high focus in fueloil and crude oil. Pour point is important in relation to storage as well. Fueloil tanks can often be heated, but most crude oil tanks do not have heating coils. Crude oil with a high pour point in tank may be a challenge in wintertime. The oil may become more solid and pumping or moving the products is nearly impossible. Storage terminals may accept high pour point crude oil in the summer but do not allow those high pour point crude oils in the winter. Most crude oil tanks are not insulated. They have floating roofs and cannot be heated. Storage terminals do not want to get stuck with unmovable oil during wintertime. See also 'ppd'.

PPD

Pour Point Depressants. Crude oil and heavy fueloils can have relatively high pour points due to paraffins present. The pour point is the temperature at which the fluid becomes 'solid'. These high pour points can cause all kind of problems especially during transport through pipelines. With a pour-point-depressant one can reduce this pour point importantly in order to ensure safe transport of these types of oils. Also, these PPDs can act as a paraffin-inhibitor, preventing wax precipitation inside 'water-dry' crude oil pipelines. PPDs are added to let oil flow easier and faster. It also helps with avoiding clingage and operational losses when discharging. See also 'pour point'.

PPM

Parts per million. Related to reported specifications of oil. Purities and impurities in oil specs are often reported in ppm, e.g. aluminium, vanadium and silicons in fueloil. When additives are added, the instruction would then be to add a certain number of ppm to a product. E.g. Add 400 ppm of paraflow into a tank with diesel in order to improve CFPP from minus 12 to minus 21. Same as in volume, milligram per litre (mg/l) or in mass, milligram per kilo (mg/wt).

PQ

Payment Quantity. In an oil contract there can be a formula related to oil quantities to be paid at a certain time. In production one never knows what the final production of a loading month will be. The seller, the producer, will make an estimation of how much oil is produced and can be loaded in a month to come. That is, in the first place, the availability. There may be a flexibility option related to the quantity and timing to be loaded. A buyer may get the option to load one or more months later or earlier. A pricing formula is then created, related to the nominated quantity for the month. E.g. a PQ of 200,000 barrels is nominated for April, but the buyer may have the opportunity to load it in May. Then it can be that from the PQ 75% is due for payment over the month average and the balance is paid basis B/L. In this example 150,000 bbls are payable in April, basis month average price and 50,000 bbls is pricing 5 days after B/L. However, it can also be that the seller has to pay the full availability and gets flexibility in return. There are many ways to price this of course. The buyer can play a bit with time and use the forward market. Load late in contango or early in backwardation. By offering such flexibility, the seller may require a small premium. Just keep in mind that in contango with late loading you are prepaying the cargo.

PRA
Price Reporting Agency. E.g. Platts or Argus which are the most well known in the oil industry.

Pre-Export Financing
Creating liquidity to a producer to make a business work. The producer receives through credit supplies by interference of a bank a kind of pre-payment. The company supplying the credit and using the bank will supply financial strength and in exchange that company has a right to purchase the production at a price level which incorporates the financing costs of such an arrangement. An interesting way to get hold of oil barrels by financially supporting a producer who is now able to pay for the production and logistic costs that are due to be paid before the oil leaves the terminal. Crude oil standard payment terms are based on late payment, 30 days after B/L. Receiving the money a month earlier makes sense for a company being short of cash. Commercial banks are specialists in these matters. This description is just to show roughly how it works, not in detail. But it is important that companies give credit with the help (at a cost) of a bank to get business in return. One may assume that the oil is sold at a discount which covers the costs of the buyer who supplies the credit.

Preference Certificates
Certificates giving advantages on duties when presented with the cargo at the customs in the port of delivery. Import duties may be free of charge or heavily discounted. E.g. Form A, Eurl and INF documents.

Preliminary Invoice
Estimated invoice based on known information and agreed preliminary price from seller to the buyer of the transaction of the goods sold. When, due to late pricing mechanism, the final price is not known before the invoice reaches its payment due date, a preliminary invoice is issued for payment in time. Large invoices are linked to big financial cost when not paid in time. When the final price is known a final commercial invoice will be issued and the difference between both invoices needs to be compensated. The invoice will be reconciled. When prices go down after the preliminary invoice and

the cargo is still pricing then it might be that the seller has to pay money back after reconciliation of the final invoice. In that case the buyer is bearing a credit risk. Therefore it is wise to find out what the financial status is of the seller.

Premium

The amount a price would be increased to purchase a better quality commodity compared with its benchmark. An eventual premium can also be based on the location of the cargo to be sourced with regards to freight optimisation schedules. In backwardation one would say that the front is traded against a premium versus the forward market. Premiums or differentials versus the benchmark are not fixed. In a tight market where Brent or crude is already high priced it could well be that the premium on top of it is also higher offered in the market. All a matter of the supply and demand balance.

Premium Diesel

The higher cetane rating is what makes a regular diesel a premium diesel, along with some type of detergent package that serves to clean the engine as the fuel is burned. Cetane is to diesel what octane is to gasoline. Premium diesel typically has a minimum 45 cetane rating, whereas regular diesel is closer to a 38 to 40 cetane level.

Pre-Payment

Advanced payment is a payment method in which the buyer pays for the goods before they are sent out. This method is used when the buyer is of unknown credit worthiness or cannot present an L/C. In the oil business prepayment is done from time to time for smaller volumes of oil products. It is applicable in international and domestic trade. A payment is committed when the receiving bank confirms that the irrevocable payment is received on the bank account of the seller. Only then loading of a vessel will commence. Pre-payments are always done on the very last day when title and risk are passing on board the vessel. The supplier wants to be secured; he avoids credit risk. In many cases last minute payment may lead to a demurrage situation. This is for the account of the buyer who paid late. A confirmation or statement from the buyer's bank that the money has been transferred is used as source of information to track the money at the receiver's bank. It is not good enough to commence loading. Maybe based on good experience and good relations between buyer and seller more credit risk is accepted and loading starts before money is received. It is up to each individual company to set working procedures and rules related to operations work involving pre-payment.

Pressure
The amount of force exerted on a unit of area by a fluid. See also 'RVP and/ or TVP'.

- **Absolute Pressure**
  The pressure referenced to a perfect vacuum as zero pounds per square inch absolute.

- **Atmospheric Pressure**
  The pressure exerted by the atmosphere. Although this pressure varies with altitude, barometric pressure and humidity, the atmospheric pressure can be defined in custody transfer contracts, or by state and federal authorities. Atmospheric pressure is most often stated as 14.696 pounds per square inch absolute.

- **Back Pressure**
  The operating pressure level measured upstream from a control valve.

- **Gauge Pressure**
  That pressure measured relative to atmospheric pressure as zero, pressure at ambient temperature.

- **High Vapour Pressure**
  A fluid which, at the measurement or proving temperature, has a vapour pressure that is equal to or higher than atmospheric pressure. Light products contain more gaseous or volatile components which cause the high RVP specification. High pressure products are therefore also low flashpoint products, like gasoline or naphtha. Due to that these oil products are to be stored in floating roof tanks to avoid emissions.

- **Low Vapour Pressure**
  A fluid which, at the measurement or proving temperature, has a vapour pressure that is less than atmospheric pressure. Heavy oil has a low RVP and therefore a high flashpoint.

- **Reid Vapour Pressure**
The vapour pressure of a fluid at 100° Fahrenheit/37.8° Celsius as determined by test method ASTM D323-58. RVP is a specification which is very important for gasoline. German gasoline has an RVP specification of maximum 90 kPa in the winter and maximum 60 kPa in the summer. See also 'vapour lock index'.

- **Static Pressure**
The pressure in a fluid that is exerted normal to the surface. In a moving fluid, the static pressure is measured at right angles to the direction of flow.

Price-Cap Contract
An agreement between heating oil distributors and consumers. Price-cap contracts establish a maximum price a customer will pay for heating oil. In contrast to price-lock contracts, the per-gallon price of heating oil can fluctuate beneath the maximum (or 'capped') price.

Price-Lock Contract
An agreement between heating oil distributors and consumers. Price-lock contracts give customers the option of locking into a fixed per-gallon price of heating oil for the duration of the heating season. Price-lock contracts are designed to protect the consumer from sudden price increases. The downside for consumers is that the price will remain fixed even if the market price of heating oil drops.

Price Discovery
The process of determining the price of a commodity by trading conducted in open outcry at an exchange. Open outcry exchange IPE is replaced by the electronic exchange, ICE.

Price Limit
The maximum advance or decline, from the previous day's settlement price, permitted for a futures contract in one trading session.

Price Quotation
Price reported by a price reporting agency on a certain day, for a certain product in a certain market. E.g. Platts quotation: 21 May 2009, high sulphur

fueloil, in ARA Rotterdam FOB barges, Platts high 'x' Dollars and Platts low 'y' Dollars per ton.

Price-Setting Market

In a perfect market, the location or hub at which supply and demand curves cross and prices are set. The Rotterdam barge market for gasoline, diesel, fueloil and other commodities. Also US Gulf coast and Singapore are price setting markets for their region. Just to illustrate Rotterdam price setting, the barge trading activity is a very active market during the quotation trading windows, from Platts and/or Argus. The fixed prices set in the Rotterdam market are used to calculate the basis value for cargoes CIF and FOB in North West Europe and possibly even as a lead for the numbers as quoted in the Med. The differential versus the barge market depends of course on the trading activity in the cargo market as such. This illustrates how important it is that price setting markets must be liquid and transparent.

Price Transparency

The ability of all market participants to 'see' or commit to a trade at the same price.

Pricing 2-1-2

The pricing of a cargo starts 2 quotations before B/L day until the 2nd quotation after the B/L day. In total 5 quotations as the B/L day is also a quotation day. If the B/L day falls on a weekend, split weekend rules will apply. See 'split weekend'. A price based on the average of a number of quotations is also called a 'floating price'. As traders like to hedge their positions they often prefer to deem the B/L before the vessel arrives at loadport. This is in the interest of both the buyer and the seller. So if for any reason the B/L delays with a day then at least the pricing days are fixed before that happens. The payment term is related to the real B/L day. See also 'deemed B/L'.

Pricing after B/L

The oil starts pricing after Bill of Lading day. The B/L day does not count as quotation day to set the final price. A price based on the average of a number of quotations is also called a 'floating price'.

Pricing from B/L

The oil starts pricing from Bill of Lading day. The B/L day is included as quotation day to set the final price. A price based on the average of a number of quotations is also called a 'floating price'.

Pricing In

When a cargo of oil is bought with certain pricing days the position will become a length when the cargo starts pricing. 10kt with 5 pricing days will price in 2kt per day. Meaning day 1 the position is 2kt long, next day 4kt long and so on till the 5th day 10kt long. The hedge should be to sell 2kt per day.

Pricing Out

When a cargo of oil is sold with certain pricing days the position will become a short when the cargo starts pricing. 10kt with 5 pricing days will price out 2kt per day. Meaning day 1 the position is 2kt short, next day 4kt short and so on till the 5th day 10kt short. The trader will probably hedge the short position and buys 2kt of paper each day his cargo is pricing out.

Pricing Option

Some deals in physical oil trades can contain a pricing option. A buyer can get the option to price B/L related, B/L plus 3 or B/L + 5 days, or the buyer can choose for month average pricing. Most often the pricing option has to be declared before the start of a loading month. There can be lots of value in such an option. In a backwardated market a buyer would price month average in case he gets early loading dates. He would sell the cargo B/L related (B/L + 3 days) and lock in time value. If the buyer would get late loading dates in a backwardated market he would prefer B/L related pricing (B/L +5 days) and sell his cargo on B/L + 3 days. Even the difference between 3 and 5 days can have some cents of time value and it can be locked in by the use of CFDs. In a contango market it would work the other way around, month average for late loading dates. One other interesting pricing option is MEO; have a look at 'MEO'. Pricing option creates value and a buyer would possibly be prepared to pay a little premium for the oil in such a case.

Primary Distillation

Atmospheric distillation. The first distillation of crude in a refinery at normal pressure. It produces: Propane, butane, naphtha, kerosene, gasoil and fueloil. These are mainly unfinished oils and need further processing and treating before it will be commercialised. Other processing is vacuum distillation, cracking, vis-breaking, hydro-treating, coking and more upgrading activity.

In refining reports you would read about the ADU and the CDU, the naming for primary distillation units at refineries. See also 'Nelson complexity index'.

Printing on the 'O'

"Crude oil prices are running, it's printing on the 'O'!" When the trade price is lower than the inside bid price or higher than the inside ask price. Overriding prices indicates tremendous urgency to either buy or sell the futures. Have a look at 'overriding prices'.

Problem

If you as a participant in oil trading related business come to this word, then please change your mind-set. Change the problem to a challenge and behave as a real trader. You need to think in creative solutions to challenges. Let this be your motivator of the day. Here I think as a physical trader related to logistic challenges when business and logistics don't go as planned. In case of a financial problem then look at 'discipline'.

Procedure

The official company process of how work has to be done. The written rules or the guidelines of the company. Deviating from the procedures could result in damage like accidents, HSE disasters and reputational damage to the company you work for. Working following procedures can lead to a cost which could be avoided without putting the company at risk. In such case a discussion can take place within the company to change or upgrade the rules. Only when a rule change has been accepted by the company one can work following the new procedures. So rules and procedures need continuous attention and can be challenged from time to time. Due to procedures and rules colleagues within a company expect a certain working attitude from each other. It leads to a well-controlled way of working and good team work, or even to company culture.

Process Gasoil

See 'vacuum gas oil' (VGO).

Processing Agreement

Contract in which two parties (one is a refiner) have agreed to refine/process crude at a refining fee. The content of such an agreement can be complex as in the agreement the type of crudes and required qualities have to be fixed as well as the qualities of products being produced. Also demurrage clauses, storage clauses etc. have to be fine-tuned. In processing deals the refinery margin and risk attached to that is for the account of the company agreeing such a deal. The refinery has no market risk. The refiner cashes money in for renting out refining capacity and refining services. He wants to be covered for refining costs plus a little extra. Such a fee is priced in Dollars per real barrel or ton refined. The credit risk is in a way limited as you deal with one company only. Selling the feedstock and buying the production is offsetting the credit risk. Besides that, in a processing deal all oil in tank is on title of the company entering the processing deal, not to the refinery.

Processing Gain
The volumetric amount by which total output is greater than input for a given period of time. This difference is due to the processing of crude oil into products which, in total, have a lower specific gravity than the crude oil processed. Opposite is shrinkage losses of blending different molecule sizes were mixed. The molecules in a refinery may change size or composition. When the overall oil export is lighter then there can be a gain in volume.

Processing Loss
The volumetric amount by which total refinery output is less than input for a given period of time. This difference is due to the processing of crude oil into products which, in total, have a higher specific gravity than the crude oil processed. The molecules in a refinery may change size or composition. When the overall oil export is heavier then there can be a loss in volume.

Processing Unit
The unit in the refinery which converts feedstock into high value oil products. The simplest processing unit is the distillation unit. After the distillation the vacuum distillation and cracking units up to the cokers are defining the complexity of the refinery. See also 'Nelson complexity index'.

Processing Unit Feedstock
After processing crude in the distillation unit next processing units at the refinery can extract better values out of the feedstock. Here an overview of different units with their required feedstocks:

· **Distillation unit** = Crude oil to straight run oil products.

- **Condensate splitter** = Condensate.
- **De-salter** = Crude oil wash out of salt and water.
- **Vacuum distillation** = Straight run fueloil from primary distillation.
- **Hydro-treater** = Naphtha and diesel desulphurisation, gasoil to diesel.
- **Catalytic reformer** = Naphtha conversion to reformate.
- **Fluid catalytic cracker** = Straight run fueloil or VGO to cracked naphtha and gasoil.
- **Hydro cracker** = Straight run fueloil or VGO to cracked naphtha and gasoil.
- **Vis-breaker** = High viscosity gasoil into low viscosity and light oil (naphtha and gasoil).
- **Kero-Merox** = Kero and jet fuel cleaning out mercaptans by caustic wash.
- **Coking Unit** = Very heavy fuels to naphtha, gasoil and coke.
- **Alkylation** = Naphtha to alkylate gasoline blending component.
- **Isomerisation** = Lightest naphtha to isomerate, a gasoline blending component.
- **Flexi Coker** = A coker unit which can take very heavy challenging oil (Low API, high metals, TAN, etc.). As one said to me: "Can make gasoline out of shoes."

Producer

Companies producing oil from a well and selling the crude oil and condensate from the well. A refinery produces oil products but is called a 'refiner'; some say 'producer' which I do not agree with – a matter of approach. Small producers which are not able to create real tradable crude oil cargoes would sell their production to the operator of the field or to another shareholder of the production field. A producer is to be seen as a marketer of crude. The producer has to sell the oil otherwise the production has to be stopped which is costly. The producer has no choice and will try to sell the oil at the highest possible price. A trader can choose to sell or buy and would sell based on the best margin to collect. (Same counts for a refiner.) The seller's job is called 'trader' as often there is much more trading activity done next to marketing the produced oil. A producer is always long oil and enjoys high prices. At low prices the margin may come down and could get below production cost. A field may limit production or even temporarily shut down when the low pricing becomes structural. Low prices would also slow down investments of producers as in those circumstances it is economically less attractive to produce more oil. Production costs for very heavy unconventional crudes would be even worse as production costs are high and the oil price is already very much discounted versus the benchmark.

Product Spread

Spread between the values of two different petroleum products. A trader can take a paper position based on a product spread, e.g. Buying a swap gasoline barges and sell a swap naphtha. Often such product swaps are done based on two different products which are correlated to each other; they must be correlated. Like naphtha/gasoline, diesel/gasoline and in fueloil there is the relation between high and low sulphur, see 'HILOS'. The change in price can be more volatile than the outright market (price per commodity). The trader will here focus on the fundamentals of the oil market, but also the historical differentials between two grades may be used as a guideline.

Products

Refined, atmospheric and cracked, consumable oil made from crude oil: Gasoline, jet, diesel, heating oil, fueloil, and many other petroleum products. The more complex a refinery is the more products it will be able to produce, including bitumen, asphalt and cokes.

Production Capacity

The maximum amount of product that can be produced from processing facilities.

Products Supplied

Approximately represents consumption of petroleum products because it measures the disappearance of these products from primary sources, i.e. refineries, natural gas processing plants, blending plants, pipelines, and bulk terminals. In general, product supplied of each product in any given period is computed as follows: field production, plus refinery production, plus imports, plus unaccounted for crude oil, minus stock change, minus crude oil losses, minus refinery inputs, minus exports.

Products Terminal

A facility used primarily for the storage and/or marketing of petroleum products which would generally have a total bulk storage capacity of 50,000 barrels/8,000 CBM up to the bigger product storage terminals of 3 million CBM/19 million barrels and there might be bigger terminals; however, those would also store crude and gas liquids. It typically receives petroleum products by tanker, barge or pipeline and serves as a loading facility for trucks to transport products to stores, stations and smaller bulk distribution plants. It has the functions for break-bulk, make-bulk. But also blending or coverage for distressed situations in the cargo market. Traders may use such a terminal for trading activity such as in the ARA barge market. Also in contango market it is great to have the possibility to put oil into storage. In backwardated markets product terminals may be rather empty. Storage prices in contango market are higher than in backwardated markets. See also 'storage'.

Products Trading

Trading of petroleum products which often refers to jet, kerosene, gasoline, diesel, heating oil and heavy fueloil. This trading can be related to business from refined production to blending, to wholesale business and pure as trading activity. Products-trading includes paper trading activity as well for the purpose of hedging and speculation. LPG and naphtha belong to gas liquid (GL) trading and in some cases condensate is part of that activity as well. Crude oil is related to feedstock trading. It is important that product traders know a lot about the qualities and understand blending and its value related to the components. Logistics is very important. The number of transactions is much higher compared with crude oil trading. The use of brokers in the products market is a given. The product market is too big to cover it on your own. Products trading can be related to the cargo market or the barge market. To learn trading physical oil I would recommend starting in trading products. The large number of transactions, the logistics, the components trading, refining understanding and blending opportunities contribute to a great learning process. But crude traders and GL traders might have another opinion about that.

Product Transfer Order (PTO)

Pipeline authorisations transferring title to a set quantity of product at a specific location to another shipper.

Profit

The income remaining after all business-expenses are paid. This is why traders are hired. They are there to make money, for growth of business and/or to secure the continuation of the business activity in a sustainable economic manner. The sum of margins and results made on time value. The main reason why a trader earns a bonus.

Profit and Loss
See 'P&L'.

Profit Taking
The action to offset a position to cash in on a sharp rise. This action pushes prices down temporarily. When traders are profit taking, the implication is that there is an upward trend in the security. Nothing is wrong with taking profit, but it is best to take profit according to the rules of trading discipline which maximises the result according to an earlier initiated plan. Taking profit too early may lead to a situation where traders take many small profits, but when they lose money on a position they lose a huge amount. See therefore the term 'net loser'.

Pro Forma
A Latin term meaning 'for the sake of form'. E.g. A pro forma invoice for the purpose of calculating the import duty duties.

Pro Forma Invoice
An invoice sent in advance of shipment, to enable the buyer to obtain an import permit or exchange permit or both. This would be a kind of value declaration. It is not the same as the final invoice.

Pro Rata
A Latin term meaning 'in proportion', share based. When a vessel has more than one discharge port, the potential demurrage might be split on a pro rata basis. That basis could be based on B/L figures. Then each receiver gets an eventual demurrage bill presented based on a pro-rata (equally shared) percentage of the total cargo.

Promissory Note
A promissory note is a signed paper promising to pay another a certain sum of money. It is in my view not as strong as a letter of credit where the bank is involved. In order to be legitimate and acceptable as a proper promissory note, the writing must contain the following elements:

- **Unconditional**

  There cannot be any conditions to payment. For instance, "I promise to pay if the cargo arrives on time." That statement makes the payment conditional on in-time arrival.

- **Promise or order to pay**

  There must be a written undertaking to pay money that is signed by the person undertaking to pay. For example, "I, Stefan Oilman, promise to pay to the order of Arthur Tankerman one thousand dollars."

- **To pay a fixed amount of money**

  The principal amount due under the promissory note must be fixed. The amount of interest due does not need to be fixed. However, the interest rate must not be unconscionable, or it may violate the Texas Usury Laws, which are state laws that specify the maximum interest rate that can be charged before it becomes unlawful.

- **Payable to order or bearer**

  The promissory note must be payable to order or to bearer. For instance, "Pay to the order of Stefan Oilman" or "I promise to pay to the order of bearer". A bearer is any person who may present the note to the person who made it ('the maker') for payment.

- **Payable on demand or at a definite time**

  The note is payable on demand if it states that it is payable "on demand" or "at sight", or if it does not state a time for payment. This means that it is payable at the will of the holder of the note. The note is payable at a definite time if it specifies a specific date for payment, or if it states a specific period of time after sight, such as "120 days after presentment for payment". However, as addressed above, make sure that there are no conditions on payment.

Prompt

A prompt cargo describes a cargo available for immediate lifting (one to two weeks). In case of prompt demand, prices will go up or premiums may be asked for supply of oil. In case of prompt availability the prices will be discounted. A strong prompt market is often the case when traders talk about a market in backwardation. Prompt cargoes may soon become distressed cargoes as no one might be willing to buy at the offered price level. During the year-end and during weak markets there may be more distressed cargoes available. When the market stays weak and too many cargoes are coming available on the market then that would indicate a possible change to a contango market. If it was already a contango market the curve would get even steeper.

Prompt Delivery (Prompts)
Designates a spot market delivery that must be made in the next few days as stipulated by the contract.

Prompt Month
The first month forward for which a futures contract is being traded. Also known as the 'front-month'.

Prop Trader
Proprietary trader, paper trader or derivative trader who is trading with their own company's money to make profit. A trader in a bank might trade with the customer's money through a fund or even a pension insurance company can speculate with their customer's money, with the awareness and allowance of their customers of course. Most customers are not aware of having money at risk, but become aware of that when they start losing money.

Propane (C_3H_8)
Gaseous paraffinic hydrocarbon (C_3H_8), present in natural gas and crude oil. A normally gaseous straight-chain hydrocarbon. H8. It is a colourless paraffinic gas that boils at a temperature of -42.04°C / - 43.67°F. It is extracted from natural gas or refinery gas streams. Propane mixture with butane is sold as lpg, fuel for cars. 60% propane and 40% butane in the winter and vice versa in summertime. LPG is good on octane value.

Propylene (C3)
An olefinic hydrocarbon recovered from refinery H6 processes or petrochemical processes. Propylene (C3) (nonfuel use). Propylene that is intended H6 for use in nonfuel applications such as petrochemical manufacturing.

PSI
Pounds per Square Inch. Common measure of pressure. Related to emissions

most storage terminals may have a licence in which it is described what the maximum psi of oil in storage is allowed to be. Especially when terminals are situated close to cities, villages or other communities. High psi relates to high flash products and high emissions. The maximum psi for a product to be stored in a floating roof tank is around 11.1 psi. Products with higher psi content should be stored in pressurised tanks.

PSM
Process Safety Management. HSE term which is the same as risk control on a terminal. PSM is a more pro-active manner related to HSE behaviour. Managing instead of controlling.

Pump Capacity
The maximum product flow a pump can handle. This is most often reported in volume. Or the maximum rate at which a vessel can be loaded or discharged. One should not forget that a pipeline can be a bottleneck as a pipeline also has a maximum capacity. Other factors which may have a negative effect on the pumping rate are the pour point and the viscosity of the product. Nevertheless if the temperature of the oil is heated enough to keep the flow going, the pumping speed would be acceptable. Furthermore when a tank or vessel becomes full the pumping speeds will decrease as resistance in the receiving unit will increase when filled up. When emptying a vessel or a tank the pumping speed would decrease as well. To avoid such delay in pumping, lots of tanks have a fixed heel so that operations are not slowed down. A terminal pumping slowly is risking a bad image. In some cases pumping has to be slowed down because of potential release of emissions during loading. The bad smell resulting from emissions may lead to complaints from neighbouring communities, which would lead to problems with the local authorities. A vapour recovery system would help with catching the emissions so that loading of cargoes can go faster. See also 'pumping rate'.

Pumping Platform
Manifold where all pipes from different tanks are directed to in order to be connected to the line (with pump) to the jetty or to another tank. At this point connections can be made between different tanks and jetties on a terminal in order to execute the planned operation on a terminal, which can be blending and loading or discharging a vessel.

Pumping Rate

Speed of pumping oil reported in Cbm per hour or barrels per hour. In some contracts with storage terminals or in charter parties a minimum pumping rate is agreed. Slow pumping might cause demurrage. Sometimes slow pumping is done on purpose in order to delay the B/L date by one day. This may be done or requested by the seller of the product for commercial reasons. A Dutch word for slow pumping on purpose is 'knijpen', 'pinching a line', that will decrease the flow.

Pumpover

Pumping of product from one tank to another tank. Reason to transfer oil may be because of blending activity, logistic optimisation or one can sell oil by pumpover if the buyer is renting a tank at the same storage terminal.

Pump Price

Self-serve price, including taxes, posted for either gasoline or diesel fuel at a station or store. VAT is calculated over excise and other duties related to the petrol at the petrol station. Tax over tax.

Purifier

A machine used for a liquid-liquid separation in which the two intermixed liquids which are insoluble in each other have different specific gravities. Solids with specific gravities higher than those of the liquids can be separated off at the same time. A purifier bowl has two outlets. One for the light phase liquid and one for the heavy phase liquid. Call it simple distillation.

Purity

As the word says: "How pure is the product?" Most often this is measured at products consisting of one type of molecule only. Ethanol is, in Europe, traded based on 95/99.9% purity. Ethanol with less than 99.9% purity could have methanol, water or other material in the product. That could affect the octane value of the ethanol. See also 'ethanol'. All molecules which differ from the main product are measured as impurities. Most oxygenates have a requirement for a certain purity level in their specifications. MTBE used to trade based on 98% purity. Oil products consist of many different type of molecules. Purity is not a specification in mineral oil.

Puvce

Percussive unconfined vapour cloud explosion. Explosion which may occur after release of liquid gas which forms a gas cloud in open air. Often a reason why use of a telephone at a petrol station is not allowed while filling a car. Also on refineries use of telephones or cameras with flashlight is not allowed. Sometimes it is also mentioned as 'uvce', but it is the same. See also 'bleve'.

Pygas

Pyrolysis gasoline. A naphtha-range product with a high aromatic content, used either for gasoline blending or as a feedstock for a BTX extraction unit. Pygas is produced in an ethylene plant which processes butane, naphtha or gasoil. Due to low aromatic and benzene specification requirements in gasoline pygas is seldom seen as blendstock in gasoline. It was popular as a blending component before the change of specifications in gasoline, year 2000. See also 'BTX'.

Pyramiding

The use of unrealised profits on existing futures position as margin to increase the size of the position, normally in successively smaller increments.

PXG

Popular abbreviation for 'pricing'. The pricing period of a cargo of oil.

Q

Q&Q 50/50

Quality and quantity inspection cost to be shared equally between buyer and seller. Both counterparties have an interest in getting the inspection done. The operators agree on the choice of inspection company. FOB sales are based on existing qualities in tank and therefore the seller is only interested in sharing cost on quantity. When a cargo is being supplied within own system then there is nothing to share. It may happen that even a third party is involved in the trade. In that case there is an opportunity to share the bill one-third each.

Q114 Q214 Q314 Q414

Q stands for quarter. Q114 is 1st quarter and '14' is the year, 1st quarter 2014. Q214 is 2nd quarter 2014 and so on. A popular abbreviation of a time period most often used for paper contracts such as swaps and CFDs.

Q88

Shipping questionnaire. Full description of the vessel. It is used to register the vessel into a company's vetting system. It does not mean that the vessel is approved. That requires more reports such as a SIRE report including the vetting inspection on board the vessel.

QA

Quality Assurance, important related to reports and requests for projects.

QC
Quality Control, going through written documentation and analyses in order to get approval for the use of such documentation. Checking the truth and completeness.

Quality
Specification of oil related to the requirements for a certain product to be delivered according to a sales contract. If the test result does not meet the required specification then the product is off-spec. When oil is nominated to be loaded, the buyer and seller agree to share the cost 50/50 for Q&Q, quantity and quality.

Quality Bank
Price penalty/reward system for oil producers who are pumping a crude oil grade into a common pipeline system. One specific crude oil grade is produced by many companies but the grade per field may differ in density, sulphur or other parameters. In the crude market the buyers require a standard crude oil with a stable quality. Producers pumping lower quality into the pipeline have to pay a small penalty as their oil is worth less than the standard requirement. A producer supplying better quality is also compensated for that by a premium. Often sulphur and density (API gravity) set the standard. E.g. Poseidon in USA and Urals crude oil use a quality bank system. Urals is (de)escalated on density, API of 32.

Quantity
The official measured content of oil in a land tank or on a Bill of Lading. Often when oil is nominated to be loaded the buyer and seller agree to share the cost 50/50 for Q&Q, quantity and quality. Quantities are important as they come on the B/L and are the commercial quantity to be hedged and invoiced. Wrong measurement may lead to oil losses. And those losses at current price levels (40 to 50 USD per barrel) are very expensive.

Questionnaire
See Q88.

Quota
OPEC sets individual crude oil production quotas for each of its 11 members. These quotas do not include condensate production. By setting quotas to

certain levels OPEC tries to set the oil prices at a good economic level. There is often discussion in the market about countries not following the quota correctly and oversupply, even in a market which is already oversupplied. If oil prices fall, the quotas will come down; the market will always correct itself.

Quotation
Official listed price of a product on a specific trading day. Example Platts cargo quotation for gasoline in NWE, basis Rotterdam, or an ASCI quotation from Argus in the USA.

Quotation Day
A day on which the oil market is open (trading day) and an oil price in a certain market can be set. Quotation days are needed to determine the price of a traded product based on formula pricing. A purchased cargo would price-in on the quotation days, getting long. A sold cargo would price-out on the quotation day, getting short. Quotation days are therefore linked to 'floating pricing'.

R

R+M/2

Research octane number plus motor octane number divided by 2, also known as the 'anti-knock index'. See also 'octane number' or 'octane rating'. The octane index is very much used in US gasoline specifications.

Rack

The loading location at a terminal for tank trucks. Linked to INCO term 'FCA'.

Rack Price

The price of petroleum products at a refinery loading rack. Rack-pricing is effectively cash and carry at the rack. Loading from the rack is done by tank trucks, supplying the oil products to the petrol stations etc.

Raffinate

The residual product left after a reforming process. The term has also been more generally used in reference to any low octane product left over after any secondary refining process. Preferable to natural gasoline in ethanol/gasoline blends because of the low RVP (4 to 8).

Rally

A swift upward movement in price. After the hurricane named 'Katrina' in August 2005, the oil price moved up 30 Dollars in two days. That was a huge rally. News items about war in the Middle East, pipeline explosions in

Nigeria or strikes in refineries or oil platforms etc. can have a huge effect on the market price. Prices may rally for some time, but soon after that the market will correct itself (after 1 or 2 days). Companies performing a lot of stress-testing may be well prepared, but once the market is in a rally it is tough to leave a position when it starts losing money. See also 'stress testing'.

Ramsbottom Coke
A carbon residue test originated by Dr J.R. Ramsbottom in England. Determination of the amount of carbon residue left after evaporation. This test is done for fueloil bunkers. Off-spec oil would cause problems in ships' engines. The Conradson carbon residue tests the same or alternative. A max specification of 0.1 % (weight) in diesel bunkers and max 1.0 % (weight) in fueloil bunkers.

Range
The difference between the high and low price of a commodity during a given trading session, day, week, month etc. Or dates in which one can load or discharge a cargo.

RAPL
Rotterdam-Antwerp PipeLine. From Rotterdam there is a crude oil pipeline going to Antwerp. Mainly used to pump crude oil to the refineries Totsa and Exxon who together are the owners of the pipeline.

RBOB
Reformulated Blendstock for Oxygen Blending. This is the gasoline as listed on the Nymex in price per gallon. Quality is fixed and should allow 10% of ethanol blending. RBOB combined with MTBE or other oxygenates at some refineries makes what we call RFM (Reformulated gasoline with oxygenates). RBOB combined with ethanol at some terminals makes what we call RFE (Reformulated gasoline with ethanol).

RBOB for Blending with Alcohol
Motor gasoline blending components intended to be blended with an alcohol component (e.g. fuel ethanol) at a terminal or refinery to raise the oxygen content. RBOB product detail by type of oxygenate was discontinued effective with data for January 2010. Beginning with data for January 2010, RBOB was reported as a single product.

RBOB for Blending with Ether

Motor gasoline blending components intended to be blended with an ether component (e.g. methyl tertiary butyl ether) at a terminal or refinery to raise the oxygen content. RBOB product detail by type of oxygenate was discontinued effective with data for January 2010. Beginning with data for January 2010, RBOB was reported as a single product.

REACH

REACH is the European Community's regulation on chemicals and their safe use. This deals with the registration, evaluation, authorisation and restriction of chemical substances. The law entered into force on 1 June 2007. The aim of REACH is to improve the protection of human health and the environment through better and earlier identification of the intrinsic properties of chemical substances. An important issue here is related to the material safety data sheet (MSDS). A document which should be available on the work floor so that each person working with chemical or oil can see what precautions to take when executing the operations. See also 'MSDS'.

Realised and Unrealised Profit

Unrealised profit is a gain from an increase in the price of a paper position that has not been closed or cashed in. Realised profits are made from the cashing in of the unrealised gain. Timing to cash in a profit or taking a loss result depends on good trading discipline.

Rebco

Russian export-blend crude oil. Urals crude from Russia. Urals crude oil is transported through pipelines in Russia: BPS, BPS2, ESPO and Druzhba. Also Kazakhstan is a big producer of Urals crude oil. They supply into the Russian pipeline systems. 60 to 70 cargoes of 725kb each (100kt) are loaded per month from Primorsk in the Gulf of Finland and with Ust Luga coming on stream this will increase. Enough oil to make it benchmark crude and that is the wish of Russia. Urals crude oil is also loaded at the ports of the Black Sea: Novorossiysk and Yuzhniy (Ukraine), in lots of 600kt (80kt) and 1 mill barrels (140kt). And of course not to forget the ESPO pipeline. Urals is therefore in Asia also called 'ESPO' crude. This is loaded in Kozmino. Urals is well traded and has its own quotations. All refineries in Russia process Urals crude oil plus some other local grades including condensate.

Recap

Sum up of a physical trade. When a trader sells or purchases a cargo of oil after long negotiations, which in most circumstances are done over the telephone, a final sum up is done by both traders. The reason for this is to mention one more time all details that belong to the deal being done. Each trader will agree on each item as it has been discussed as being part of the committed contract. The second reason is to have all recorded details on a taped line. It can happen that a deal is done from a mobile or private phone. In such a case it is very common that both traders agree to call each other from an office taped line and do the final recap. It is often company policy to have each deal agreed on a taped telephone. In case of disagreement in a later stage, traders could listen to their tape to find out what exactly has been discussed. It does not happen very often that traders send their tapes to each other to prove that they are right. A tape could be used in court cases, although traders prefer commercial solutions. Also called 'voice log'.

Recap Content

A recap or a deal done can contain the following items being agreed: Deal date, buyer, seller, commodity, quantity, type of delivery, delivery window, price, pricing days, credit open or covered, inspection, location loading or delivering with options at charter party differential, charter party rate, demurrage rate, laytime, (de) escalation, country law and location of arbitration, specs guaranteed and/or typicals, payment day, nomination procedures, anti-corruption clause, GT&C, vessel approval and in some cases trader might add some small notes like draft restrictions or pumping rate guarantee, etc. Contract departments from both companies will be in contact with each other when finalising the last details which are often related to text, formats and anti-corruption or other clauses.

Recycle

The use of water or wastewater within (internally) a facility before it is discharged to a treatment system.

Recycled Feeds

Feeds that are continuously fed back for additional processing.

Red-Dye

Diesel fuel is dyed red to denote it is being used for tax-exempt purposes.

Entities that are tax-exempt (agricultural use) use red-dyed fuel because it is tax exempt. There is no difference in red-dyed product specifications. Red-dyed prices typically are 0.25 to 0.35cts per ton higher than clear prices to recoup the charge for the dye and dyeing process. Fuelling a car with red-dyed diesel for common use is illegal and not smart to do. The furfural in the diesel works like a finger print and even after 10-20 times refilling the tank with clean tax paid diesel, the onetime use of red-dye can still be tracked. Police or tax authorities may be entitled to take a sample from your tank.

Reduced Crude Oil
Crude oil that has undergone at least one distillation process to separate some of the lighter hydrocarbons. Reducing crude lowers its API gravity, but increases the handling safety by raising the flash point. Such activity may happen at the producer. The light fraction is used for other purposes.

Redwood Viscosity
The number of seconds required for 50 ml of an oil to flow out of a standard Redwood viscosity meter at a definite temperature as per British viscosity standard.

Reference Point (Gauge Point)
The point from which the reference height is determined and from which the ullages/innages are taken.

Refined Petroleum Products
Products produced by a refinery. Such as propane, butane, naphtha, gasoline, jet, kerosene, gasoil, heating oil, diesel, VGO, fueloil and residues. From this range of products, propane, butane and naphtha are traded and/or marketed by the so-called GL traders. See also 'light ends'. Gasoline, jet, kerosene, gasoil, heating oil, diesel, VGO, fueloil and residues are traded by the so-called products traders.

Refiner
A person or company that has any part in the control or management of any operation by which the physical or chemical characteristics of petroleum or petroleum products are changed through processing units. A refiner is always long oil. Income is generated by earning a refinery margin and optimisation related to the refining activity.

Refinery

A plant used to separate the various components present in crude oil and convert them into usable products or feedstock for other processes. There are simple refineries with limited cracking capacity. They sell finished products but also straight run fuel, VGO and blending components in the market. The complex refineries keep cracking their oil until the last drop. They squeeze the maximum values out of the oil. The residue of such a refinery may be sulphur, cokes, bitumen or even asphalt. See also 'Nelson complexity index'.

Refinery Capacity

The maximum processing capacity of refinery in barrels per day. Refinery capacity is always expressed based on feedstock – how much crude per day does the refinery process? Traders always ask for the refinery capacity of a refinery. It gives an impression to the trader of how attractive his counterparty is. A big refinery would buy more crude or sell more products. There is more to trade. If you are a trader working for a refinery it is therefore recommended to know your refinery capacity because your counterparty will always ask the question. How would you feel if you cannot answer such a question?

Refinery Capacity Utilisation

Ratio of the total amount of crude oil, unfinished oils, and natural gas plant liquids run through crude oil distillation units to the operable capacity of these units. If not used at maximum capacity, then there must be economic reasons for that or the refinery is in maintenance. The worst reason is due to a failure of the trader. He did not supply his crude in time, empty on feedstock or products are not sold in time and production tanks are running full. As a trader you must always know how your refinery is running and what the stock situation will be during the next days and weeks. A trader would also like to know what other refineries are doing.

Refinery Complexity

The degree to which refineries are equipped with conversion capacity to convert heavier residual streams into lighter fractions.

Refinery Fuel

Crude oil and petroleum products consumed at the refinery for all purposes, i.e. Heating or generating energy. Flare gas is not part of refinery fuel.

Refinery Gain

Heavy oil molecules cracking to lighter molecules, long chains to short chains leads to more volume. So as the refineries try to maximise values they keep on cracking and processing oil. Most value is in light products. The gain in refineries is based on a gain in volumes, not in weight. Of course there are also refinery losses, for sure in weight percentage.

Refinery-Grade Butane (C_4H_{10})

A refinery-produced stream that is composed predominantly of normal butane and/or iso-butane and may also contain propane and/or natural gasoline. These streams may also contain significant levels of olefins and/ or fluorides contamination. Butane has a good octane level and is used as blendstock for gasoline. Gasoline contains typically 4% of butane in summer and 8% in winter. Furthermore butane is also used in LPG as car fuel. In the winter season refiners may use some of the propane and butane production to fuel the refinery.

Refinery Input, Crude Oil

Total crude oil (domestic plus foreign) input to crude oil distillation units and other refinery processing units (cokers, etc.). This is crude oil only. Feedstock such as straight run fueloil and VGO are not part of this calculation.

Refinery Input, Total

The raw materials and intermediate materials processed at refineries to produce finished petroleum products. They include crude oil, products of natural gas processing plants, unfinished oils, other hydrocarbons and oxygenates, motor gasoline and aviation gasoline blending components and finished petroleum products. See also 'unfinished oil'.

Refinery Losses and Gains

Processing gain and loss that takes place during the refining process itself. Excludes losses that do not take place during the refining process, i.e. Spills, fire losses, and contamination during blending, transportation, or storage.

Refinery Margin

The difference between refineries' cost to produce a product and the amount it will procure from the sale of the product. Often traders refer to the weighted sum of the product cracks when talking about refinery cracks. See also 'topping margin' and 'crack spread'. When margins are bad the refineries will cut throughput and refine at a lower speed. Fewer products are produced and prices for products may increase unless it is cheaper to import products from other trading areas. A situation which is called a reversed arbitrage.

Refinery Production

Petroleum products produced at a refinery or blending plant. Published production of these products equals refinery production minus refinery input. Negative production will occur when the amount of a product produced during the month is less than the amount of that same product that is reprocessed (input) or reclassified to become another product during the same month. Refinery production of unfinished oils and motor and aviation gasoline blending components appear on a net basis under refinery input.

Refinery Unit Abbreviations

These abbreviations are very often used in reports related to refinery activity:

- **ADU** – Atmospheric distillation unit.
- **AU** – Aromatic unit.
- **CCR** – Continuous catalytic reformer.
- **CRU** – Catalytic reforming unit.
- **CDU** – Crude distillation unit.
- **DCU** – Delayed coking unit.
- **DSU** – De-sulphurisation unit.
- **ECU** – Ethylene cracking unit.
- **DHDS** – Diesel hydro-de-sulphurisation unit.
- **FCC** – Fluid catalytic cracker.
- **FCU** – Fluid coking unit.
- **HCU** – Hydro cracker unit.
- **HDSU** – Hydro de-sulphurisation unit.
- **HDT** – Hydro-treater.
- **HOU** – Heavy oil upgrading.
- **HVU** – Heavy vacuum unit.
- **KHDS** – Kerosene hydro-de-sulphuriser.
- **KHT** – Kero hydro-treater.
- **KHU** – Kerosene hydro-treating unit.
- **KMU** – Kero merox unit.
- **MHC** – Mild hydro-cracker.

- **NHDT** – Naphtha hydro-treater.
- **NHT** – Naphtha hydro-treater.
- **RDS** – Residual de-sulphuriser.
- **RHU** – Residue hydro-de-sulphurisation unit.
- **RFCC** – Residual fluid catalytic cracker.
- **SR** – Semi-continuous reformer.
- **SRP** – Sulphur recovery plant.
- **SRU** – Sulphur recovery unit.
- **VRU** – Vapour recovery unit.
- **VDU** – Vacuum distillate unit.
- **VBU** – Vis-breaker unit.

Refinery Yield

Refinery yield (expressed as a percentage) represents the percentage of finished products produced from input of crude oil and net input of unfinished oils. Each refinery is different and would therefore require different feedstock as basis. It is calculated by dividing the sum of crude oil and net unfinished input into the individual net production of finished products. See also 'assay'.

Refining

Manufacturing petroleum products by a different set of processes that separate crude oil into its major components and blend or convert these components into a wide range of finished products, such as gasoline or jet fuel. See also 'processing unit feedstock'. The refining steps most known by traders include:

- Atmospheric distillation.
- Vacuum distillation.
- Alkylation.
- Reforming.
- Hydro-treating.
- Solvent extraction/De-waxing.
- Acid treating/Sweetening.
- FCCU.
- Vis-breaking.
- Delayed cooking.
- Thermal cracking.
- Catalytic cracking.

- Hydro cracking.
- Steam cracking.
- Co-cracking.

Plus more processes per refinery. See also 'simple and complex refinery' and 'refinery unit abbreviations"

Reformate
A high-aromatic, high-octane gasoline component made in a reformer and used to blend motor gasoline. Density is heavier than the gasoline standard (density 0.755) and aromatics can be a challenge. Reformate with a very high aromatic and benzene content can be too challenging for gasoline blending purposes. Those may be seen as a BTX stream and may be sold into the petrochemical market.

Reforming
Catalytic reforming is a process in petroleum refining used to make from low octane naphtha a high octane gasoline blending components, called 'reformate'.

Reformulated Gasoline
Finished US gasoline formulated for use in motor vehicles. This gasoline is required in order to reduce smog in areas that exceed the federal health standard for ozone in the USA. Emissions such as VOC (volatile organic compounds) and NOx (nitrogen oxides). RFG is specified to contain 2.7% oxygen. Due to this oxygen content in gasoline the exhaust of toxic air is significantly reduced. Some spec requirements to show that the gasoline became 'cleaner': Aromatic down to 25% Max, benzene 1%, a requirement of 2% - 2.7% oxygen. (Oxygen comes from MTBE blending or from bio ethanol.) Octane index to be 83.7 (R+M)/2.

Reformulated (Blended with Alcohol)
Reformulated gasoline blended with an alcohol component (e.g. fuel ethanol) at a terminal or refinery to raise the oxygen content.

Reformulated (Blended with Ether)
Reformulated gasoline blended with an ether component (e.g. methyl tertiary butyl ether) at a terminal or refinery to raise the oxygen content.

Reformulated (Non-Oxygenated)
Reformulated gasoline without added ether or alcohol components.

Reg. Unl.
Abbreviation for regular unleaded gasoline. Research octane number of minimum 91, motor octane number of minimum 81 (RON/MON 91/81) and density based on 0.745 mg/l at 15°C/60°F. For the record, premium gasoline has octane RON/MON 95/85 and density is based 0.755 mg/l at 15°C/60°F. Regular unleaded is cheaper than premium gasoline. Not only in price per ton, but even cheaper per litre due to the standard density. 1 ton of regular gasoline contains more litres than 1 ton of premium gasoline.

Regular Emulsion
This consists of small water droplets suspended in a crude oil phase. Various contaminants form a film around the water droplet preventing combining or coalescing of the water droplets.

Regulatory Regime
The laws and government regulations governing the oil and gas industry within a country.

Reid Vapour Pressure (RVP)
RVP is used to measure pressure in terms of pounds per square inch (psi), although in gasoline we look at RVP reported in kPa. In terms of gasoline, RVP is used as an ozone control mechanism. German summer gasoline has a maximum RVP of 60 kPa in the summer and a maximum of 90 kPa in the winter. In Norway summer gasoline has a maximum of 70 kPa and during winter it has a maximum of 100 kPa. One can conclude that in Norwegian gasoline more butane or other light components can be blended than in German gasoline and therefore Norwegian gasoline is relatively cheaper to produce.

Relative Strength Index, RSI (Technical Trading)
The RSI is a price-following oscillator that ranges between 0 and 100. A popular method of analysing the RSI is to look for a divergence in which the price of the oil futures makes a new high, but the RSI fails to surpass its previous high. This divergence is an indication of an impending reversal. When the RSI then turns down and falls below its most recent trough, it is

said to have completed a 'failure swing'. The failure swing is considered a confirmation of the impending reversal in the price of the oil futures.

Re-let

To rent out something that has been rented already. This can be done with allowance from or in cooperation with the owner of the asset. In storage it could be the case that a tank is not needed or unused for a certain period of time by the company who has rented the tank in the first place. Instead of terminating the storage contract it is better to re-let the tank. If the tank is rented out at a higher price compared with the original contract then the storage company could split the difference with its customer at an agreed ratio. When the original customer wants his tank back, he will give notice. Such notice will be given at an agreed timing before that customer requires his tank back. By that one can be sure that a good storage position is not lost. The storage company keeps the long term contract with the original customer and makes some extra Dollars when re-letting the tank – a risk free and smart way to cash in money. However, it may frustrate other potential customers looking for storage capacity.

Remaining on Board (ROB)

Sum of measured liquid volume, including free water, and measured non-liquid volume but excluding vapours, in cargo tanks on completion of discharge.

Renewables

A power source that is continuously or cyclically renewed by nature. Solar, wind, hydro-electric, geothermal and biomass electricity generation are examples of renewable energy sources. Supplies of renewable energy are unlimited and therefore an important source for the future.

Renewable Fuels (Other)

Fuels and fuel blending components, except biomass-based diesel fuel, renewable diesel fuel, and fuel ethanol, produced from renewable biomass.

Repeatability (Product Analyses)

The closeness of the agreement between the results of successive measurements of the same quantity carried out by the same method, by the same person, with the same measuring instrument/equipment at the same location, over a short period of time. Specifically it would be the ability of a meter and prover system to repeat its registered volume during a series of consecutive proving runs under stable operating conditions or a gauger getting the same gauge three times in succession. See also 're-testing sample'.

Replacement Cost

Cost of replacing a cargo after one other supply arrangement failed. In some cases the costs may be claimed if the original supplier has failed on delivery.

Replacement Gas

Gas for replacement of minor losses under normal operation.

Representative Sample

A small portion extracted from the total volume of material that contains the same proportions of the various flowing constituents as the total volume of liquid being transferred. The precision of extraction must be equal to or better than the method used to analyse the sample. A top-middle-bottom average sample is often seen as a representative sample if taken from a tank with homogenous product. Still it is just a few litres out of a tank containing millions of litres. A representative sample has to be taken preferably from a homogeneous tank. A ship composite sample can also be seen as a representative sample by agreement. If a tank is off-spec it is officially not allowed to take another sample which may turn on-spec and then become the new representative sample. A small manipulation on the tank should have been done. Maybe an hour's homogenation might work.

Reproducibility

The closeness of the agreement between the results of measurements of the same quantity where the individual measurements are made by different methods, with different equipment, by different observers, at different locations after a long period of time or where only some of the factors are different. Specifically it is the ability of a different set of meters or a different gauger using different equipment to measure a volume and arrive at the same volumes as the first meter or gauger. If a tank is off-spec often new samples are taken, and there is a chance based on reproducibility and repeatability that the specification of the product turns out to be approved. See also 're-testing sample'.

Resale

Trader's activity. Buy oil and sell at a profit by using time value, a small upgrade, supplying a niche market or take advantage from a good logistic solution. The trader will have a market view and buy a cargo from another trader or a producer or marketer. A cargo to make profit by resale. See also 'back to back'.

Resids

Oil market jargon for residual fueloil.

Residual/Residual Fuel/Residue

Alternative names for straight run fueloil, high-sulphur fueloil (HSFO), low-sulphur fueloil (LSFO) and low-sulphur waxy residue (LSWR).

Residual Fueloil

Heavy fueloil produced from the non-volatile residue from the fractional distillation process. Heavy oils that are 'leftovers' from various refining processes. Heavy black oils used in marine boilers and in heating plants.

Residuum

Residue from crude oil after distilling off all but the heaviest components, with a boiling range greater than 538 °C / 1000 °F.

Resistance (Technical Trading)

A horizontal price range where price hovers due to selling pressure before attempting a downward move.

Retail Margin

The difference between the cost to acquire product at wholesale and the selling price of the product at street locations (store or station), exclusive of taxes.

Retail Marketing

The marketing and sale of refined oil products to end users.

Re-Tested Sample

When the outcome of a quality check turns out to be an off-spec product on a small differential of one of the parameters the trader or operator may ask for a new test. It is best to take a new sample after maybe 1 hour of homogenising the tank. Then based on reproducibility and/or repeatability the 2nd test might turn out to be on-spec. This extra cost is not that high. It is less time consuming compared with re-blending the tank. See also 'repeatability', 'reproducibility' and 'off-specification product'.

Return on Investment

Defined as the percentage earned back or rate of return per unit of capital invested per year.

Reverse-Demulsifiers

The water-soluble reverse-demulsifiers can be used to treat contaminated cutting oils, but also for other industrial oil-in-water emulsions, as can be encountered in various industries. Clarification of the water phase is the main objective. Coalescence agents are used to destabilise these type of emulsions by increasing the size of the oil-droplets present. They can be used together with flocculation agents to accelerate the separation process and/or to improve overall clarification.

Reverse Emulsion

This consists of small oil droplets suspended in a water phase, which typically occurs where the percent water content or B.S. & W. exceeds 50 to 60 percent.

Revocable Letter of Credit

A Letter of Credit that can be cancelled or altered by the drawer (buyer) after it has been issued by the drawer's bank. A very unsafe way of getting credit covered and therefore not recommended. See also 'Letter of Credit'.

RFG (Reformulated Gasoline)

Finished US gasoline formulated for use in motor vehicles. This gasoline is required in order to reduce smog in areas that exceed the federal health standard for ozone in the USA. Emissions such as VOC (volatile organic compounds) and NOx (nitrogen oxides). RFG is specified to contain 2.7% oxygen. Due to this oxygen content in gasoline the exhaust of toxic air is significantly reduced. Some spec requirements to show that the gasoline became 'cleaner': Aromatic down to 25% Max, Benzene 1%, a requirement of 2% 2.7% oxygen. Oxygen comes from MTBE blending or from bio ethanol. Octane index to be 83.7 (R+M)/2.

RFP
Request For Proposal.

RFQ
Request For Quotation.

RFS
Renewable Fuel Standard.

Rich Gas
A hydrocarbon or mixture of hydrocarbons and non-combustible gases in the gaseous state, which is extracted from the reservoirs in a particular field in its natural state or together with the liquid hydrocarbons, processed and exported in dense phase. Natural gas that contains significant amounts of heavier hydrocarbons which act to increase the calorific (or heating) value of the gas and hence its value.

Right of First Refusal
It can be agreed in a contract for a term supply contract or for a storage contract for example that when the contract expires, the counterparty will have the right to get a last look at the final offer in the market and be prioritised for the next contract in case he accepts that offered price. When a contract expires and the business between both parties has been good, the prolongation will just be renegotiated between the parties. The price has to be a reasonable market price. For other companies it will be very difficult to get business as storage capacity, for example, is very tight. Until the market becomes backwardated, then the appetite to take on storage is less.

Risk
Exposure to price fluctuation as a result of a position taking in a trading book. An unhedged position taken by a trader based on his market view, with a possibility that the result of his trading book will change as a consequence of volatile market prices. Big risk positions may cause big result changes; it can result in a profit or loss. Traders will adjust their risk position if their market view has changed. Most traders would minimise that risk by hedging activity. The traders need to know their exposure each minute of the day and so P&L reports need to be received by the trader in time and should be accurate. A P&L mistake can be expensive especially in high volatile markets. It takes a

lot of trading discipline, maybe the most challenging part of a trading job, to manage risk in a professional way. A trader or a trading book is monitored by the risk controller. The main task of the controller is to monitor that the trader is following the rules and that the trading book is handled within mandates as set by trading management. He keeps an eye on it that all input into the P&L is done in a correct way and he creates the P&L report on a daily basis before the start of the trading session so that the trader knows exactly what his position is for that day. Also stress testing and more support activity are part of a controller's job. See also 'stress testing'.

Risk Averse
Seeking stability rather than risk. A trader who wants to avoid risk unless the payoff is worth taking the risk. A calculated risk decision in that case.

Risk-Free Rate
Back to back deal with a counterparty in which all terms and conditions of the purchase-contract are exactly the same as in the sales-contract with the other counterparty. The only difference may be the price. The difference of price between the earlier purchase contract and sales contract is the margin, a loss or a profit. Also called 'mirrored deal'. A deal, free of risk.

Risk Management
The employment of financial analysis and use of trading techniques to reduce and/or control exposure to financial risk.

RME
Rape Methyl Ester, biodiesel made from rape seed oil.

RMF
Retail Motor Fuel.

RMR Naphtha
Pipeline from Shell Pernis, Rotterdam going to Germany. Rhine-Main-Ruhr pipeline used for naphtha only. This naphtha is meant as petrochemical feedstock for further processing in Germany, Ruhr area.

Road Oil
Any heavy petroleum oil, including residual asphaltic oil used as a dust

palliative and surface treatment on roads and highways. It is generally produced in six grades from zero, the most liquid, to five, the most viscous.

ROB

Remains On Board. After discharging a vessel the inspector checks if all tanks of the vessel are completely emptied. The inspector will also look at the OBQ. If the OBQ and the ROB are showing the same result then one can conclude that the whole cargo on board has been discharged. Without those checks, part of the cargo could be left on board, which would mean a loss of product. 1,000 barrels (0.1%) sounds like a little, but at a price over 100 Dollars per barrel it suddenly becomes a big financial loss.

ROB TCV

Total calculated volume of all oil, sediments and water including free water and measured non-liquid volume but excluding any vapours, measured in the ship's tanks, including slops, after discharge, remaining on board. See also 'crude oil voyage loss calculations' in the back of the book.

ROB Water

On board quantity of all free water measured in cargo and slop tanks after discharge, remaining on board. See also 'crude oil voyage loss calculations' in the back of the book.

ROCE

Return On Capital Employed. A measure of how productively the company manages its refining, marketing and transportation assets. ROCE is the ratio of operating profits generated to the amount of operating capital invested. A good reason for having low oil stocks at the year-end. Lots of big oil companies delay their purchasing until the New Year. Cargoes which may arrive during the last week of December may have to be sold. For traders a good opportunity to get a cheap barrel as a result of distressed cargoes being available.

Rocket Line

When a tanker has to load crude oil from an offshore field, a hose needs to be picked up out of sea. The vessel will shoot a line out to the operator of the offshore field in order to connect that line to the hose. The tanker pulls in the hose to connect to the vessel. After connection, the vessel is ready for loading. The line they shoot for this purpose is called a 'rocket line'.

Roll Over

The transfer of a position from one futures period to another involving the purchase (sale) of the nearby month and simultaneous sale (purchase) of a further-forward month. Rolling position is simply needed because futures during the front month are expiring while the hedge is still needed. When you are long oil in a contango market such rolling activity can be rather profitable as often the structure differentials are most often the strongest in the front month.

Rolling Position

When a physical position is hedged with futures and that position will stay for a longer time then obviously the futures being used to hedge might expire in the futures market. As the meaning of the futures position was to hedge the physical position, one needs to liquidate the prompt futures position and take a new futures position based on the forward months contract. By this the physical position is still hedged but now with another futures month contract. The futures hedge has been rolling from one to the other month. Traders like to roll from one month to the other at highest spread in contango markets and at minimum spreads in backwardated markets. See also 'CFD'.

RON

Research Octane Number. Gasoline octane is reported in MON and RON, but also as octane index. The average octane or even called PON, pump-octane-number. RON number is an important rate for the slow and relaxed style of driving a car, while the MON number is an important rate for the more speedy and aggressive style of driving a car. RON is the 91-95-98 as we see at European petrol stations. The MON is usually 10 points below the RON, as according to European gasoline specification requirements. More information is available at 'octane number' and 'octane rating'.

Rotterdam

A port in The Netherlands. The most prevalent transaction point for spot market petroleum on the European continent. The second largest refining centre in the world after Houston. Most oil quotations in North West Europe are related to Rotterdam as a base location. Rotterdam is the main location in the ARA and therefore in Europe very important as price setting market. There are five refineries in Rotterdam, storage companies and many pipeline systems for different oil qualities are connected to Germany and Belgium. The connection with the 'hinterland' Germany by the rivers makes Rotterdam a logistic centre for Europe. Also the infrastructure, such as connection over road and by train system to Germany, is impressive. Rotterdam is the biggest harbour in Europe and well used for oil logistics including its bunker market.

RRP

Rotterdam Rhine Pipeline. Pipeline for crude oil from Rotterdam storage and refineries to Germany owned by Shell Petroleum, BP, Ruhr Petroleum and Shell Germany.

RRR

Rotterdam Running Refinery. When I traded gasoline barges (1999-2005) there was a difference in price for gasoline ex storage and gasoline from a refinery (RRR). That difference could go up to 5 Dollars in the benefit of the refiners. The assumption was, and may be still is, that oil loaded from the refineries contained less 'questionable' blending components compared with blended gasoline from storage. Refinery product was worth a premium over storage product. Probably due to the quality changes like aromatics and benzene to lower levels, the blending concept has changed in the gasoline market. In the Platts/Argus window there is no difference for gasoline barges loaded from a refinery or storage. The difference between the high and low quotations were roughly in that time around as said 5 Dollars. The low quotation represented gasoline value from storage and the high quotation was the Rotterdam running refinery production. There might still be a little value differential between storage or refinery barrels when it relates to long-term contracts. Refined quality and quantity guarantees and loading from Rotterdam must have some value over blended gasoline in Amsterdam. Now since quotations are based on Platts/Argus windows 'the market on close' the differential between high and low is not more than a Dollar.

RVP

Reid Vapour Pressure, a measure of a gasoline's volatility. Measured at 100° Fahrenheit/37.8° Celsius. In summer the max allowed RVP in gasoline is less than in winter spec because of the outside temperatures in the different seasons. A car with a high RVP gasoline would produce too much gas in the engine in the summer and a car with a low RVP would not produce enough gas to start the engine in the winter. RVP may differ from country to country. North is colder than South. Due to this there are many different gasoline specifications per country. RVP in gasoline specs are reported in the unit 'Kpa'. German gasoline has a maximum RVP specification requirement of 60 Kpa during summer and maximum 90 Kpa during winter time; in Norway it is winter 100 Kpa and in summer 70 Kpa. RVP is a vapour pressure at 100°F/37.72°C while the TVP is the vapour pressure at operating temperatures.

RWA

Ready Willing and financially Able. An intermediary who is acting as a private agent in the position of a seller on any given side becomes 'RWA' when the financial instrument is issued from the end buyer to the seller. One cannot be RWA to supply goods. Only RWA in being ready to issue payment. In my opinion this term, in combination with all other popular abbreviations like POP, LOI, PCO, FCO, is used a lot in offers by jokerbrokers and there are a lot of those in the market. Also with such offers we see unreasonable high quantities and prices which are way off from market levels. Get a proper IDD check with new counterparties – it gives some certainty related to counterparty risk.

S

Safe Port or Berth

In charter parties, a port at which vessels can safely enter, or which, at least, has a safe anchorage outside, where it can lie and load, or discharge. It is a requirement in nominations that a vessel is directed to a safe port and always afloat (AA). An HSE related requirement.

Sailing Advice

Also called sailing instruction. It is part of the document instruction. In the sailing advices, all details are written that are important to make the order to the vessel, the voyage order. Destination, receiver, terminal, inspection at disport or loadport at written in this order. It also contains the order to the captain to give regular updates related to arrival time for load and disport. Sometimes there are special instructions related to sampling or NOR to be tendered. Based on ETA and expected loading time the operator can make an estimated Bill of Lading date, which relates to pricing and therefore to hedging activity of the trader. See also 'voyage order'.

Sailing Telex

When a vessel is ready with loading, a terminal may send a full overview of the operation. Main items are loaded quantities (B/L numbers), loading times (B/L date) and some qualities like density, BS&W, salt, Tan. An operator will forward this information into his or her operations system as this is important for the trader's P&L. It has to be precise as a mistake could lead to severe losses as a result of wrong hedging. When loaded quantity differs significantly from the planned quantity then the trader needs to be informed as the exposure will change. See to it if the quality is on spec before the sailing telex is filed. The receiver may complain and ask questions when the sailing advice is different from the expected delivery.

Sale and Purchase Agreement (SPA)
A definitive contract between a seller and buyer for the sale and purchase of a quantity of oil, natural gas or LNG for delivery during a specified period at a specified price. See also 'GSPA'.

Salinity
Expected salt content. Salt is here often causing the BS&W.

Salt content
A measured salt content of a crude oil reported in PTB (pounds per thousand barrels). Salt is normally dissolved in the water or oil phase. On rare occasions salt can exist as crystalline salt. Inorganic salts are present on the water phase. Organic salts are present on the oil phase. High conductivity in de-salters does not necessarily come from high salt content but from other properties as Ca-Naphthenate or other organic salts.

Salt requirement of max 100 LBS PTB = Salt max 300 milligrams per litre

Sample Handling
The extraction, transport, mixing, and transfer of the representative sample from the pipeline to analytical glassware or centrifuge tubes. Also the time between taking a sample and doing a test is important, e.g. RVP testing cannot wait too long. Gaseous components may be released when a sample is standing too long. Could become a good result for the gasoline blender as the RVP might be reported at lower level. Also the type of bottle and the colour of the sample bottle are important when sampling. Inspection work has to be done accurately and according to the rules as set for sampling methods, e.g. ASTM standards and European norm (En228).

Sample Preheater
A device used to heat samples before S&W or API gravity or related density tests are performed.

Sample Receiver (Receptacle)

A receptacle that is usually part of an automatic sample system to contain the collected sample.

Sampling

The process of obtaining a sample of the material in the tank, container or pipeline to be used for testing or other purposes. This can be achieved by automatic or manual means. See also 'representative sample'. The following are the most common types of samples taken:

- **All-Levels Sample**

  A sample obtained by lowering a weighted, stoppered bottle or beaker or bottle to a point 1 foot (0.3 metre) above the free water level and then, with a sharp jerk of the line opening the sampler and raising it at a rate that it is about 75% full (a maximum of 85% full) as it emerges from the liquid.

- **First Foot Sample**

  When loading a jet A1 cargo it is important to know if the oil on board the vessel is not becoming contaminated with anything which was still in the line system of the vessel. After loading one foot of jet A1 into the vessel the pumping will be stopped and a sample will be taken. If the quality is good the loading will commence. If something goes wrong the vessel has to discharge the first foot out again. Thereafter the vessel has to be declared clean again and another attempt to load the vessel will be taken. Often then the first foot sample looks fine and the full cargo can be loaded. The off-spec jet A1 will be used for gasoil or diesel blending. It loses a little bit of its value. But at least due to the first foot sample the off-spec situation was found before it would have huge consequences related to the financials and the performance on the delivery.

- **Absolute Bottom Sample**

  Sample taken from the bottom of the tank. This sample is taken by the use of a special sample tool which can be opened from the bottom. The oil from that sample might contain water, sediments, slurry or, if you are lucky, good oil. When using a tank for a long time it is good to know what substances are lying on the bottom of the tank. The substances on the bottom may affect the quality of the oil in tank, but also when one wants to empty a tank he might supply some slurry to his customer. That would make a cargo off-spec.

- **Automatic Sample**
  A sample taken by automatic means. Sample from a pipeline taken during loading, sometimes called a 'drop sample'. A well accepted method for making a representative sample for a cargo. Nevertheless, ship composites are also taken as back up.

- **Flow-Proportional Sample**
  A sample taken by an automatic sampler from a pipeline at a rate that is proportional to the liquid flow rate.

- **Time-Proportional Sample**
  A sample taken from a pipeline at regular intervals during a batch transfer period.

- **Tap Sample**
  A sample taken from a valve or connection on a tank or pipeline.

- **Upper Sample**
  A spot sample obtained at the midpoint of the upper of the tank contents.

- **Upper, Middle, Lower Samples**
  Spot samples taken from the upper third, the middle and lower thirds of the liquid in the tank. The samples so taken may then be composited or analysed separately. Also called 'top-middle-bottom-sample'.

- **Bottom Sample**
  A spot sample taken from the material at the bottom of the tank. Not the same as absolute bottom. Sample is taken at one foot from the bottom of the tank.

- **Lower Sample**
  A spot sample obtained at the midpoint of the lower third of the tank contents.

- **Middle Sample**
  A spot sample obtained at the midpoint of the middle of the tank contents.

- **Running Sample**
  A sample obtained by submerging an unstoppered beaker or bottle from the surface of the liquid to a point as near as possible to the shore tank draw off point or about one foot above the level of the free water in a ship tank, and then raising it without letting it rest, at a rate so that it will be about 75% full as it emerges from the liquid.

- **Spot Sample**
  A sample taken at a specific 'spot' within a tank using a stoppered bottle or beaker and lowering it to the level of desired sample then opening it and allowing it to remain at that level until full. A thief or a zone sampler may also be used to obtain spot samples.

- **Ship Composite**
  Set of samples taken from each tank of a cargo from a vessel. The quality of all samples together represents the quality of the oil on board the vessel. These qualities are often compared with the onshore-tank qualities before loading or after discharging. Nevertheless, it does not mean that the title holder on board the vessel has a right to claim when something is off-spec. Right to claim depends on the terms according to the contract. FOB is related to the quality in tank before loading.

- **Composite Sample**
  A sample made up of equal portions of two or more spot samples obtained from a tank or pipeline. See also 'ship composite'.

- **Line Sample or Inline Sample**
  Sample taken from the line. It is taken during loading or discharging a cargo. Can be taken during the whole operation and will be used to represent the quality of the cargo.

Sandwich Car
Super insulated train tank car.

Scac Number
Standard Carrier Alfa Code. A code used as ID for Transportation companies. This contains 2 to 4 letters (not numbers). This code is mainly used in the USA. This code has to be used on shipping documentation.

Scale Inhibitors
All produced formation water contains salts in solution. When dissolved they are divided in cations and anions. As water has a limited capacity for maintaining these ions in solution, the solubility of some of these combinations can be exceeded if a change in physical conditions or water composition occurs. Salt will precipitate as solids out of the water, which may form scale. Scale formation can result in many different process operation problems. To prevent scale formation one must select an effective scale inhibitor based on a thorough water analysis together with a good understanding of the process conditions. There are specialist companies who can advise here if required.

Scalper
A trader who trades for small, short term profits during the course of a trading session, rarely carrying positions overnight. Also called a 'day trader' and/or a 'jobber'.

Scrammers
Leaving, get out. One moment a trader is in the market with a bid or offer and suddenly they pull out. Pushing numbers into the market may have a price setting effect as others would utilise these numbers as a signal in the market and therefore set their benchmark on such a price level. Scramming sometimes occurs during the Platts/Argus window. Almost the same as 'flaker'.

Screen
When traders talk about the screen, they talk about the online prices for crude oil and other oil products traded on the exchanges. One can see the forward market on the screen, make graphs, technical analyses and much more online information is available on that system. Reuters and Bloomberg are well known reporters providing the trading environment with information on screens.

S/D
Shutdown at a refinery. Can be planned or unplanned. A planned shutdown is often done for maintenance purposes and unplanned shutdown may be caused by a blackout, production failure or an accident. Traders like to keep unplanned shutdowns quiet for as long as they can. As due to an unplanned shutdown the trader needs to cover unforeseen physical shorts or lengths. Also

the expected position of the book will change. New paper hedges to cover the changed exposure in the P&L have to be arranged in the market as well. This can be a hectic period for a trader and requires a lot of the trader's creative mind-set to balance the physical and paper position. Planned shutdown or turn-arounds are often known and announced in the market. Wire reporters even publish complete lists with refinery shutdown schedules. Maintenance is preferred to be done in the months March/April or September/October. During the summer season when gasoline and diesel consumption are high the expectation is that the refinery margins are best. Therefore summer is not a good time for a shutdown. Shutdown during winter periods does not work. Weather conditions would cause trouble and delays during that season.

SDS
Safety Data Sheet or also called a 16 point SDS. The 'old' MSDS is being replaced by this new sheet and complies with the REACH-, CLP- and OSHA standards. The CLP regulation (classification and labelling of chemicals criteria) that came into force already in 2009 and complements the REACH regulation. OSHA relates to the (USA) occupational safety and health administration into its new hazard communication standard (HCS). The final rule is called 'HazCom 2012'. So one can conclude that this sheet is the standardised description of the oil or oil product on a vessel, truck or shore tanks. This document should be in the hands of people working with it and it should be carried with the means of transport. A document issued according to latest guidelines in the oil industry. The supplier of the product must be able to hand over the SDS; he is obliged to do that when requested. If no SDS is available, why would you accept to operate this oil? HSE rules must be followed. Authorities can block an operation and impose a fine for violation of rules. If an accident happens and it turns out that no SDS was available then problems can be rather big. Do not take a risk and insist on the document at any time.

SDWT
Summer deadweight.

Sealed Tank
Tank sealed/closed/locked by at least two different companies, most often by a surveyor and a storage company. Both have their own logo on the lead part of the seal when they lock the tank. By sealing a tank one can be 100%

sure that no one can pump something in or out of the tank. The quality
and quantity is by that action secured. Sealing a tank can be done when the
content is in tank for strategic storage. By that no manipulations can be done
for a long time. Also in case of contamination of oil quality in a tank it can
be smart to seal the tank. This will be done in cooperation with an insurance
company. If operations on the tank have to be done the seal has to be broken
by both companies.

Seasonality (Technical Trading)
All energy futures markets are affected to some extent by an annual seasonal
cycle or 'seasonality'. This seasonal cycle or pattern refers to the tendency of
market prices to move in a given direction at certain times of the year.

SECA
Sulphur Emission Control Areas. The SECA is an area from the North of
Europe (incl. Norway) to the South of Spain. Rules are set in that area to
reduce sulphur emissions from vessel engines. The sulphur specification for
bunker fuel is set to maximum 0.1% versus 3.5% in the rest of the world. Main
reason for SECA comes from the busy shipping traffic in the Baltic Sea. A
SECA fee is part of the freight cost in that area. The SECA fee is roughly 1.5
Dollar-cents per barrel or 10 Dollar-cents per ton.

Security
Oil paper (swap, futures or option) meant to hedge, insure or minimise risk.
A trader buys or sells securities. Also 'derivative'.

Sediment and Water (S&W)
The non-hydrocarbon solid material and water in suspension in petroleum
liquid.

Seds
Sediments or total sediments. One of the parameters of the fueloil
specifications. Sediments in bunker fuel may cause problems in engines such
as a complete stoppage of operation and combustion, blocking and plugging
of burner tips and screens and corrosion. It also causes a loss of heat release.
Therefore the maximum allowed content of sediments in bunker fueloil is
1.0%.

Segregated Ballast

Ballast water that is contained in dedicated ballast tanks serviced by dedicated ballast pumps and lines with no permanent connection to the cargo system. As there is no chance for contamination with oil, this could be considered as clean ballast water.

Segregated Ballast Tankers (SBTs)

Vessel having sufficient dedicated ballast tanks to enable safe sea going operations under normal weather conditions. Often sea water is then used as ballast; it stays clean. See also 'heavy weather ballast'.

Segregation on Board

When more than one quality of oil is planned for a vessel or barge, then the owner or the captain will show how his plans are on board the vessel or barge to place the different qualities on board. Take a look also at 'cargo plan'. Due to segregation it is not always possible to use the full capacity of the cargo tanks on board the vessel. Most likely no cargo tank on board the vessel is 100% used. Segregation therefore leads to higher freight cost per ton or barrel for the whole cargo. Some deadfreight is due.

Seller

The company which will receive money for the supply of a certain commodity. The seller will pass title and risk of the commodity at a certain moment in time. That moment of passing over risk and title is based on the delivery terms. The seller will get shorter on a commodity in paper or based on his physical position. The reason to sell may be because of marketing of production or other obligations to supply as a consequence of an earlier taken position. But also in a backwardated market one prefers to sell early to keep storage empty in order to avoid hedging at loss. Another reason to sell is just to take a position. In that case the commodity needs to be bought again at another moment in time depending on delivery dates – an activity with a certain risk. Just remember to sell high and buy low. See also 'buyer'.

Seller's Market

A situation in the market where there are more buyers than sellers. There is too little oil in the market and the seller can sell at a high price. The market will become strong and as a result of that the forward curve will show a backwardated market. The opposite is a 'buyer's market'.

Seller's Option
Look at 'SO'.

Service Contract
A contract related to logistic service in physical oil trading. That can be storage, shipping, inspection, etc. Service may add quality and value if used in the right way. Service is in some cases something that is required. Without service contracts the business would have to invest in those activities themselves which can be costly. Service is required to show qualities to the market, to supply the oil to the buyer and to make or break bulk or for blending purposes. There are many reasons to buy service. Nevertheless that service should be bought at the lowest possible price without loss of quality. Service providers would probably disagree with that statement. In the oil market it is preferred that the service provider acts as an independent company. See also 'independent inspector' and 'independent storage company'.

Settlement Price (The Closing Price)
The last price paid for a futures contract on any trading day. Settlement prices are used to determine open trade equity, margin calls and invoice prices for deliveries.

Sevan
A variation on FPSO. Basically just a storage block connected to offshore crude oil production. Size matters here. It depends on the production capacity and quality of the oil production. Also the requirement for cargo's size is important related to the size of the sevan. Local markets would accept smaller lots, while for arbitrage cargoes bigger lots would be better. So based on production and quality the trader can advise how to market and will require flexible options related to that. Therefore very much linked to logistics.

Seven Sisters (After World War II)
Seven Anglo American oil companies have dominated the petroleum industry since World War II. Companies were Standard Oil of New York (Mobil), Standard Oil of California (Chevron), Standard Oil of New Jersey (ESSO), Gulf Oil, Texaco, Royal Dutch Shell and Anglo-Persian Oil Company (BP). Abbreviation for Standard Oil became S.O. pronounced as Esso.

Seven Sisters (The 'New Seven Sisters')

Mainly state owned and most influential oil companies: Saudi Aramco, Gazprom (Russia), CNPC (China), NIOC (Iran), PDVSA (Venezuela), Petrobras (Brazil), Petronas (Malaysia). SOMO from Iraq is not in this list yet. See also 'NOC'.

SG

Specific Gravity. Look at 'API gravity' and/or 'density'.

Shale Oil

Oil which is extracted by heat, from clays that are impregnated with oil (much like oil sands). Simply explained, old empty oilfields may get into production again due to the above mentioned new techniques. Oil being trapped in the formations of the field can be produced. Other words for shale oil are 'tight oil' and 'trapped oil'. Production of shale oil requires a lot of energy. New or more sophisticated systems are required to produce the shale oil in the most efficient way.

Shark

Those market players who want to take advantage of another trader's squeezed position. The sharks are ready to 'help' and offer to buy your product at a heavily discounted price or they sell oil to you at a price with a big premium. The shark will screw the squeezed trader. Sometimes you can be a victim and sometimes you can be a shark. It is important to have good business relations that are willing to not to screw you too much. Trading can be tough. Therefore, solve your problems before your squeezed position becomes public. Sometimes a PR-department in a big company has an interest to send out information into the market because they need to be loyal to their shareholders' requirements, stock-exchange rules and related to the responsibilities towards various stakeholders.

Shell Storage Capacity

The design capacity of a petroleum storage tank which is always greater than or equal to working storage capacity. Also called 'max capacity' or 'gross capacity' of a tank. The real ullage in tank, the work capacity, is a bit less capacity. Most storage rental invoices are calculated over the shell storage capacity.

SHEX
Saturday and Holidays EXcluded.

Shifting Cost
The cost for moving a vessel from one jetty to another jetty within the same port, e.g. In Rotterdam a lot of terminals are located close to each other. When a vessel in one port has to discharge at more than one berth (double port discharge) the charterer has to pay shifting costs. Sometimes shifting can be done by the use of tugboats when the 2nd jetty is available If that jetty is occupied the vessel may have to sail back to the pilot station and wait for instructions to re-enter the harbour. Waiting time leads to demurrage, so proper planning is important.

SHINC
Sundays/Holidays INCluded. SHINC is often mentioned as part of the laytime clause in a charter party.

Ship Composite
Set of samples taken from each tank of a cargo from a vessel. The quality of all samples together represents the quality of the oil on board the vessel. These qualities are often compared with the onshore-tank qualities before loading or after discharging. Nevertheless, it does not mean that the title holder on board the vessel has a right to claim when something is off-spec. Right to claim depends on the terms according to the contract. FOB is related to the quality in a shore-tank before loading. Related to CIF supplies the buyer is the owner of the oil on board the vessel. And off-spec oil is then basically the titleholders' problem.

Shipper
The company that sells a cargo of oil. When you buy a cargo of oil from two customers and you load it onto your vessel, then you have two shippers and you probably get two B/Ls. One B/L from each shipper or also called supplier. When you then sell that cargo on to the company who buys it, then that company buys the cargo from one company only. He considers the seller as one shipper. So in trading the shipper is not always meant as the company chartering the vessel. In trading language there is a difference between the 'shipper' and the 'charterer'. Many people might not agree with this, but remember this book is about the meaning of words in trading jargon.

Confusion might be caused when lawyers are having a discussion with traders and both persons use different interpretations for the word 'shipper'.

Shipping Meeting
Traders and charterers say they have a shipping meeting and by that they mean a meeting in the pub, networking and socialising.

Shipping Size
Size matters; volumes are transported in different quantities and type of vessels. It depends on loading capacity, available quantity, draft in the ports and much more. The bigger the quantity the cheaper the price per ton or barrel. Some type of vessels:

- ULCC   320,000 – 549,000
- VLCC (Very large crude carrier)   280,000 – 320,000
- Suezmax   120,000 – 150,000
- Aframax   80,000 – 110,000
- LR1 Large/Long Range   45,000 –   80,000
- Panamax   50,000 –   60,000
- Handy size   25,000 –   35,000
- GP general purpose   16,500 –   25,000

Ship's Agent
A person or firm who transacts all business in a port on behalf of ship-owners or charterers. Many agents hold fantastic statistic reports related to activity per port. Based on good relations they might share this information. Also called 'shipping agent' or 'agent'.

Short
Having an outstanding position to supply wet barrels, a physical short. Or a sold futures contract causing a short position. When having a speculative 'short' the trader would be hopeful of an oil price decline so he could eventually buy back his futures position at a lower price. A market with too many short traders is often described as oversold. See also 'wet barrel' and 'outright short'.

Short Covering
Description which usually pertains to a market where speculative shorts are

covering or cancelling out their positions by buying product. A rally from short covering is not indicative of new buying and is often violent but brief.

Short Freight

You are short freight when you have a cargo and you need ships. When you are short physical freight then you buy the FFA.

Short Position

A position assumed when traders sell oil they do not own or just by selling paper contracts like futures or swaps. A trader wants to be short when he believes that market prices will come down, he is bearish. See also 'flexi short'.

Short Residue

Fueloil that is left over after processing of oil in the vacuum distillation tower. This oil is heavier than VGO. It may be processed at temperatures up to 600°C. This residue may stream into the straight run fuel oil which is then exported to refineries that can process it in the cracking unit. Short residue does not contain cracked material. See also 'long residue'.

Short Selling

Selling oil positions in the market that have not been covered by own production or purchase contracts. "Buy what you don't need and sell what you don't have." Short selling can also be based on a market view where the trader decides to take a short paper position by selling derivatives. Short selling of a physical basis is not necessarily a speculative position. You can be short physical oil and long paper. It is easy to sell the paper position again when the products have to be delivered. So even though the position was hedged the trader is still short physical oil. A refinery trader would take up long term shorts as he knows that the refinery will also produce the products in the next month or year to come. Maybe the trader would sell more products than the expected production. In that case the refinery can pick and choose which petroleum qualities are most profitable to produce. The shorts left over, the products which the refinery does not want to or cannot produce, will have to be covered in the market. Short selling can be a good way of refinery optimisation.

Short Ton

USA unit for measurement. 1 short ton is equal to 2000 US pounds which is equal to 907.18474 kilograms.

Shot Coke

A hard type of coke in the shape of hard round balls, like ammunition for a shotgun. Very low gravity product. Due to the hardness of this shot coke it is more expensive to use it for further production. Refiners prefer to produce sponge coke which is more porous and easier to handle for the next process. Often low in sulphur and low in metal. Shot cokes contain a lot of sulphur and metals. In some cases a refinery may produce needle coke. That is even better quality than sponge coke. Take a look at 'sponge coke' and 'needle coke' in this book.

Show Stopper

When two traders are negotiating a deal and one of the terms related to the deal is really unacceptable and also not negotiable then this is a serious issue for the on-going discussions. If both counterparties cannot give in or agree on something else then it might be that the negotiations have to stop. No business is possible at that stage unless new mandate is given. Show stoppers can be related to issues in HSE regulations, anti-corruption clauses, payment terms, embargoes etc. Commercial terms like price, nomination and volume are always issues that can be discussed, although lack of mandate can be a show stopper as well. A trader should be well prepared before he enters a market or negotiation meeting.

Shrinkage of Oil

When oil is blended then the oil molecules shuffle into each other with the result that the total volume will shrink. One litre plus one litre of oil with different densities together is not always exactly 2 litres. Imagine a 10 litre bucket filled with tennis balls. When you add one litre of sugar to it, you still have a bucket with a content of 10 litres (tennis ball/sugar blend). The (heavy density) sugar molecules found space between the (light density) tennis balls. This hopefully visualises how it works with oil molecules as well, but not as extreme as this example. The only change is the density. When oil is priced in weight and that price is corrected by a density escalator then basically no money is lost based on that density. Gasoline in Europe is (de)escalated at 0.755. In crude oil there are not always density standards. One can get a better price for quality, but the shrinkage factor can become a part of the blending cost. Understanding shrinkage may help storage companies explain a loss of volume after discharging. And for traders and operators it is good to understand why there is less volume after blending.

Shut Down
Refinery stop, most often temporary. There are planned shutdowns due to maintenance programmes or investments programmes. And there are unplanned shutdowns as a result of technical problems, black out or accidents. Other reasons for shutdown can be based on security and safety due to bad weather like during the hurricane season in the US gulf coast area. Concerning planned shutdowns, refiners typically avoid maintenance programmes during wintertime due to weather conditions and summertime due to the driving season with best cracks. See also 'turn around'. Planned maintenance shutdowns are often announced in the market and published by the wire-reporters. Unplanned shutdowns are kept quiet as long as possible. Traders will unexpectedly have to solve their supply challenges or even sell feedstock which was planned to discharge at the refinery. It can become very costly when the market finds out too early as then the trader will get squeezed by the market. See also 'S/D' differently explained.

Shuttle Tanker
An offshore loader which continuously has the same offshore load place and discharge port. The vessel is in service to keep the production process running at the oil platform at sea. Often these types of vessels are owned by the oil producers or they are chartered on long term TC contracts. In most cases these vessels sail for one charterer only between fixed loading fields and different locations which are in the nearby market. The shuttle tanker has to be in time back to load the next cargo. When a vessel arrives too late at the loading place then it would stop the field production. The operators will have good track on this and may have to reschedule another vessel originally meant for another field. A stop production can be very expensive, so some creative mind-set is required. A stop production would be seen as a result of non-performance in operations and trading. See also 'floating pipeline'.

Side Stream
Oil components which are produced during a chemical process. These components can be of use in blending fueloil or gasoline. Also in chemical

plants there may be side streams which are heavy or light. Often they have a low value and the chemical plant wants to get rid of it quickly. This oil can be a challenging blending component as it could contain high aromatic contents and other substances. Some components if available could be used as cutterstock in heavy fueloil. However, one has to be careful: chemical contents are contributing to non-environmentally friendly exhaust. It is important that the finished products which are delivered are on-spec as according to standard requirements for finished grades.

Silent Payment Guarantee

When a buyer cannot or does not want to supply an L/C and open credit is not available, then it will become challenging to get a deal done without risking credit. A solution could be to talk with a bank. The seller would in that case try to find a bank that is willing to take over the credit risk. This is not for free and banks also have their ratings versus the various companies in the oil business. The bank and the seller have to negotiate a fee for such a payment guarantee. The price will become part of the sales price and it is a question of whether the buyer is willing to pay a premium for the oil-cargo in such a case. For the buyer it looks like he gets open credit when he pays a premium for it. So in this case the bank would cover the seller at a fee. I would almost call it credit insurance.

Silver Corrosion

Corrosion of silver components in fuel systems caused by sulphur in gasoline. The sensors of fuel gauging systems in most modern cars make use of silver components. Silver is normally not so much exposed to corrosion in gasoline. But due to the gasoline specification changes since 2000 until today challenges have been notified. The sulphur came down in gasoline but the processes to make the low sulphur components have changed as well. By hydro-treating the sulphur level in oil would decrease but the gasoline would also lose its kind of protection against silver corrosion, it missing some lubrication properties. Silver corrosion in car tanks can cause trouble in the car's gauging system. Some failure in fuel-sensors in cars happened in 2004. I heard a consumer driving in a desert in the USA running out of gasoline while his car indicated a full tank of gasoline. The supplier of the gasoline got a claim and had to go to court. The specification of gasoline has been changed based on that. Lubricating additives are now added in refineries or by marketers to ensure that such problems are avoided. So if your fuel sensor is not working because of corrosion then maybe the problem is linked to this definition.

Simple Refinery

Opposite of complex refinery, also called a topping refinery or a skimming refinery. A simple refinery often consists of limited different units for processing oil. Atmospheric distillation and vacuum distillation are available and maybe it includes some oil treating facilities such as hydro-treating (desulphurisation unit). A refinery with a simple set up has done fewer investments for further processing of the heavier production. Straight run fueloil or other feedstock or unfinished products will be available from those refineries for export. The total refining costs per ton or barrel are lower than at a complex refinery. But then again one needs to understand that due to fewer investments in the refinery, a simple refinery will never be able to extract the maximum value out of the crude oil being processed. These types of refineries were built in the first place for the purpose of supplying the local market with gasoline, jet fuel and diesel. Other products got less attention and were not needed in the local market. Take a look a 'complex refinery' and 'Nelson complexity index'.

Singapore International Money Exchange (SIMEX)

A futures exchange in Singapore trading fueloil.

Sire Report (Shipping)

Ship inspection report. A report which is required by a vetting department in order to make a decision if a vessel is approved or not for the use of next voyage. If a new vessel comes on the market the owner of the vessel has to make a request to all different oil companies to have his vessel inspected. Without that inspection companies would not use the vessel. Each company may have different requirements based on HSE. Each company has a programme to commit physical inspections of the vessel as well. This 'sire report' just shows the latest official known status of the vessel, showing that no damages have occurred since her last voyage. See also 'vetting' and 'Q88'.

Skimming Refinery

Refinery with limited refining capacity mainly used to supply local markets. See also 'simple refinery'.

SLCO
Saudi Arabian Light Crude Oil.

Sleeving
A transaction whereby a counterparty, which does not have credit with another counterparty, asks a third party that has credit with both parties to be the middle person to facilitate a trade. Sometimes a 3rd party can offer to sleeve when two counterparties cannot or are not willing to trade with each other. For the 3rd party involved it is just easy money, often 25 to 50 cents per ton straight into the P&L.

Slippage
Trading orders that get filled at disadvantageous higher or lower prices than planned.

Slops
Oil, oil/water/sediment, and emulsions contained in slop tanks or designated cargo tanks. The mixture usually results from tank stripping, tank washing, or dirty ballast phase separation. When slops are in tank, water will be separated and oil-slops are left over. In some cases these slops may be re-processed and therefore still have a value, although a vessel which wants to get rid of slops has to pay for it. Slops may contain chemicals and you do not want those in a refinery. Companies who are specialists in processing slops are available in bigger ports.

Slop Tank
Vessel tank(s) utilised as a reservoir for COW medium and receipt of tank washings. Most vessels are able to heat up the oil in a slop tank. This is needed in order to prepare for the COW, crude oil wash. The heated crude in the slop tanks can be of use for the COW. Cleaning ship, spraying tank ship wall in order to minimise the amount of oil sticking to the walls. You may conclude that slop tanks are also being used as cargo tanks – it is part of freight optimisation and loss control.

Slow Steaming
To let a vessel sail slowly to the place of destination. A reason to do that is for the seller of the product, the charterer, to get late pricing days connected to the structure in the market or to avoid demurrage as the vessel might arrive

before the agreed discharge window as described in the commercial contract. Sometimes the owner of a vessel may ask for it to save on fuel consumption or for other commercial reasons. It can also be that a company has a vessel on time charter and would prefer to slow steam in order to save on the use of bunkers. Call it 'economic steaming'.

Sludge

A highly viscous mixture of oil, water, sediments and residue. Mainly found on bottoms of tanks after being in service for some years. Heavy oil which has been in tank for a long time may have settled and all dirtiness has gone down to the bottom of the tank. To avoid that one can homogenise the tank once in a while. It would cause trouble for the next cargo when a tank is empty and sludge is left behind. It could even lead to a situation where the tank has to be cleaned which is done at very high expense. Therefore it is important to homogenise a tank before emptying it. Besides that you would avoid oil losses.

Slurry

Cutterstock for blending purposes in fueloil. The density is most often higher than 1.0000 at 15°C/60°F and the viscosity may vary between 30 and 100 centistokes at 50°C/122°F. This blends well with Russian M100 with a lower density and a higher viscosity. That blend would turn into a good bunker grade. Whether that is profitable to do also depends on the blending value. I have seen both products/blendstock being sold with a premium over barge quotations. Then it is impossible to make money when blending for bunkers, unless the premiums in the bunker market are at a high level.

Smart Pig

An internal inspection tool used in the pipeline industry to detect anomalies or irregularities on the walls of a pipeline. Also called an 'intelligent pig'.

Smell of Money

When people are at a refinery or an oil terminal they would say that it smells bad and unhealthy. A trader would call it the 'smell of money' and sees a machine consuming crude and making products to trade. A potential place for the sourcing of oil business opportunities.

Smoke Point

Specification in jet A1 referred to the maximum flame height of jet without smoke observation. The minimum flame height according to the specifications is 25 millimetres.

SO

Seller's Option. A quantity is bid or offered with a certain loading tolerance but it is in seller's option related to the quantity (within the tolerance agreed) to load on board a vessel. CIF and DES cargoes are assumed in seller's option as in that case the seller is fixing the freight and logistics. But also some FOB sales may be based on seller's option, e.g. Russian crude oil supplies which are offered on FOB basis in seller's option (so).

SOF

Statement Of Facts, the time sheet of a vessel or terminal. This document shows all relevant times and events that are connected to the operation of a cargo. E.g. NOR tendered, pilot on board, start mooring, mooring completed, inspection on board, hoses connected, loading started, loading completed, hose connected, bunkering started, vessel unmoored, vessel departed, etc. Based on all the information the time used for this vessel can be compared with the contractual agreement related to the available hours. Too much time used in disport or loading port may lead to a claim for demurrage. This documentation is important and has to be accurate. Vessel, agent, terminal and the inspector are all making their own time sheet. They report those to the customer or file it in their system in case of a claims situation. A SOF or timesheet is part of the document instructions for oil cargoes to be loaded and/or discharged. Furthermore for each discrepancy during loading from which a terminal, vessel, inspector or agent finds himself not to blame for, a letter of protest is made. Those letters of protest are used to evaluate the time used related to the lay-time agreed. See also 'port log' and 'lop'.

Sodium

Salt. Some grades of oil contain sodium. It can have a negative effect on refinery equipment as it may cause corrosion of the hardware like pipes and units.

Soft Market

More potential sellers than buyers, which creates an environment where rapid price falls are likely. See also 'buyer's market'.

Soft Offer

Offer indication where the buyer has the option to take delivery but is not obliged to do so. The buyer would in such a case only take delivery when he can sell it at a profit. Oil traders do not like to give too many options away. So soft offers are rare or must be based on very good business relations.

SOLAS

Safety Of Life At Sea.

Solvent

A substance, normally a liquid, which is capable of absorbing another liquid, gas, or solid to form a homogeneous mixture.

Solvent Extraction

Process in petroleum refining to produce refined lubricating oil.

Solvent Naphtha

Light naphtha or mineral turpentine. A solvent (from Latin solvere, 'loosen') is a liquid, solid, or gas that dissolves another solid, liquid, or gaseous solute, resulting in a solution that is soluble in a certain volume of solvent at a specified temperature. This type of naphtha may have a good value for the chemical industry.

Sour/Sweet Crude

Definition which describes the degree of a given crude oil's sulphur content. Sour refers to a high sulphur content (>1.0%) and sweet refers to a low sulphur content (<0.5%). The sulphur range from 0.5% to 1.0% is often called 'medium sulphur'. In earlier days when oil was just discovered some analysts tasted the crude oil. The high sulphur crude tasted very sour. Therefore high sulphur crude is called sour crude. WTI and Brent on the exchanges are sweet crudes. The majority of the produced Middle East crude is sour crude but the producers/sellers use the sweet crude exchange prices, WTI and Brent, as benchmark. West African crude is sweet as well. South American is a mixture, but they have a lot of very heavy crude oil production as well. North

Sea crude is sweet (Brent related) and also in the USA the majority of the production is sweet. But there is a sour quotation as well. Read more about that at 'ASCI'.

Sour Trader/Sour Desk
A trader or desk being responsible for the trading activity of all crudes with sulphur of more than 1.0%. Medium sulphur crude is often traded by the sweet desk. Although it also depends on each individual company. It is related to the way they have organised their trading system.

Sourcing Intermediary
This is an agent/consultancy who acts between a producer of oil and a buyer. Some markets are difficult to enter. Sometimes because you do not want to travel there and in some cases because of language problems. Besides that when entering a new market it can be great to have some advice. A sourcing intermediary is paid based on performance. A good agent has a big network and has therefore easy access to the producers. Often when a company is getting established in the new market they will be able to create the business without the help of an intermediary. So intermediaries are useful for creating new business as long as they add value. They are not the same as a broker who can trade from behind a desk, a telephone and a screen. A sourcing intermediary will also introduce a trader to producers, write letters to get invitations. They help you in building up a network.

South East Pipeline
Multiproduct pipeline connecting a refinery from Fawley to Eastern UK includes jet pipeline to the London airports.

Sp.Gr.
Specific gravity.

SPA
Sales & Purchase contract Agreement.

Spec(s)
Specification(s). Quality of crude oil or petroleum products. Traders like to talk about the specs or request for a spec sheet. The abbreviation became a

word originated from oil trading jargon. Spec is also used as abbreviation for speculative trader, a spec trader.

Special Naphtha

All finished products within the naphtha boiling range that are used as paint thinners, cleaners, or solvents. These products are refined to a specified flash point. Special naphtha includes all commercial hexane and cleaning solvents conforming to ASTM specification D1836 and D484, respectively. Naphtha to be blended or marketed as motor gasoline or aviation gasoline, or that are to be used as petrochemical and synthetic natural gas (SNG) feedstock are excluded.

Specifications

Term referring to the properties/characteristics of a given crude oil or petroleum product, which are 'specified' since they often vary widely even within the same grade of product. In the normal process of negotiation, the seller will guarantee the buyer that product or crude to be sold will meet certain specified limits, and will agree to have such limits certified in writing. Crude oil is traded based on the quality as given in the assay. The most important specifications are always mentioned such as API, sulphur, viscosity and if needed TAN. Most refiners are very familiar with the crude they order; they might ask for a test sample of crude or check the assay. Only refinery-approved crude will be bought when the price is right. Petroleum products have standard specification related to the consumer market, e.g. Diesel, gasoline, jet a1 and bunker fueloil. Blending components have specifications which might be of interest due to specific qualities which a blender is looking for. Guarantees may be required on certain specifications when those keypoints are very important to the buyer. See also 'keypoints'.

Specific Gravity

This comes from the USA calculations system. It is the weight in kilos per litre at 60°F, i.e. 0.8457. In Europe call it density and it concerns the weight in kilos per litre at 15°C. Look also at 'API Gravity', a result indicating the specific gravity in a calculated number. Crude barrels API of 36.43 (= Sp. Gravity 0.8457).

Specific Heat

The quantity of heat required to raise the temperature of a unit weight of a substance by 1 degree which is usually expressed as calories/gram/C or BTU/ lb./F.

Specific Gravity

A way of naming density. The ratio of a liquid's density compared to water. A liquid with a specific gravity less than one is less dense than water. Water has a density of 1.0000 at 4°C/39.2°F.

Spec Sheet

Specification Sheet. Detailed information of the qualities of petroleum product or crude. Also called a quality report. Before a trader buys or sells a product a spec sheet is required. Based on that sheet the trader can see if the oil is on-spec or if there is some good value as blending component. In some cases a better sulphur level, viscosity, density, octane, RVP or other parameter can be seen as giveaway and have a good value for the blender. A spec sheet is not always to be seen as the definite quality of the oil. It has to be treated as a good indication of what you can expect. When buying oil a trader can require the same guarantees of certain parameters. The more guarantees a trader requires the more expensive the oil may become. But some key qualities are just important for blending purposes. Finished oil must apply according to the specs as set by the international market standards or according to the requirements as set per country. Gasoline and diesel have many different requirements per country and season.

Spec Trader

Trader who buys and sells derivatives and accepts risk with the purpose of making profit. A spec trader can be a proprietary trader or a trader speculating on behalf of his customers, e.g. a bank or insurance (life or pension). See also 'proprietary trader'. A good spec trader is excellent in reading markets and takes positions based either on fundamentals or purely on the technical by reading the graphs. Trading discipline and a good trading plan are important for speculative traders. See also 'discipline' and 'net loser'. Spec trading is not an unlimited activity. A spec trader has mandates as well. Trading out of mandate can cause huge losses. Some companies have suffered from spec traders going out of mandate. If that happens out of sight of a controller and management then one can consider this as illegal practice. Such a trader could land behind bars. Fortunately, it happens rarely.

Specification Salt Content: 100 LBS PTB mg/l

Different geographic areas have different methods and reporting requirements. I see this requirement popping up sometimes. Traders or operators intend to give instructions to inspection companies. However, sometimes a trader sells his cargo with a max guarantee on salt content. In most countries, we are used to giving such guarantees in ppm, not in lbs. A trader needs to know such a calculation from lbs to ppm before he gives any guarantee. Therefore the example here below:

100 LBS = Apr. 45 kilos

PTB = per thousand barrels

A heavy crude density 0.909 kilos per litres at 15°C

1,000 barrels of heavy crude = 1,000 x 158.98729 x 0.909 = 144.519 kilos

45 kilos/144.519 x 100% = 0.03%

0.3% = 300 ppm

Ppm volume = milligram per litre

Speculator

A market participant who tries to profit from buying and selling futures and options contracts by anticipating future price movements. Speculators assume market price risk and add liquidity and capital to the futures market. Speculation can be done by day traders who do not take overnight positions. Their trade is based on their view of the market activity per day, technical indicators, volatility during the day and often this is done in small lots. The major speculators like banks, hedge funds, trading companies, oil companies etc. have a longer market view and trade bigger volumes. Such a view is based on fundamentals and technical indicators. Following rules of trading discipline is the most important part of the job; a good trader makes profits, but a great trader knows when to cut losses. Such discipline is the most difficult part of business as human beings are more emotional than rational. Cutting a loss? No one likes to lose money!! Follow the rule of trading discipline!!! You can also trade and speculate privately if you fancy risk. You will find out how difficult trading discipline can be.

Spill

Oil getting into the sea or vapour released in the atmosphere in any amount for any reason caused by human activity. A spill happens by accident due to errors in the process. Dumping oil in sea is not a spill, which is a crime. An aircraft may dump kerosene above sea in case of an emergency. That is allowed and the oil spill does not harm the sea too much as light material will evaporate very fast. See also 'oil spill'.

Spike

A large, quick, temporary rise or fall in price often followed by a correction in price. It may be caused by a 'fat finger' or a short market reaction on unexpected news which may affect the oil market. When prices suddenly go up and stay up it is called a 'rally' and when it suddenly goes down and it stays down it is called a 'crash'.

Split Weekend

If a payment day or a quotation day falls on a Saturday or Sunday then buyer and seller agree in their contract that if the due day falls on Saturday it will be replaced by the Friday before that due day and if a due day falls on Sunday it will be replaced by the Monday following that due day. Such rules do also apply for the 2-1-2 B/L pricing. If the B/L day is on a non-quotation day then the nearest days with a quotation will count as B/L-quotation-day.

Sponge Coke

A porous type of coke. A grade of coke from the coker-unit which meet the specs for the production of anodes that are needed for the steel and aluminium industry. Often low in sulphur and low in metal. See also 'calcined coke', 'needle coke' and 'shot coke'.

Spot

Single trade contract for one cargo of oil. In spot markets each cargo is traded separately. Opposite of 'long-term' in which more cargoes over a longer period are agreed.

Spot Contract
Physical oil contract for a sale or purchase of one or more deliveries of oil within a short period of time.

Spot Market
Physical cargo market which trades on a daily basis and are to be used by the reporters such as Platts and Argus to create the assessments, the price quotation, for the next day. The traders dealing with physical cargoes in the spot market will be very busy talking with the market trying to find the best buyers. The traders need to watch the logistics and the specification. Spot cargoes are normally sold in good time before loading. Could be max a week for products or 10 to 14 days for a spot crude cargo. If a cargo remains unsold and the trader has a problem finding a home for the cargo he might get squeezed by the market. He would have a distressed cargo on his hands. Pricing of these cargoes may be B/L related, floating or in some cases also at a fixed price. The biggest spot market is the barge markets in ARA. Where the market pays fixed prices. I would call it a reasonable liquid market with lots of activity. Spot markets are price setting markets. The opposite is related to long term contracts; those prices are not published and use the benchmark quotations to set the prices of the different oil products.

Spot Price
A cash market price for a physical commodity that is available for immediate delivery.

SPR
Strategic Petroleum Reserve in the US. In the USA a lot of crude and oil products are placed in storage for potential threats when oil supply problems may be the case. At high stocks and high prices the USA can release some of their strategic stock into the market. By that the demand for oil at the producers will lag behind due to a temporary oversupply of oil. This can result in oil prices coming down. When stocks are at a low level the SPR has to be filled up again. That goes slowly and controlled. So the SPR can be used as a tool to influence market prices. Lower oil prices support the economy in a better way. Global strategic petroleum reserves ('GSPR') refer to crude oil inventories (or stockpiles) held by the government of a particular country, as well as private industry, for the purpose of providing economic and national

security during an energy crisis. Holding of strategic stocks, as basically done by countries in the world, calling it 'compulsory stock obligations'.

Spread

The price difference between two related markets, commodities or time. Spreads can be more volatile than the outright market (price movement per commodity). There are different spread-types described in this book such as 'time spread', 'product spread', 'location spread' (arbitrage) and 'crack spread'.

Spreading

The simultaneous buying and selling of two related markets or commodities in the expectation that a profit will be made when the position is offset.

Spread Crack

Crack is the margin per barrel for a certain product (crude per barrel versus product per barrel). Gasoline is priced in tons. It can be calculated back from price per ton to price per barrel. The differential between the crude price per barrel and the gasoline price per barrel is the refinery margin per barrel or the gasoline crack. The value fluctuates depending on the activity and price fluctuation in the crude market and gasoline market. One can buy or sell the crack expecting or hoping for a change in one of the markets in order to buy or sell that position back. When cracks are very good a refinery can consider selling the cracks by which the refiner would lock in a certain refinery margin. A high crack is a result of a strong market at the front. It may cause a backwardated market. See also 'crack spread'. In the back of this book you will find more information about the calculation of cracks.

Spread Markets

Arbitrage or location spread. Difference in prices between different price-quoted geographic areas. As an example the difference between ARA quotations and the USGC quotations. World economies and prices are changing all the time. With open arbs cargoes move Trans-Atlantic until prices are changing as a result of oversupply. Also heavy demand for freight would increase freight rates which will cause a closed arbitrage. Traders are always looking for the opportunity to export and lock in (hedge) the arb and move oil in order to take profits. With closed arbs the activity slows down rapidly. Shipping prices go down due to lack of transport demand, which could cause another open arb possibility because of cheap freight. Arbitrage trading is most often seen as an opportunistic trade. However, some flows will never stop due to long term obligations. Also called location spread.

Spread Product
Spread between the values of two different petroleum products. A trader can take a paper position based on a product spread, e.g. Buying a swap gasoline barges and sell a naphtha swap. Often such product swaps are done based on two different products that are correlated to each other. Like naphtha/gasoline, diesel/gasoline and in fueloil there is the relation between high and low sulphur, see 'HILOS'. The change in price can be more volatile than the outright market (price per commodity). The trader will here focus on the fundamentals of the oil. The historical differentials between two grades may be used as a guideline.

Spread Time
Time spread is a position taken based on time value in the forward market. One can buy a futures contract gasoil in June and sell a futures contract in August. When the market is in contango then one can be long physical oil on the prompt basis (product in storage) and hedge it in the forward market. Look also at 'front to back' and 'contango'. One can also speculate on spreads. A trader who believes that a market will flip from contango to backwardation can buy a time spread (buy the front and sell the back) and cash in later. When you sell a time spread, you sell the front and buy the back. If in that case the market might change from backwardation to a contango situation again money may be cashed in. Time spreads are less volatile than product spreads or location spreads.

Squeeze
A market situation in which due to the lack of supplies buyers are forced to cover their positions by offset at higher prices. When a refinery has an unplanned shut down and the market finds out very quickly, then the suppliers would try to squeeze the refiner who needs to cover his shorts in a prompt matter. When you get squeezed you are either forced to buy high or to sell low.

Squiggly Lines
A trader drawing a lot of squiggly lines on his chart. The lines are used by the

trader as technical indicators. Creating trend lines, support and resistance lines etc.

SSHEX
Abbreviation for Saturdays, Sundays and holidays excluded. Refers to loading and discharging of cargo as agreed to in the charter party. This indicates when time does not count in the calculation of demurrage and despatch.

ST
Shuttle Tanker, in this context connected to offshore crude activity. A vessel sailing from a selected number of offshore fields to disports that are not too far off. If the destination is too far from the offshore field then such a vessel cannot be back in time to load again from the offshore field. Besides that, transport by offshore shuttle tankers is rather expensive. If the disport is relatively far away from the offshore field then it can be an economically preferable solution to go for an STS operation into a conventional vessel. A matter of logistic optimisation. A shuttle tanker always sails back empty to the offshore field while a conventional vessel will try to find a next loading order close to the place where she just discharged.

Stabilised Condensate
Non-refrigerated C5+ product produced from unstabilised condensate.

Stadis
Additive for jet A1, often added before the product is pumped into a pipeline system for supply to an airport's tank terminal. Stadis is meant to decrease the static electricity level caused by friction of the product when pumped. See also 'conductivity'.

Standby L/C
Payment guarantee used in case the credit taker fails to meet its payment obligations in part or in full. With this document money can be cashed in at the bank that issued the document. See also 'Letter of Credit', 'silent payment guarantee' and 'credit risk'.

Standard Gallon
Net or temperature-assigned gallon (231 cubic inches at 60°F). 42 gallon is 1

barrel. One gallon is 3.785 litres. One lot of gasoline in USA is 42,000 gallons (1,000 barrels).

Standpipe

The vessel's deck fitting through which closed system measurements are taken. It contains the necessary valves and fittings to allow the closed system measurement unit to be lowered into an inverted, pressurised, vessel tank to take the required measurements. It is also referred to as a pressure or vapour lock system.

Start-up

The moment that a refinery is starting up its production after a shutdown period. Or starting up for the first time when newly built. Traders are always interested in start-up dates of refineries as more feedstock may be required in the market and at the same time more products will be supplied to the market.

Static Hedge

A hedge that does not have to be changed once it is initiated. Can be as in an arbitrage hedge. The physical sale may price out while the paper hedge (the swap) is pricing in. E.g. If you sell a cargo of heavy fueloil in Singapore at October average pricing, then you like to lock in your sales price as part of an arbitrage hedge. You would then sell an October fueloil swap. When it is October the physical cargo starts pricing out each day. That would make you short. The paper position in October would start pricing in each day. That would make you long. Long plus short at the same volume makes the position balanced. So nothing needs to be done. Your position is not changing due to the hedge.

Stats

Weekly presentation (API) of the stocks of crude, gasoline and heating oil in USA. These numbers are shown in the market each Wednesday or each 3rd working day in the week. The market prices (screen levels for oil related futures) include the expectations of what the stats outcome will be. If there are big surprises like a stock build instead of a stock draw then the oil prices on the oil exchanges will fluctuate immediately. A trader having a big outright position, when the stats come out, takes a big risk on outright exposure and has to act fast when markets move in the wrong direction.

Steam Cracking

A petrochemical process which produces olefins, particularly ethylene, and, in some cases, aromatics. The most common feeds are ethane, butane, and naphtha. Residual fueloil from steam cracking is sometimes blended into heavy fuels.

Stem

The stems for a cargo are the planned/expected loading or discharge activity for an oil cargo at a fixed location. Date, product and quantity are important. When loading programmes for crude are broadcasted the traders of different oil companies will start working on their cargo tracking. They want to know which companies have a stem on the different loading dates for each cargo.

Stick

A full point (or Dollar). Charts can contain candlesticks; when a trader says that the market went up 3 sticks he means 3 full Dollars.

Still Gas (Refinery Gas)

Any form or mixture of gases produced in refineries by distillation, cracking, reforming, and other processes. The principal constituents are methane, ethane, ethylene, normal butane, butylene, propane, propylene, etc. Still gas is used as a refinery fuel and a petrochemical feedstock. The conversion factor is 6 million BTUs per fueloil equivalent barrel.

Stochastics (Technical Trading)

Stochastics is a data series which oscillates between 20 'oversold' and 80 'overbought'. Many traders use stochastics to try to pin-point long or short entries into markets.

Stock Change

The difference between stocks at the beginning of the reporting period and stocks at the end of the reporting period. A negative number indicates a decrease (i.e. A drawdown) in stocks and a positive number indicates an increase (i.e. A build-up) in stocks during the reporting period. Stocks are changing due to production, import and export. But also losses cause stock changes. Losses do also cause financial losses straight into the trader's P&L. Measurements have to be accurate, but operational losses are just part of the business.

Stop Loss

When a trader has a trading position he likes to let profits run, but as soon as the market goes down or in the wrong direction the position starts to become a losing position. The stop loss number is the moment where the trader decides to leave the position when a certain loss from peak level has been reached. In that case he cuts losses. The moment you reach that level you get to a stop loss position and action has to be taken. Following this rule is based on strong trading discipline. Sometimes a push from a controller would help. If it really goes wrong and trading discipline is lacking, the financial losses would become huge. That could even lead to a temporary 'stop trade'. See also 'loss from peak'.

Stop Order

An order that becomes a market order when the futures contacts reaches a particular level. A sell stop is placed below the market and a buy stop is placed above the market.

Stop Trade

When a trader starts losing on a continuous basis and those losses are out of proportion then the loss controller or trading management might pull back all mandates. The traders are getting a stop trade signal. A strict way to stop a trading activity from a trend in the wrong direction. Time for traders to make up their mind and maybe evaluate why business went wrong. In some companies it would mean for a trader an exit through the backdoor and in other companies the business will be picked up after some time with the same trader. A stop trade can last for some days or even a month or longer. After a reset the trader enters with a fresh mind back into the market, but probably he has to earn his mandates back again by starting small. Another lesson learned so to speak.

Storage

On-land tank facilities for short- or long-term storage of crude or oil products. This may be land tanks (above ground) or caverns (underground). Storage can be used for trading activity and logistic activity such as break of bulk, gathering small cargoes to make a big cargo (make bulk), blending activity, contango activity, back up for refinery, compulsory stock obligations, etc. Storage is expensive during contango markets as everybody wants to rent a tank for oil storage. In contango market the front market is weak and freight prices may come down as well. In that case some vessels may come available as temporary floating storage. Often it is cheaper than storage on land. A vessel used as temporary floating storage could sail to a certain destination and stay there until it gets the instructions to discharge. There also exists fixed floating storage. Those are often old VLCCs or other big vessels which are stationary. Those that cannot sail from A to B. See also 'floating storage'.

Storage Facilities
Sites, offices, buildings, tank storage areas, tank installations, wharfs, quays, piers, loading and unloading docks, pipelines, blending equipment, in which, by or for the storage company, activities are performed, regardless of whether these activities occur on the site of the storage company itself or elsewhere.

Storage Fee
The fee payable for the storage related services, use of the storage facilities, the leasing of the storage tanks and the insurance costs. The storage fees can vary a lot depending on market situations like contango and backwardation. Also the performance of a storage company has impact on the storage fee. Storage fee can contain tank rental plus 1 or more throughputs per month. It can also be just tank rental plus a separate fee per throughput. Storage fees may also include other services such as pumpover fee, homogenation fee per hour, butanising, heating and even customs documentation. The storage fee often differs from location to location and from commodity to commodity.

Storage Related Services
Making storage space available, take delivery, store and re-deliver the product, and in tank transfers and pump-over to other storage tanks and/or refinery pipes. Issuing documents, customs, blending, adding additives, heating etc. (administrative processing). Also some good advice and good information related to operations is part of the service that may be expected from a storage company.

Straddle (Technical Trading)
An option portfolio consisting of one call option and one put option, both with the same underlying direction (long or short), strike, and expiration date.

Straight or Non-Negotiable

A Bill of Lading in which the merchandise is consigned directly to a designated party, generally the buyer, but not to his 'order'. Delivery of the merchandise is made only to the designated party, usually without surrendering the Bill of Lading.

Straight Run

Material which has come straight from an atmospheric distillation unit and has not been cracked or reformed, and which is usually used as a feedstock or as a blending component. Straight run production comes from simple refining. A product available at each refinery before it is further processed in crackers, vis-breakers, etc. Straight run oil is also called 'unfinished oil'.

Straight Run Fueloil Synonyms

- **Atmospheric residue**.
- **Atmospheric Tower Bottoms**
- **Atres** – Atmospheric residue.
- **Black Oil** – Straight run oil, but could also be cracked fueloil.
- **Cat. Feed** – Straight run fueloil as feedstock for the catalytic cracker.
- **Distillate Fueloil**.
- **E4** – Russian high sulphur straight run fueloil.
- **Feedstock** – Straight run fuel is a feedstock to a refinery, also crude.
- **FO SR** – Fueloil straight run – sulphur level is mentioned separately.
- **Heavy shit** – Can be straight run fueloil, maybe more heavy than expected, probably discounted.
- **HSAR** – High sulphur straight run residue.
- **HSSR** – High sulphur straight sun.
- **LFSR** – Low sulphur straight run.
- **Long residue** – Straight Run fuel are long hydrocarbon chains.
- **LSAR** – Low sulphur atmospheric residue.
- **Refinery name** –Some straight run fuel oil are named after its origin (Ilsky)
- **Resids** – Residual - Residual Fuel – Residue
- **SRHSFO** – Straight run high sulphur fueloil.
- **SRLSFO** - Straight run low sulphur fueloil.
- **Straight Run Residual Oil**.
- **Tower Bottoms** – Residue from the distillation tower.
- **Unfinished Oil** – Oil from the refinery meant for further processing.

Straight Run Gasoil

A middle distillate that is produced from refinery distillation at temperatures usually ranging from 200° to 350°C/392° to 662°F. Usually it is used for heating oil or diesel fuel. However it may need further treatment or processing before it can be commercialised as heating oil or diesel.

Straight Run Residual Oil or Residue

The remaining portion of the crude oil feedstock that does not vaporise in the refinery distillation process. This product can be used directly as a boiler fuel, or it can be used as feedstock for vacuum distillation units or into the fluid cat cracker unit (FCCU).

Strategic Stock

Stock required to be kept in a separate tank in case of urgent need as a result of any type of oil crisis. Most countries require a stock big enough to cover the most essential needs for 90 days. See also 'compulsory stock' and 'compulsory stock ticket'. Very well known as the 'SPR' and 'CSO'.

Strategic Petroleum Reserve (SPR)

Petroleum stocks maintained by the Federal U.S. Government for use during periods of major supply interruption. Lots of that storage is available in Cushing. A place where you find more tanks then people. As the USA is not yet consuming as much as they produce this stock has increased significantly in the USA. It is one of many reasons why WTI is lower priced than Brent. Export crude from USA is not an option. USA law prohibits it.

Stratification

Occurs in blended fuels that have a compatibility problem. It is usually experienced when paraffinic based oils are mixed with asphaltic based oils, causing asphaltenes to precipitate and settle at the bottom of the tank. See also 'compatibility'.

Stress Testing

Testing of the impact of extreme market moves on the value of a portfolio. Stress testing is often done to be prepared on seasonal changes or is executed based on expected events according to the news which may affect the fundamentals. Hurricane season is a good reason to stress test in order to be prepared for volatile markets. But also a threat of war can be a reason for stress testing. Nevertheless, once a market rallies or crashes it will be very difficult to leave a position. See also 'rally'. Due to stress testing one can see what changes can happen in the P&L based on the actual position. One may consider reducing risk before certain expected events may happen, although it always depends on the trader's and company's risk appetite.

Strike Price
The price at which an asset may be bought or sold in an option contract.

Strip
A straddle plus another put option.

Strip
When a trader buys or sells a number of swaps from different months he pays an average price for the whole set. One average price for the strip. Some months will be registered over-priced and some months will be registered under-priced. Think about a quarterly strip or a whole year.

Stripping
Stripping a tank, popular way to say: "Emptying a tank", the last cubic metres and litres of oil to be pumped out of a tank. When a tank has to be completely emptied the pumping speed can be very low at the end of an operation. 'Stripper pumps' may be used to empty the tank as best as possible. When a tank is emptied some losses might be caused as a result of clingage. Compare it with a glass of water. When you turn it around the glass is empty but there are always some drops left behind. Crude tanks are not emptied completely. There is often a heel to be left behind in the tank. Therefore the pumping rate related to crude tank should always be reasonable.

Structure
This is the way the forward market looks like. Contango or steep contango and otherwise backwardation or deep backwardation. Or what also can happen is a contango market changing into a backwardated market and vice versa. The structure is changing in that case. If the forward market shows equal or close to equal oil prices then there is no contango or backwardation. That is called a flat market. See also the 'curve'.

STS

Ship To Ship. One vessel pumping oil products or crude oil over to another vessel on open sea. Ship to ship activity can be very costly. Fenders need to be hired and tugboats are often required for such an operation. Due to challenging logistics the vessels related to the STS operation are much exposed to demurrage. Often one vessel needs to wait for the other vessel. Furthermore in case of fog or rough weather conditions the vessels may not be connected as that can be dangerous which causes even more demurrage. The risk of an oil spill is high. But keep in mind that everybody understands that risk. The HSE-focus on the operations during STS activity is enormous. Therefore it happens rarely that an oil spill occurs. There is a possibility that balances of oil stay behind in the supplying vessel if the receiving vessel is lacking ullage. Then extra costs are made by the supplier as the supplying vessel needs a second discharge place to unload the balance cargo. The extra logistic costs which may be expected need to be estimated before committing to a deal. See also 'lightering'.

Subs

When a nomination is sent then one would see the vessel name 'X' or subs. Meaning, in case vessel 'X' is cancelled a substitute vessel will be nominated. But traders use the term subs also when to lift subjects from a contract, subject to management approval etc. They would lift 'subs' as the trader would call it.

Sub Octane

Usually applies to a gasoline that does not meet the 87 octane (index R+M/2) standard which most suppliers mandate for regular unleaded distinction. Sub-octanes are typically utilised by those using oxygenated components.

Subject to

When negotiating a contract and finalising the deal there are often a last few remaining matters to be clarified before confirming the business as final and binding. Deals can be done subject to vessel approval, management approval, vetting approval or credit approval. This approval has to be clarified within reasonable time. When everything is approved then subject or subs will be lifted and the deal is confirmed.

Suezmax

The maximum sized ship that can sail through the Suez Canal generally considered to be between 135-150,000 DWT depending on ship's dimensions and draft. This vessel size is used for crude and heavy fueloil. This is a dirty vessel.

Sulphur

A yellowish non-metallic element, sometimes known as 'brimstone'. It is present at various levels of concentration in many fossil fuels whose combustion releases sulphur compounds that are considered harmful to the environment. Some of the most commonly used fossil fuels are categorised according to their sulphur content, with lower sulphur fuels usually selling at a higher price. Diesel is currently reported as having either a 0.05% or lower sulphur level for on-highway vehicle use or a greater than 0.05% sulphur level for off-highway use, home heating oil, and commercial and industrial uses. This also includes ultra-low sulphur diesel (<15 ppm sulphur). Residual fuel, regardless of use, is classified as heavy fueloil having either no more than 1% sulphur (low sulphur) or greater than 1% sulphur (high sulphur). Coal is also classified as being low-sulphur at concentrations of 1% or less or high-sulphur at concentrations greater than 1%. Crude oil is also classified on sulphur: low sulphur (<0.5%) is sweet crude and high sulphur (>1.0%) is sour crude. Crude with a sulphur-level between 0.5% and 1.0% is called a middle grade. Sulphur content in oil is very important. In crude and all products sulphur is one of the key qualities. After stricter sulphur levels were announced the refineries had to find solutions to secure the deliveries. Most refineries were forced to invest in de-sulphurisation capacity. To avoid such an investment a refinery would have to change crude slate and process low sulphur (sweet) crude only. Sulphur spec requirements are related to crude oil, gasoil, gasoline and fueloil. Low sulphur oil has a higher value than high sulphur oil. Bunker oil in seca-area has a max sulphur spec of 0.1%. However, outside the seca-area in international waters, tankers may use bunkers with a sulphur specification up to 3.5%. It is expected that in 2020/2025 the sulphur in bunkers, globally, will at least be not more than 0.5/1.0%. It remains to be seen what the exact goal will be.

Sulphur Content

A measure of the presence of sulphur in crude oil and oil products, which is a key determinant of quality. Sulphur content is measured as the percentage of sulphur by weight in the oil. Crude oil grades that are high in sulphur are referred to as sour crudes and those that are low in sulphur are referred to as sweet crudes.

Summer Peak/Driving Season

The period after May when people in the USA take their holidays and start driving their cars for long distance voyages. Gasoline prices, but also diesel prices increase. Cracks are up and the crude slate at the refineries which are processing is to maximise gasoline and diesel production. Driving season is mainly related to the petrol consumption in the USA. Refineries would avoid turnarounds during those months.

Summer Spec

Gasoline and diesel have to perform during the whole year. Therefore the cold properties in summertime are different compared with those in wintertime. E.g. German gasoline in summer has a RVP of 60/70 and in winter 90/100. In diesel summer spec and winter spec differs based on cold properties such as cloud point and CFPP. See also 'cold properties'.

Super Major

Non-state owned biggest and richest oil companies: ExxonMobil, Shell, BP Chevron, Total and ConocoPhillips.

Supply-Side

Supply side is 50% of the traded volume in trading. One sells and one buys. Supplies come from production. That can be crude oil production, refining and blending. Supplies can be local supplies and supplies coming from imports from the local trading area or from arbitrage business. The supply volume tells if there is easy access to oil as feedstock or petroleum products for consumption. When the market is undersupplied the market becomes a sellers' market. Prices will increase and markets may fall into backwardation. With high demand the refinery cracks would look healthy and refiners may even invest by upgrading their refinery units. Refineries will maximise production. In case of oversupply the market becomes a buyers' market. Prices may collapse into contango. At low prices the refinery cracks may go down. Refineries will suffer and minimise production. Opposite of supply side is the demand side. Supply-demand will always try to get in balance. In a sellers' market prices are high but may soon come down as a result of over-production in all refineries. In a buyers' market prices will be low but then the refineries will undersupply until there is a short in the market. In general one could say that there is an overcapacity in refining in some parts of the market and there is too little refining capacity in other parts of the world. That makes arbitrage business an interesting trading activity. Supply and demand in the oil business is therefore challenging to keep in balance per trading area. Markets are volatile and traders need to extract the maximum value out of that by placing their cargoes in the most profitable markets.

Support (Technical Trading)
A horizontal price range where price hovers due to buying pressure before attempting an upward move.

Support Area (Technical Trading)
A price level where a descending price movement is likely to encounter resistance.

Swap
OTC contracts for the exchange of a fixed price against a floating average or index price, whereby the buyer of the swap buys a fixed price and sells a floating price over the stated calendar period of the agreed contract. Swaps are used to lock in a fixed price. A hedging tool for products. In crude oil there are CFDs which work in the same way with a floating leg and a fixed leg. But those are much more sophisticated. Look at 'CFD' to learn more about that. Swaps are based on month averages and sold in lots of 5, 10, 15 or 20kt. Swaps are traded in the forward market pricing on Platts and Argus quotations. In Europe swaps are pricing most often on barge quotations as that is the most liquid market for products, although they are an easy target for leverage games. HILOS in the fueloil market is a bit special as that is the difference between high sulphur barges and low sulphur cargoes.

Sweet Crude
Crude oil with low sulphur (below 0.5%) content which is less corrosive, burns cleaner, and requires less processing to yield valuable products. Refineries without desulphurisation capacity prefer to buy sweet crude only. Sweet crude is not necessarily more expensive than sour crude. It depends on the yield.

Sweetening
A process at a crude production site where the bad smell of crude is removed.

The bad smell is often caused by the content of acid gas like H_2S and mercaptans. On some occasions it happens that fueloil cargoes contain too much H_2S on arrival at disport. In that case that oil needs to be treated on board the vessel before it can arrive at the jetty. In the worst case scenario a refinery would refuse the cargo. The trader needs to know the refinery requirements. In this case it is often an HSE issue and should be part of the contract requirement from the buyer. So with crude oil we call it sweetening and in products it is called H_2S treating or removal.

Sweet Sour Spread

Difference in value between sweet crude and sour crude. Most refineries with good de-sulphurisation capacity can be very sensitive to the sweet/sour spread. Based on the difference in price they could easily change feedstock at their refinery.

Sweet Trader/Sweet Desk

A trader or desk being responsible for the trading activity of all crudes with sulphur of less than 1.0%. Medium sulphur crude (sulphur between 0.5 and 1.0) is often also traded by the sweet desk. Although it also depends on the company related to the way they have organised their trading system.

Swing Trading

Speculative trading activity in the paper market whereby the trader buys and sells derivatives following the waves of the volatility of a commodity. Target per trading range is to sell close to a peak and buy at a dip. Some technical trading knowledge is required. Following the volatility based on Fibonacci and Elliot wave theory are good examples. A swing trader keeps overnight positions, but those positions are not as big as a trend trader.

Synthetic Crude

Extremely heavy, difficult crude, such as sand oil, which is upgraded to a floating and logistic transferable type of oil and can be processed in a refinery as crude. Without such upgrade the original heavy crude would not be ready for transport. Sand oil is very heavy and is unconventional crude. It even needs some extra treatment to be usable crude. Sand oil is a good example of synthetic crude. Sand oil is mainly produced in Canada and Venezuela. Converting difficult to handle crude into easy logistic to handle and marketable crude, that becomes a 'synthetic crude'.

System

Tools to support trading on a bigger scale such as storage, flexi shorts, supply contracts, shipping system, refinery, marketing outlet etc. If that is organised in your trading activity then it is much easier to take positions and earn money. A trader sees his system as a backup for his trading activity. When something goes wrong the trader will find a solution by placing his cargo in his system. See also 'back up'.

System Trader

A trader who is generating his activity from the production of a refinery or from crude oil production activity. Also traders working for a wholesalers do have a great system of short supplies. The system trader is basically a marketer on behalf of his company. A system trader can create more business around the existing system. He could sell more than the production of the refinery and create a short. Also related to purchases of feedstock a system trader can create some interesting trading strategies. For a system trader there is business created each day, there is always good activity. A 'normal' trader starts his day every time with a blank sheet. He has to make something from nothing. He needs to take more risk but can in some cases also choose to not trade. The choice to not trade is not available for the system trader. Production never stops and tanks may run full. If production has to be stopped as result of lack of sales the costs for missing production will be high. That would be considered as non-performance of the trader.

Systematic Risk

Risk that cannot be eliminated by diversification.

T

T1

Customs document to be used for transport of Non-EU (import duties unpaid) products from one bonded warehouse to another bonded warehouse within the EU. By paying import duties T1 material gets the status of imported product and can be sold into the consumption market in the EU. Not all oil needs to be import duty paid. For products which undergo a process in a refinery or other plant you do not need to pay import duties. The products which are produced are automatically free of import duties. Crude, condensate and naphtha are feedstocks and free of import duties. Straight run fueloil and VGO were coming available from distillation but still they are a feedstock as well. So also those products are free of import duties. Bunkers fueloil is used for consumption on board sea going vessels. But that is not really seen as imported oil; besides that a vessel may leave the EU region. So for bunkers fueloil no import duties are applicable. Fueloil used by utilities for burning purposes to create energy is seen as consumption goods being imported into a country. Import duties are due. Blending components for gasoline has to be imported like all products. You can say that it undergoes a blending process and the oil changes from composition, but blending material does not go through processing units. Components with T1 status must be imported before they can go to the end consumer in the EU.

T2

T2 is the old customs document that states that the oil covered by that document is free of import duties within the EU. Either import duties have been paid over the imported oil or the oil is produced within the EU and no import duties are due in such a case. The market would call it EU qualified product or EU certified product. The T2 document does not exist any longer and has been replaced by the AAD or EAD. The market still uses the term T2 when talking about EU qualified oil, –some old habits never change, and T2 is typical of good old fashioned oil business jargon, a word from the past still used today. Just keep in mind that EU qualified oil loses its status when leaving the EU. When it comes back from a non-EU country then it gets T1 status. For some countries that have an agreement with the EU it would be possible to make a T2L.

T2L
Customs document used for transport of EU products (import duties in EU paid) from one place to another Non-EU member country, but with special connection to EU (e.g. Switzerland). If the product is in transit and final destination is within the EU, then this document is valid to prove that import duties in the EU have already been paid. If product would go to USA and back to EU again, then it would have lost its EU Status. Often one can issue a T2L with destination 'Sea'. If the vessel holding the T2L documents is sailing into international water, the T2L has lost its status.

TA
Trans-Atlantic. Vessels with cargoes crossing the Atlantic Ocean are going Trans-Atlantic. TA is therefore related to arbitrage business. See also 'Atlantic basin'.

T/A
Maintenance shutdown in a refinery. See 'turnaround'.

Tag-Robinson Colorimeter
An instrument used to determine the colour of oils. Important for gasoil. Colours may vary from very yellow to dark brown. Each colour is classified with numbers. A well-used colour scale is the Saybolt colour scale.

Tail Production
Production from an old oil production field that narrows the end of its lifetime. Quality might change slightly, API gets slowly higher. Other specs might change as well. See also 'brown field'.

Tailor Made Crude Blend
Crude oil blended on specification requirements of a buyer for processing purposes at a specific refinery. Often a blend of 2 or 3 standard grades. A refinery can order the required crude for processing purposes from a company having infrastructure in place to blend. In USA supplies of tailor made blended crude are more common than in Europe. In a backwardated market it would be much more efficient for refiners to buy tailor made blended crude. In that case it would be easy to keep stocks at lowest level as keeping high stock, in backwardated markets, for blending purposes in the refinery can then be avoided. In a contango market tanks are preferred to be full at both the refineries and at the blending terminals.

Take or Pay
A term used in contracts to specify a minimum amount of gas a buyer must pay for regardless of whether the gas is taken or not. For example, in a 1.0 mmtpa contract with a 90% take or pay level, the buyer has an obligation to pay for 0.9 mmtpa even if he only takes 0.7 mmtpa. Take or Pay terms are frequently used in long term contracts but the take or pay level will be dependent on the individual arrangement between the buyer and the seller. Depending on contract conditions, buyers may also have the option to take additional volumes (carry forward) or take less volumes (make up) in a given period (usually a year) which may be balanced out over the duration of the contract.

Talking a Book
Traders are talking their own book. It means that traders try to talk the market into a direction which is based on their position, their trading book. Preferably they discuss that with the reporters writing the stories and reporting the quotations. They may use a lot of arguments why the price should go up or down. In some cases they try to find other traders with the same thoughts about the wanted market directions. A trader being long positioned would tell the market and the reporter that the market is tight and that the fundamentals look bullish. A trader being short positioned would prefer lower market prices to indicate bearish signals to the market. If other traders in the market would agree with the opinion of that trader then it would give him a confident feeling; his view is confirmed in the market. Reporters often agree with any trader's view. They need to write the stories.

TAME

Tertiary Amyl Methyl Ether. An oxygenate blendstock formed by the catalytic etherfication of isoamylene with methanol. A gasoline blending component, ether to oxygenate fuel.

TAN (High/Low)

Total Acid Number. Refiners consider low acid crudes to contain less than 0.5 mg koh/g. and observation of acid contents higher than 0.5 mg koh/g are considered as high TAN. A TAN of 4 is often seen in high TAN crudes; I have seen 10 TAN crudes as well. In biofuel components the high TAN content may also be an issue. High TAN oil causes corrosion, it eats the steel away. Maintenance programmes in refineries and other systems are well monitored. High TAN crudes are well discounted versus other crudes because of its challenge. Also the market for high TAN crude is much smaller. If the price for high TAN is not low enough, then high TAN refineries may buy normal grade crude.

Tandem Operation

Describes the normal method of loading from a ship shaped FPSO, where the tanker keeps station astern of the FPSO on approximately the same heading relative to the weather. Either one or both vessels will have some means of propulsion and certainly the off-take tanker. There are similar types of off-take operations undertaken such as from a spread moored FPSO and while these have similar elements as regard to tandem mooring, these differences should nevertheless be understood. See also 'FPSO'.

Tank

Storage unit on land for the purpose of storing liquids, which in this book is meant for crude oil or oil products. Tanks can be classified in low flash and high flash tanks, but also clean or dirty. Tanks can vary from 20 Cbm slop tanks up to a 120.000 Cbm or maybe bigger if they exist. From 3 metre height up to 35 metres. Tanks are built in different sizes which depend on the need of the market related to the oil commodity. Crude goes in big cargoes and requires bigger tanks and ethanol goes in small lots and smaller tanks are required for that. Each tank has its challenge as some tanks are emptied all the time and for some tanks it is preferred to not empty the tank and instead keep a heel (a minimum quantity in tank). Most tanks are filled up and emptied through the entry, the pipeline, at the bottom. There can be three spots in the tank to make it empty. Those spots are the high suction with a big pump to speed up the operations; the low suction which has a line into the middle of the tank towards the bottom to empty the tank as best as possible; and the drain line connected to the bottom of the tank. Often used to get rid of free water before a manipulation (load or discharge) will start. Crude tanks do not always have the drain line. Those tanks are first homogenised and mixed before oil is loaded from the tank. See also the tank drawing of a crude oil tank.

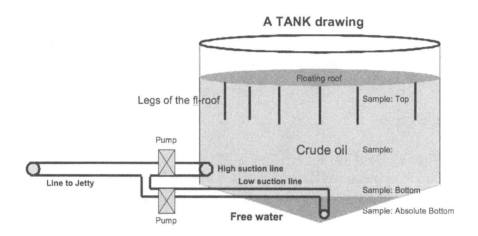

A TANK drawing

Middle of tank = lowest point in bottom

Tank Bottoms

A mixture of oil, waste, and other heavy sludgy material that collects in the bottoms of storage tanks and must be cleaned or pumped out on a regular basis. Cleaning tanks is expensive and time consuming. When a tank is homogenised on a regular basis most of the tank bottoms will become mixed into the oil. It depends on the oil quality in tank if that is wise to do. For dirty oil it would make sense.

Tank Farm

A group of tanks connected to a pipeline through which oil is moved.

Tank Heel

Minimum required quantity in a crude tank. See 'heel'. Net tank capacity minus heel is usable capacity of the tank.

Tank Top

In crude production, logistic people talk about tank tops, meaning the moment or the risk that during the oil production the tanks are running full. When tanks are running full and nothing is planned or able to load then production has to stop. In wintertime with rough sea, wind and high waves, loading at an offshore terminal is not possible until the weather improves. The logistic plan during winter is to keep storage as empty as possible so that a delay of a certain number of days does not result in a tank top situation. Stopping production because of a tank top situation should be avoided. A halt in oil production is also stopping the money machine. We are talking here millions of Dollars of loss if production stops at a big field. It requires a lot of logistic flexibility and certainly includes a lot of vessel planning and rescheduling.

Tank Types

- **Floating Roof Tank**

  Needed for gaseous and so low flash oils like crude, gasoline and naphtha. As the roof is floating on the product, the emissions are minimised and so are product losses. If the oil level in tank is very low the floating roof is standing on legs. Due to the room between the roof and the product gas comes free and that gas often stays also on top of the roof in the open tank column. Sampling is a dangerous job in such a case and is not always allowed. To avoid rainwater handling on a floating roof most storage companies have built a dome on top of a tank, just like the function of an umbrella. In addition to that the oil is also protected against the heat of the sun. The dome helps in further reducing the emissions as well. Most floating roof tanks can handle a product with a TVP of max 11.1 psi. Products with higher pressure should be stored in pressurised (bullet) tanks.

- **Fixed Roof Tank**

  Cheaper to build than a floating roof tank and used for high flash products like fueloil and gasoil (heating and diesel). Do not underestimate the fact that high flash does not burn that easily. Often a tank being empty from gasoil is very dangerous. 'Heavy' gas gets easier satisfied with air and can be very sensitive for static electricity. Unfortunately sometimes an accident happens during the cleaning of empty tanks. Friction causes static electricity and a disaster takes place as the mixtures of gas and air were just waiting for ignition. Fueloil tanks are insulated in most terminals.

- **Fixed Roof with Inner Floater**
  This is a tank meant for jet A1, fuel for an aircraft. The aim is to avoid any water into the product and control losses as a result of gas leaving the tank. Often these tanks have a special coating inside or are made from stainless steel as the jet A1 has to stay clean and free from water and other particle matters in order to meet the product requirements as set for consumption by aircrafts.

- **Insulated Tank**
  A tank protected against the exposure to cold temperatures caused due to weather conditions. The purpose is to maintain the product at temperatures in tank and to minimise the loss of temperature when stored. These types of tanks are meant for high viscosity oil, often fueloil. It is easier and more energy efficient to keep a fueloil tank at a certain temperature when the tank is insulated. Insulated tanks save a lot of energy for the terminal and heating costs to the owner of the product in tank. Products in insulated tanks can also be heated to higher temperatures if required. There are heating coils on the bottom of the insulated tanks for that purpose. Pay attention also to 'heating coils' or 'traced pipeline'.

Tank Washing

The cleaning of a vessel's tanks. It is divided into two types of activities:

- **Water Washing**
  The use of a high-pressure water stream to dislodge clingage and sediment from the bulkheads, bottom, and internal tank structures of a vessel.

- **Crude Oil Washing**
  The use of a high-pressure stream of the crude oil cargo to dislodge or dissolve clingage and sediment from the bulkheads, bottom, and internal tank structures of a vessel during the discharge operation. Also done with light cycle oil (LCO, cutterstock).

Tankers

Size is typically measured in deadweight tonnes (cargo capacity for carrying water). Ships fitted with tanks to carry liquid bulk cargo such as crude petroleum and petroleum products and other liquid and gaseous commodities.

Here are tanker sizes and typical abbreviations (in deadweight tonnes):

· **Product tankers**	2,000	–	20,000
· **GP General Purpose**	16,500	–	25,000
· **MR Medium Range**	25,000	–	50,000
· **Handy size**	35,000		
· **LR1 Large/Long Range**	45,000	–	80,000
· **Panamax**	65,000	–	80,000
· **Aframax**	80,000	–	110,000
· **LR2 Large/Long Range**	80,000	–	160,000
· **Suezmax (1 million barrels)**	130,000	–	150,000
· **VLCC (2 million barrels)**	160,000	–	320,000
· **ULCC**	320,000	–	550,000

Tanking
Tanking is the jargon which expresses that the market takes a sharp turn for the worst. So when the market is tanking you'd better leave your position.

Taped Line
Telephone which is taped by the company you work for. Traders handle business where lots of money is involved. Business agreed by phone is equal to agreed contracts. Therefore one needs to listen back to the conversation on a taped line in case of disagreement with the counterparty. It seldom happens that a tape is used, but it is a security in case of disagreement. See also 'recap'.

TBA
Tertiary Butyl Alcohol. An alcohol primarily used as a chemical feedstock, a solvent or feedstock for isobutylene production for MTBE; produced as a co-product of propylene oxide production or by direct hydration of isobutylene.

TBA
To Be Appointed or To Be Advised. In case an inspector is lacking on a nomination. Apparently, the buyer and seller have not yet agreed which inspector to use. Sometimes there is other information in a deal or nominations not yet available. That information is advised at a later stage.

When a nomination is sent early not all details are known, so fill in 'tba'. The receiver will accept the nomination and immediately request the information that is most important for him.

TBN
To Be Nominated. When a vessel or quantity is unknown or not yet chartered and a first loading or discharge instruction has to be sent to the buyer or seller, then often a vessel name is TBN, meaning vessel name will follow later.

TC
A charter for varying periods of time, usually between two and ten years, under which the owner hires out the vessel to the shipper fully manned, provisioned, stored and insured. The charterer is usually responsible for bunkers, port charges, canal tolls and any crew overtime connected with the cargo. The charter rate (hire) is quoted in terms of a cost per day or month per deadweight ton, excluding the use of bunkers and harbour dues etc. You control every movement of the vessel. Perfect for freight optimisation, but you have to be sure that there is enough work. In some cases you can make your vessel available for 3rd party voyages. It is to avoid having a vessel doing nothing or some additional income can be made due to high freight prices in the market.

TC
Temperature Compensation. Relates to measured volume and difference between actual temperature of the oil and the density at 15 °C or 60 °F.

TCV
Total Calculated Volume on the Bill of Lading. The total volume of all petroleum liquids and sediment and water. See also 'crude oil voyage loss calculations' in the back of the book. Gross barrels on the B/L.

TCV Vessel After Loading
Total calculated volume on board after loading, including slops. See also 'crude oil voyage loss calculations' in the back of the book.

TCV Vessel Before Discharge
Total calculated volume on board before discharge, including slops. See also 'crude oil voyage loss calculations' in the back of the book.

Technical Analyses

An approach to analyses of a futures markets which examines patterns of price change, rates, and changes in volumes of trading, open interest and other statistical indicators. Someone who follows technical rules (called a technician) believes that prices will anticipate changes in fundamentals. 90% of paper trading market consists of traders using technical analyses in order to take trading decisions. This means that if all of this 90% of paper traders in the market see the same bullish buying signal, then many of those traders will buy and the futures price will indeed increase. Most technical traders do believe in 'the trend is your friend' and often therefore the trend will go on. But even then trading paper on a speculative basis requires some trading discipline. Big fundamental events may affect technical patterns.

Technical Value

Differential in quality value of a certain origin of crude oil compared with its benchmark crude. The technical value depends very much on the differences in yield. Each refinery would compare the different crude value depending on their refinery abilities to process the crude and products lifting programme. Traders may use the technical values in order to set or evaluate the market price of the crude oil cargoes to be sold or purchased. See also 'refinery margin' or 'topping margin'. Most companies, especially crude oil producers, have analysts working for them. They enter the qualities of the different crudes in their system which generates a technical value. The calculation of the value depends on market prices for crude oil and the setup of the system. That system has run the crude in a simulated refinery set up. That set up may differ from company to company and is something which is not shared in the market, "the chef's recipe of cooking oil". Technical value is only an indication of the crude value. The market price may be different. Based on the comparison between the market price and the technical value one can decide to buy or to sell. This is a good way for refinery optimisation when it concerns the supply side of feedstocks into the refinery.

Technical Weather

On oil terminals operators enjoy the weather better when it is warm and sunny. People become a bit more relaxed. When business goes slow in operations, they blame it on technical weather.

Temperatures in Distillation Curve

You will see this when you get the distillation curve reported by the inspector. Starts with IBP and ends with FBP. These terms are also in this book.

· **T10** Temperature on the fuel distillation curve at which 10 percent of the fuel has distillated or transitioned from a liquid to vapour state.
· **T30** Temperature on the fuel distillation curve at which 30 percent of the fuel has distillated or transitioned from a liquid to vapour state.
· **T50** Temperature on the fuel distillation curve at which 50 percent of the fuel has distillated or transitioned from a liquid to vapour state.
· **T70** Temperature on the fuel distillation curve at which 70 percent of the fuel has distillated or transitioned from a liquid to vapour state.
· **T90** Temperature on the fuel distillation curve at which 90 percent of the fuel has distillated or transitioned from a liquid to vapour state.

Tender

Request or invite to the market, a reasonable number of potential candidates, wherein a company is asking for offers or bids on a certain contract (in this case to buy or offer oil) at best price. The bids or offers are not shown publicly and have to be received before a certain time and date as mentioned in the tender invitation. The company showing the best price wins the business and has to fulfil the contract. It may happen that after receiving a first bid on the tender a second tender-round may follow. The seller wants even better prices. If the market is used to that practice then the first bid would automatically become a conservative bid to show interest and willingness to seriously participate. The second round will be the seriously taken bidding round. It looks a bit like auctioning. Not really the way a tender should work. See also 'auctioning'.

Term

Longer period. A term contract in oil trading is minimum a year contract. 3 months to a year is often called a mini term. A term customer is a company one has a term contract with. Term is the opposite of 'spot'. In the gas business a term contract may last up to 20 or 25 years. Different markets, different habits.

Terms and Conditions

Often referred to as GT&C, general terms and conditions. The rules setting out the parties' rights and obligations related to a commercial agreement. You always sell basis your own terms and conditions, but when you sell a product on to another party on a back-to-back basis then you may use the terms and conditions that were used for your earlier purchase. To many traders and operators terms and conditions can be complicated; however, you just have to know them as it says something about how to behave related to your deal. Knowledge of the terms and conditions can give you a commercial and logistic advantage over those who do not read them. The GT&C are an appendix to the contract. In the contract, there may be items agreed that differ from the rules according to the GT&C. In that case, the contract text overrules the wording in the GT&C. Main clauses to focus on in the GT&C as operator or trader are demurrage rules, nomination procedures and claims procedures. Read them and highlight what is important to you. In nominations to your customers you may even refer to these clauses. The receiver of your nomination also has obligations. The purpose of not following nomination procedures is to gain flexibility on one side. Otherwise, your counterparty may not have read the GT&Cs. They were made for a reason, so use the rules. GT&Cs are also made to give the seller a benefit but mainly protection, therefore I repeat: "Read your GT&Cs." Knowledge is power.

Terms of Sale

The point at which sellers have fulfilled their obligations so the place where the goods in a legal sense could be said to have been delivered to the buyer. Terms of sale are related to the International Chamber of Commerce terms of trade (INCOTERMS), effective July 1990: exw, fca, fas, fob, cfr, cif, cpt, cip, daf, des, deq, ddu and ddp.

Terms of Sale Types (INCO)

- **EXW (Ex Works)**

  A term of sale which means that the seller fulfils the obligation to deliver when he has made the goods available at his premises (e.g. Works, factory, warehouse, etc.) to the buyer. In particular, the seller is not responsible for loading the goods in the vehicle provided by the buyer or for clearing the goods for export, unless otherwise agreed. The buyer bears all costs and risks involved in taking the goods from the seller's premises to the desired destination. This term thus represents the minimum obligation for the seller.

- **FCA (Free Carrier)**
  A term of sale which means that the seller fulfils their obligation when he has handed over the goods, cleared for export, into the charge of the carrier named by the buyer at the named place or point. If no precise point is indicated by the buyer, the seller may choose, within the place or range stipulated, where the carrier should take the goods into their charge.

- **FAS (Free Alongside Ship)**
  A term of sale which means that the seller fulfils his obligation to deliver when the goods have been placed alongside the vessel on the quay or in lighters at the named port of shipment. This means that the buyer has to bear all costs and risks of loss of or damage to the goods from that moment. See also 'STS'.

- **FOB (Free On Board)**
  An international term of sale which means that the seller fulfils his obligation to deliver when the goods have passed over the ship's rail at the named port of shipment. This means that the buyer has to bear all costs and risks to loss of or damage to the goods from that point. The FOB term requires the seller to clear the goods for export. Risk and title goes over from seller to buyer as soon as the oil is pumped through the ship's manifold during loading. Quality is based on specifications in tank at loadport.

- **CFR (Cost and Freight)**
  A term of sale where the seller pays the costs and freight necessary to bring the goods to the named port of destination. The risk of loss or damage to the goods, as (continued) well as any additional costs due to events occurring after the time the goods have been delivered on board the vessel, is transferred from the seller to the buyer when the goods pass the ship's rail in the port of shipment. Risk and title goes over from seller to buyer as soon as the oil is pumped through the ship's manifold during loading.

- **CIF (Cost, Insurance and Freight)**
  A term of sale where the seller has the same obligations as under the CFR but also has to procure marine insurance against the buyer's risk of loss or damage to the goods during the carriage. The seller contracts for insurance and pays the insurance premium. The CIF term requires the seller to clear

the goods for export. Risk and title goes over from seller to buyer as soon as the oil is pumped through the ship's manifold during loading.

- **CPT (Carriage Paid To)**
  A term of sale which means that the seller pays the freight for the carriage of the goods to the named destination. The risk of loss of or damage to the goods, as well as any additional costs due to events occurring after the time the goods have been delivered to the carrier, is transferred from the seller to the buyer when the goods have been delivered into the custody of the carrier. If subsequent carriers are used for the carriage to the agreed upon destination, the risk passes when the goods have been delivered to the first carrier. The CPT term requires the seller to clear the goods for export.

- **CIP (Carriage and Insurance Paid To)**
  A term of sale which means that the seller has the same obligations as under CPT, but with the addition that the seller has to procure cargo insurance against the buyer's risk of loss of or damage to the goods during the carriage. The seller contracts for insurance and pays the insurance premium. The buyer should note that under the CIP term the seller is required to obtain insurance only on minimum coverage. The CIP term requires the seller to clear the goods for export.

- **DAF (Delivered At Frontier)**
  A term of sale which means that the sellers fulfil their obligation to deliver when the goods have been made available cleared for export, at the named point and placed at the frontier, but before the customs Terms of sale border of the adjoining country. Risk and title goes over from seller to buyer as soon as the oil is pumped through the ship's manifold during discharging.

- **DDU (Delivered Duty Unpaid)**
  A term of sale where the seller fulfils his obligation to deliver when the goods have been made available at the named place in the country of importation. The seller has to bear the costs and risks involved in bringing the goods thereto (excluding duties, taxes and other official charges payable upon importation) as well as the costs and risks of carrying out customs formalities. The buyer has to pay any additional costs and to bear any risks caused by failure to clear the goods in time.

- **DDP (Delivered Duty Paid)**

Delivered duty paid means that the seller fulfils his obligation to deliver when the goods have been made available at the named place in the country of importation. The seller has to bear the risks and costs, including duties, taxes and other charges of delivering the goods thereto, clear for importation. While the EXW term represents the minimum obligation for the seller, DDP represents the maximum.

- **DAP (Delivered at Port/Place)**

A term of sale where the seller fulfils his/her obligation to deliver when the goods have been made available to the buyer on board the ship, un-cleared for import at the named port of destination. The seller has to bear all the costs and risks involved in bringing the goods to the named port destination. DAP is the same term as DES in the old days. Quantity is based on out-turn figures unless otherwise agreed. Risk and title go over at disport.

- **DEQ (Delivered Ex Quay [Duty Paid])**

A term of sale which means that the DDU term has been fulfilled when the goods have been available to the buyer on the quay (wharf) at the named port of destination, cleared for importation. The seller has to bear all risks and costs including duties, taxes and other charges of delivering the goods thereto.

Termination of a Contract

If both buyer and seller agree that a certain agreement does not work for both then a contract can be terminated. Or when a buyer or seller is not performing to the contract the affected company in the contract may have the right to terminate the contract with a certain notice of time. The contract will in such a case stop before it has reached its date of expiry.

Testing Method

The procedure of a test. There are many different ways to test a certain specification of a product. The market standard has its requirement for how to test different specifications of a product. The test outcome can be qualitative, positive or negative and in quantities, such as measurement of content, what percentage sulphur, while appearance is a visual test. See also 'ASTM', 'DIN' or 'EN590/228'. All methods are numbered and described.

Sometimes a different method is used for testing. When the required method cannot be done because a laboratory is lacking the correct equipment for the test, a waiver may be requested to deviate from the standard requirements. Normally it would not be such a problem. Most results will be equal. It could be that one test method is much more accurate and reliable than another test method. Therefore standard requirements are important.

'The trend is your friend.'

Looking at the bar chart of the oil prices or other commodities the trend-line over time goes one direction, up or down in a reasonable regular time/trend. When this trend is indicating that the price is going up then the trend is your friend and it is indicating that you'd better follow it and go long. It is very theoretical as the oil price may collapse even if you follow the fundamentals; however, the whole market knows and believes that 'the trend is your friend' and so many market participants will trade accordingly. See also the chapter 'words of wisdom' for many more trading expressions like this one. Traders speak about uptrends and downtrends. Find them in this book.

Thermal Cracking

Cracking of atmospheric/vacuum residues. A refining process in which heat and pressure are used to break down, rearrange or combine hydrocarbon molecules. Thermal cracking is a process, at a temperature up to 800°C/1472°F and a pressure up to 700 Kpa, used to crack distillate and heavy oil into smaller molecules with better antiknock properties. Thermal cracking includes visbreaking, fluid coking, delayed coking and other thermal cracking processes.

Thin Market

A market in which the trading volume is low and in which consequently bid and ask quotes are wide and the liquidity of the commodity traded is low. The market here is lacking liquidity and can be risky to enter. A thin market can easily be manipulated and that results in a lot of unexpected volatility.

Third Party Access (TPA)

The right for a third party to use a specified pipeline or facility of another company.

Threshold Limit Value (TLV)

The lime-weighted average concentration of a substance to which workers may be repeatedly exposed, for a normal 8-hours workday or 40-hours workweek, day after day without adverse effect. High focus on HSE required.

Throughput

A term used to describe the total volume of raw materials that are processed by a plant such as an oil refinery in a given period. In storage it is the total volume of crude oil and refined products that are handled by a tank farm, pipeline, or terminal loading facility. Number of throughputs per month indicates the activity in that period and says something about the utilisation of a terminal.

Tick

The smallest allowable increment of price movement for a futures contract. Also referred to as 'minimum price fluctuation'. The life graph on the screen is called 'the ticker'.

Tight Emulsion

This consists of many very small water droplets that do not separate readily due to high surface tension, or due to emulsifying agents that prevent coalescing.

Tight Oil

Another word for 'shale oil'. Opposite of conventional oil (traditional way of oil production). Shale oil can also be called 'trapped oil'.

Time-Charter

A charter for varying periods of time, usually between two and ten years, under which the owner hires out the vessel to the shipper fully manned, provisioned, stored and insured. The charterer is usually responsible for bunkers, port charges, canal tolls and any crew overtime connected with the cargo. The charter rate (hire) is quoted in terms of a cost per day or month per deadweight ton, excluding the use of bunkers and harbour dues etc. You control every movement of the vessel. Perfect for freight optimisation, but you have to be sure that there is enough work. In some cases you can make your vessel available for 3rd party voyages. It is to avoid having a vessel doing nothing or some additional income can be made due to high freight prices in the market. See also 'charter types'.

Time of Analysing

When an oil sample is taken the traders prefer to know the test results as soon as they are available. Only when the traders know the result they can start selling and when it is off-spec they need to use more time to make a quality on-spec. When can you expect your quality sheet on your desk? That depends on the time which is needed for analyses related to the qualities that need to be reported. But remember your sample is not the only one which needs to be tested; there may be waiting times and delays at labs. Here an overview of analysis time use per quality. Depending on which method, underneath is the average (however several methods can change significantly). Normal time spent for analyses:

- **Density** – 10 minutes.
- **RVP** – 1 hour.
- **Sulphur** – 0.5 hour.
- **Viscosity** – 1 hour.
- **Pour point** – 3 hours.
- **CFPP** – 2 hours.
- **Cloud point** – 2 hours.
- **Colour** – 0.5 hour.
- **Copper corrosion** – 4 hours.
- **Silver corrosion** – 4 hours.
- **Flashpoint** – 1 hour.
- **Smoke point** – 1 hour.
- **RON/MON** – 4 hours.
- **Doctor test** – 1 hour.
- **Distillation curve** – 2 hours.
- **Al + Si** – 8 hours.
- **Vanadium** – see above (together 8 hours).
- **Purity** – 2 hours.
- **Conductivity** – 1 hour.
- **Water** – 1 hour.
- **BS&W** – 2 hours.
- **CCR** – 3 hours.
- **C4** – 2 hours.
- **Piona-test** – 3 hours.
- **Compatibility** – 2 hours.
- **Aromatics** – 2 hours.

- **Benzene** – 2 hours.
- **Crude Yield** – 10 days.
- **Crude Assay** – 10 days.
- **TAN** – 1 hour.
- **Sediments** – 2 hours.
- **Oxygenates** – 2 hours.
- **Caloric Value** – 2 hours.
- **Lead** – 2 hours.
- **Appearance** – 0.5 hour.
- **Cetane** – 3 hours.

Time of Sampling

When a vessel arrives or when a blend is ready then traders' and operators' biggest concern is time. Waiting time needs to be set to a minimum and qualities must be reported as fast as possible; time is money. But sampling, testing and measurement take time. An inspector needs to be called into a refinery, there must be an order to the terminal, the vessel and the inspector. The instructions must be clear, there is time to take a sample and there is time to bring a sample to a lab. And then the analyses take time as well. See here an estimation of time used for sampling. Depending on several circumstances (safety regulations, weather conditions) these are average times normally used.

- **Tank sampling (roof on top)** – 1.5 hour.
- **Tank sampling (roof halfway down)** – 3 hours (breathing apparatus – 2 man).
- **Rhine barge sampling** – 2 hours.
- **10 kt products tanker sampling** – 4 hours.
- **50 kt products tank sampling** – 4 hours.
- **Aframax sampling** – 4 hours.
- **Suezmax sampling** – 5 hours.
- **VLCC sampling** – 5 hours.
- **Sampling during STS activity single vessel** – sampling during STS is not permitted (4 hours).
- **Sampling during STS activity multi vessel in to VLCC** – sampling during STS is not permitted (4/5 hours).
- **Time sample to laboratory** – depending on location (buoys, traffic jam) 1 / 2/ 3 hours (varies depending on actual circumstances).

· **Time sample at lab to start analyses** – after registration 10 minutes; however it depends.

Time Spread

Time spread as a position taken based on time value or the forward market. One can buy a futures contract gasoil in June and sell a futures contract in August. When the market is in contango then one can be long physical oil on the prompt basis (product in storage) and hedge it in the forward market. Look also at 'front to back' and 'contango'. One can also speculate on spreads. A trader who believes that a market will flip from contango to backwardation can buy a time spread (buy the front and sell the back) and cash in later. When you sell a time spread, you sell the front and buy the back. If in that case the market might change from backwardation to a contango situation again money may be cashed in. A producer or refiner is always long physical oil. That oil position is often hedged by paper related to the forward market. Therefore time spreads in physical oil business cannot be avoided. Time spreads are less volatile than product spreads or location spreads.

Time Value

Value of the structure, the value of the difference between the months in the forward futures market. See also 'contango', 'backwardation', 'forward market' and 'structure'.

Title

A set of documents defining that the holder of such owns the goods being transacted upon. The most important of such being the Clean on board Bill of Lading, and seller's invoice.

Title Point

The place where risk and title of the cargo to be loaded or discharged go over from seller to buyer. At loadport when CIF, CFR or FOB deals are done, and at discharge port when a DAP (old DES) deal is done. See also 'manifold'.

Toluene ($C_6H_5CH_3$)

Colourless liquid of the aromatic group of petroleum hydrocarbons, made by the catalytic reforming of petroleum naphthas containing methyl cyclohexane. A high-octane gasoline-blending agent. Aromatics in gasoline are limited to maximum 35%. Most refineries have produced reformate and cracked naphtha that already contain many aromatics, therefore toluene is not used anymore as blending component. That was used before the mid-nineties. Toluene was in the past combined with xylene. The experienced gasoline blender may recall the use of tx-blend.

Ton Mile

The movement of one single ton of commodity freight by train for one mile. Used to calculate the total amount of commodity in weight (tons) that is shipped by a transportation company.

Topped Crude Oil

Oil from which the light ends have been removed by a simple refining process. Also referred to as 'reduced crude oil'.

Topping Margin

The value of the products minus the cost of the raw material. Example: Crude oil value $120 per barrel and processed in a fictive refinery. The column 'Raffi %' you see the percentage production after primary distillation, crack value is the margin per barrel per refined product, calc. is calculation to get a weighted average. Topping margin is 2.02 USD. This is not much to cover refinery cost and does not include costs of the cracking processes of a refinery.

Product in bbl.	Raffi %	Crack	Crude oil	Calc.
Butane, Propane	5.00%	-1.00	120.00	-5.00
Gasoline blends	3.50%	3.75	120.00	140.63
Diesel, Jet Fuel	37.50%	5.10	120.00	191.25
Fueloil, Resids	20.00%	-6.25	120.00	-125.00
Total Value	100.00%	2.0188	122.02	201.88
Topping Margin		USD	Per barrel	+ 2.02

Topping-Off

Filling up cargo tanks which were only partially filled at the loading port because of port or canal draft restrictions. The filling up occurs outside the loading port through lightering activities, or at another loading port. A reason for lightering could be draft restrictions at loadport. Therefore as an example much activity takes place just outside the 'Big Belt' area at Skaw where due to draft restrictions VLCCs are topped off by STS operations.

Topping Refinery

Refinery with limited refining capacity mainly used to supply local markets. See also 'simple refinery' and 'Nelson complexity index'.

Top Up

Extra quantity of oil a trader would look for in the market in order to optimise the sold contract quantity up to its maximum limit, or to buy additional volume on top of an existing cargo as part of a freight optimisation. The operational process to load the vessel to the maximum is called topping-off. Freight cost per ton comes down when one maximises the quantity in a vessel.

Tolerances

Quantity instructions in nominations. See 'loading tolerances' for a full overview.

To Order/Negotiable

A Bill of Lading in which the merchandise is consigned directly 'to order' or 'to the order of' a designated party, usually the shipper or a bank. The phrase 'to order' or 'to the order of (a designated party)' signifies negotiability permitting the title of the merchandise to be transferred many times by means of appropriate endorsements.

Total Acid Number (TAN)

Expressed in milligrams of potassium hydroxide, the TAN reflects the number needed to neutralise the acid in one gram of oil. The TAN is an especially important parameter for refiners, as the higher the number the more corrosive the crude can be and thus the more difficult and more expensive it is to handle. A high TAN affects crude prices negatively. TAN in crude oil causes corrosion when heated. Nevertheless, some refineries can handle high TAN crude and may take the benefit of the 'discounted' prices in the market. See also TAN (high/low). High TAN crude can be blended with low TAN crude at the refinery.

Total Existent Sediment

Combination of inorganic and hydrocarbon sediments existing in a fuel as delivered. Sediments in bunker fuel may cause problems in engines such as a complete stoppage of operation and combustion, blocking and plugging of burner tips and screens and corrosion. It also causes a loss of heat release.

Therefore the maximum allowed content of sediments in bunker fuel for vessels is 1.0%.

Total Observed Volume (TOV)
The total measured volume of all petroleum liquids, BS&W and free water at observed temperature. Expressed in cubic metre or/and barrels.

Tower
The distillation unit in a refinery. See also 'column'.

Tower Bottoms
Straight run fueloil from the distillation tower at the refinery. Feedstock for the vacuum tower or cat cracker.

Towing Assist Vessel (TAV)
Vessel which has sufficient power, manoeuvrability and equipment to perform towing assistance to shuttle tanker or FPSO.

Traced Pipeline
Pipeline which can be heated and is therefore insulated. Heavy fueloil with a high viscosity can get stuck in a pipe when the temperature comes down. Pipelines above ground at a terminal can be traced. Lines underground are not traced. They are also not really exposed to extremely cold temperatures.

Trade Date
The date on which a trade occurs, also 'contract date' or 'deal date'.

Traders
Buyers and sellers of large quantities of petroleum products. They use the spot markets as a basis for their deals. They also buy and sell derivatives for hedging and speculative purposes. The core task is to make money. They do that by earning margins on trades, by earning money on time value, by optimising refining and marketing systems, by blending and by taking risk positions and many more activities related to trading. Their trading power depends on the company profile they work for. Financial strength and good reputation are important but also a good trading management giving the mandate to trade. A trader starts each day with a blank sheet of paper and has to create positions to make money. They can choose to buy, to sell or to wait

and do nothing. That decision is based on their market view, but they must at least make a decision. A marketing trader, working for a refiner or crude producer, has no choice. Production keeps coming and not selling is not an option. Marketing traders will sell their oil at the highest price they can get at that moment, on that day they must sell their oil. The trader would buy and sell with the goal of getting the highest margin possible. If there is no money to make, he decides to do nothing and will track the market until something profitable crosses his path. In most companies that should happen fast, as traders are hired to create business and make money.

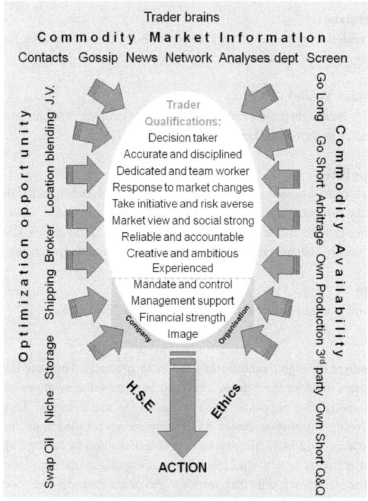

Trades

Purchase, sale or swap of any commercial products as from time to time included in a company portfolio, including paper transactions. Paper trades are done when bid and offer match each other. Physical oil trades are more complex as it involves logistics, quantities, qualities, time value, credit and much more.

Trading

Buying and selling or the holding of any position, paper or physical oil, for a period of time with the intent of preventing a loss or making a profit on the difference between purchase price and the market price at time of sale of the asset or output from the asset. The intention defines the kind of trading: Speculating, hedging, market making, etc.

Trading at Market (TAM)

Also called TAMM, trading at morning marker. A trader can give a TAM offer or bid for futures. The prices will be related to a morning marker. The exchange has set a fixed time of one or two minutes' trading session and calculates the average price level as settlement price. All TAM bids and offers will be matched by the exchange at the end of the day. This matching will be based on a first come first served basis. Deals which cannot be matched are cancelled. The traders with a matched deal get their deals confirmed. See also 'trading at settlement'. In crude, gasoil or gasoline at Nymex this marker session is calculated based on activity between 4:29 and 4:30 p.m. London-time, which is equal to TAS Brent futures (ICE). An arbitrage hedge gets the same moment/time of settlement here.

Trading at Settlement (TAS)

A trader may during the day bid or offer futures for a certain month at settlement level. All TAS bids and offers will be matched by the exchange at the end of the day. This matching will be based on a first come first served basis. Deals which cannot be matched are cancelled. The traders with a matched deal get their deals confirmed. TAMM is based on a morning marker USA, Nymex based, a settlement price of a small morning session of one or two minutes. See timing at 'trading at market'. A bid TAMM versus an offer TAS works as a great Brent/WTI spread.

Trading Discipline

The ability of the trader to follow the trading rules and act accordingly. "Cut losses and let profits run." "Do not fall in love with your position." Also stay within 'mandate'. You will find these words and expression in this book. Following these rules of discipline is probably the most difficult part and an important part related to paper trading. A technical trader has to take rational decisions, not emotional. Taking a loss is something no one likes. But often a trader just has to cut losses. Maybe out of 10 trades he might have to cut his losses 8 times. If he does that according to plan those losses would be relatively small. The 2 positive trades would make a lot of money if the trader is able to let profits run. Cashing in a trade as soon as it is in the money would mean that the trader takes small gains only. That would not be enough to cover the losses. Therefore traders must be patient and create a loss from peak rule. As long as the price is going in the right direction his profit will grow. As soon as the price moves to the loss from peak level the trader must cash in his profit. The result would be great. No trader can take all his profit at the peak. Traders taking a profit at a peak apparently did not introduce a discipline plan, even though the result is good when the price was at peak it could have gone up further. There was still more potential 'to ride the profit'. Traders who do not cut losses and only take small profits become a net loser. See also therefore the description of a 'net loser'. So make your trading plan before you step into the market and then 'stick to the plan'. Trading discipline is not only important for paper traders like speculators, also physical traders have positions, like time spread and product spreads. See also 'loss from peak'.

Trading Network

A forum of traders who trade different strategies and have ideas about how to make money in the markets. They come together to discuss these topics to educate themselves and learn new ideas and tactics for making money. But the network of a trader also means the people he knows. His friends and relations in the business. From his network he would receive market information and offers or bid on products. The quality of his network and his decisions depends on the personality of the trader. Network building is done by meeting the market and getting introduced. The better and bigger the network the more business opportunities a trader will create. That creation of business depends again on the mandates and the image of the trader and the company he works for. As network is important, a trader should not sit behind his desk the whole year. Circulate and supply your business cards into the market, meet people, make friends. A trader's network also includes relations with people in different departments of the company he works at. Cross commodity network is important.

Trading Psychology

One of the key factors in success or failure at trading. The ability to control fear and greed will determine a trader's long-term success. Traders who are too greedy will overtrade and make many mistakes. Traders who are too fearful will have 'analysis/paralysis', always seeking perfect answers and afraid to pull triggers on their trades. Fearful traders delay their decision long enough so that the trading opportunity has disappeared when he is obviously ready to pull the trigger. Training on such trading behaviour would be very helpful to make even experienced traders much stronger. Internal meetings should not be the excuse for not making a decision. Decision making is very important. It is part of personality and self-confidence. Decision making can take a lot of energy but is also something one can learn.

Trading Range

The prices traded between the high and low for a specific time period (day, week, month, contract life, etc.).

Trading Software

A tool used by traders to identify the trend. Some include charts, technical indicators or proprietary 'black box' indications that the market is going higher or lower. See also 'screen'.

Transaction

An agreed deal, a trade done and confirmed. Price reporters try to gather as much information as possible about each transaction. They need that to create their assessments. The number of transactions depends on the cargo sizes traded and of course on the activity of the traders. The number of crude oil transactions in a company, which trades all commodities, is relatively small compared with the number of transactions done by the traders being active in the barge market. Cargo trades involve a higher volume of oil per transaction and therefore more risk. If a trader is a dollar off from market value then he will lose more money on a big cargo and on a small barge. Barge trades are done in smaller lots and therefore the number of transactions is much bigger. That creates a bigger workload for product operators and back office. See also 'back office'.

Transaction Cost
The cost of carrying out a trade. The total costs are related to the trading activity, which means that costs related to barge trading is more expensive than cargo trading. See also 'cost of carry'.

Transfer Point or TP
The inlet flange of an outgoing pipeline from a production measurement point where the transporter/charterer/buyer shall receive petroleum production or crude from an operator/seller. Where oil passes the flange at the manifold of the vessel or barge, the risk and title will pass from seller to buyer. For FOB, CFR and CIF sales that happens at loadport. For DAP (old DES) sales the risk and title goes over at disport.

Transit Time
The period of time designated by a pipeline company for petroleum products to become available at the destination.

Transition period
The period from summer to winter and winter to summer related to the diesel and gasoline specification. Some extra requirements on specification are added to the petrol, mainly related to emission reduction and requirements on cold properties. In those periods the gasoline and diesel has intermediate grade specification. So there are summer specs, winter specs and intermediate specs requirements for gasoline and diesel during the year. See also 'cold properties'.

Transparency
In relation to a market, this refers to the tendency for price signals and other market information to be easily visible to all participants and for market pressures to be quickly reflected in price levels. See also 'liquid and illiquid markets'.

Trapped Oil
Another word for 'shale oil'. Opposite of conventional oil (traditional way of oil production). Shale oil can also be called 'tight oil'.

Treating Processes

Additional processes carried out at refineries prior to the petroleum products being marketed. Treating is used to 'clean up' products. E.g. The reduction of sulphur content in gasoline or hydro-treating where gasoil becomes de-sulphured and low sulphur diesel is produced. See also 'sweetening'.

Trend

A direction that the market is headed in where it appears that all major market indicators are moving in the right direction. It can be an uptrend or a downtrend. Important advice is to trade with the trend. See also 'trend trader'.

Trend Lines

A line drawn that connects either a series of highs or lows in a trend. The trend line can represent either support as in an uptrend line or resistance as in a downtrend line.

Trend Trader

A trend trader takes positions based on longer term investments. Such a position can remain for weeks or months. The trend is his friend. A good trader would not make the mistake of trading against the trend. When the trend breaks its pattern then the trader would leave his position and invest in another commodity with a clear trend (up or down).

Trigger Pricing

Sale of oil on a formula based price but where the buyer has the possibility to pick the pricing day(s). That pricing decision has to be on a day on which no official quotations have been reported yet.

Trim (Draft)

The difference between the fore and aft draft of the vessel. When the aft draft is greater than the forward draft, the vessel is said to be trimmed 'by the stern'. When the aft draft is less than the forward draft the vessel is said to be trimmed 'by the head'. If the vessel is perfect (horizontal, water pass) lying in the water then we call it 'even keel'.

Tripping

A pump is tripping or a system is tripping. Means there are failures in the systems caused by overpressure or lack of feed. The pump suddenly stops pumping or is stuttering. When oil is pumped and the tank gets empty, air will come in the pipe, in the product. If that air comes into the pump, the pump will get a failure message, as it registers 'no-feed'. The pump stops so it needs to be re-started. A vapour recovery unit can get saturated when there is too much gas and the system will stop working, the capacity of the VLU is not big enough or the oil is too gaseous. Tripping can cause delays in some cases.

True Vapour Pressure (TVP)
The absolute pressure exerted by the gas produced by evaporations from a liquid, when the gas and liquid are in balance at the actual temperature. RVP is a vapour pressure at 100°F/37.72°C while the TVP is the vapour pressure at operating temperatures. TVP is often linked to HSE requirements related to the type of tank. A kind of indication says that if the TVP is below 11.1 psi the oil could be stored in a tank with a floating roof. When it comes above 11.1 psi then pressured tanks are required. These numbers are according to my understanding and have been checked in the storage market. Nevertheless the rules may be different between different storage companies.

Trunk Line
A main pipeline.

TS-1
Jet fuel produced and used in Russia and other CIS-states. Due to different regulation related to the certification jet fuel, TS1 may be cheaper than jet A1. Quality requirement for the use as aviation fuel is the same as jet A1 and is therefore well accepted and used as such. See also 'jet A1'.

TTO
Tanker Take-Over. Selling a loaded crude oil cargo including the charter party. Unfortunately, in my opinion, one has to be careful when seeing terms like this in oil offers as this term has been used a lot in fake offers from 'jokerbrokers' and there are a lot of those in the market. TTO is often used then in combination with many other abbreviations such as LOI, IPCO, TTT, RWA, SPA or POP etc. The price levels are most often way off market level and it includes unrealistic huge quantities. I heard traders asking for the offer and as a reply they got the message: "Not available anymore."

TTT

Tanker to Tanker Transfer. Better call it ship to ship transfer (STS). Often these terms are offered by brokers showing Bonny light crude oil (BLCO). Unfortunately, in my opinion, one has to be careful when seeing terms like this in oil offers as this term has been used a lot in fake offers from 'jokerbrokers' and there are a lot of those in the market. TTT is often used then in combination with many other abbreviations such as LOI, IPCO, POP, RWA, SPA or TTO etc. The price levels are most often way off market level and it includes unrealistic huge quantities. I heard traders asking for the offer and as a reply they got the message: "Not available anymore."

TTT

Tank to Tank Transfer. Pumpover from one land tank to another land tank at the same terminal. Sales term 'ex-tank' will be used in this case. Qualities are as per tank certificate and quantities are often based on the ex-tank numbers. Risk and title goes over as soon as the oil leaves the tank.

Tugs

Tugboat. Used to guide big tankers into the harbour or to control stability of a vessel when doing ship to ship operations. At an STS operation at Skaw, Denmark where a VLCC is loaded, lots of tugs are used for a safe operation. Two tugs control the VLCC. Two tugs control the suezmax and one tug is available as standby in case of problems. There is also a need for fenders. The whole operation including potential demurrage is not cheap and is part of the calculation for arbitrage business when fueloil is supplied to Singapore.

Turnaround

Periodic, planned shutdown of a refinery or processing plant during which preventive maintenance, inspections, safety checks, repairs, cleaning and overhaul of units are conducted. Often these turnarounds are published and noticed in the market. See also 'shut down'. During bigger turnarounds, which happen once in every 4 or 5 years, a refinery may get modified. This is the chance to realise new investments in the refinery. If not done, then wait another 4 or 5 years. Shutting down a refinery just for the sake of investments is very costly for the refinery as such.

Type of Oil

Oil can be classified based on quality or geography. But for environmental purposes related to accidents the US environment protection agency has classified the crude based on weight and viscosity. A classification related to oil spill response. That leads to the following classifications, the heavier the oil the bigger the visual impact on the environment. Light oil is much more gaseous and flammable.

· **Class A:** Light, volatile oil.
· **Class B:** Non-sticky oil.
· **Class C:** Heavy, sticky oil.
· **Class D:** Non fluids.

The market classifies the crude oil based on sulphur, TAN and gravity reported in API. Based on sulphur there are three classes. Those are sweet with sulphur below 0.5%, medium sulphur crude with sulphur between 0.5% and 1.0 %, sour crude is all crude over 1.0 % and heavy sour crude could be based on all crude with sulphur above 3%. On TAN we speak about high TAN and low TAN; every crude with a TAN specification over 0.5 is by definition a high TAN crude. The classification on API is very important and relates very much to value. Low API is heavy and lower priced and vice versa. Heavier crude is more difficult to market and to process. Condensate can be light enough to become available for the petrochemical industry. Here an overview based on API.

· Crude oil with API < 20 is extra heavy crude.
· Crude oil with API >20-<28 is heavy crude.
· Crude oil with API >28-<40 is medium crude.
· Crude oil with API >40-<50 is light crude.
· Crude oil with API >50 is condensate.

Typicals

Typical specification or standard spec without any guarantees mentioned. The market knows what qualities of a product are being produced. The seller will inform the buyers what the specification of the oil is before offering. The buyers would trust the seller and buys oil on typicals. This happens often in the fueloil market where M100 is traded according to the typical specs. Also in crude the qualities are standard and may fluctuate from the typicals, but here the typicals are related to the assay. A crude quality which is far off from the assay quality is an off-spec crude. Once in a while (in some years) a new standard spec will be published. When the real quality is just a bit off from the typicals then it would be accepted. In some cases the specs are much too different from the typicals as agreed. That can happen due to production changes or because of wrong information that has been supplied. In principle the contract does not cover guarantees and the chance to cash in money from a claim is difficult. A company having good relations would compensate for the failure. I would at least try to get a guarantee on the parameters (in oil products) which are most important at the moment of purchasing. So basically unfinished oil and blending components can be traded and valuated on typicals. Finished oil is sold on standard specifications as set in the international market. Standard specifications have guaranteed requirements on all specs. Off-spec supplies on standard products are not allowed to be marketed at the petrol stations or other consumer markets, unless a waiver has been given.

U

UKC

UK-Continent. Tanker market term for the UK and North West European (NWE) region closest to it. Worldscale rates are quoted by reporters based from one important loading point to the UKC. See also 'flat rate' and 'worldscale' for further explanation about freight rates.

UKC

Under Keel Clearance. The space between the sea or canal bottom and the keel of the vessel while sailing or in anchored position. A vessel that is sailing is deeper in the water and that has an effect on the UKC, therefore slow sailing is recommended in low draft areas. Vessel owners have a certain UKC requirement for their vessels, an HSE Standard. E.g. An owner can have a UKC requirement of 10% for their vessel. When a vessel goes to a port with draft restriction, the canal to that port may have a low draft as well. When a vessel loads up to 14-metre draft, sailing 5 knots to the terminal through a canal with 15 metre draft, then the speed of the vessel could give a 0.4-metre squad effect. The 14.0-metre loaded plus 0.4 metre = 14.4 metre draft. 10% is 1.44 metres. The canal draft 15.0 metre minus 1.44 metre is a UKC requirement of 13.54 metres. This means that even though the draft at disport is 14 metres the vessel can only take oil in the cargo until 13.54-metre draft. The canal to the port and the HSE standard of the owner is the port restriction. Most orders are loading up to safe arrival draft at disport. A 50-centimetre difference in draft can be roughly 50-60kb crude oil less loaded on an afra-max vessel. So as an operator do not look only at draft at disport but think also about the draft of the canal to the terminal including UKC requirement of the vessel owner. Just before loading the master of the vessel checks with the agent in the arrival port, what the draft will be in disport. Now loading can commence. Contractual agreed tons or barrels that cannot be loaded on board due to draft restrictions or ullage restrictions at the receiving end will be charged as deadfreight to the buyer. If you would like to push the vessel to go for more draft then the owner would require a letter of indemnity. Then as charter you would take too much risk, you would be chargeable when a vessel is grounded. Better accept what the owner advises, the risk is too big as a vessel repair is very expensive.

UKCS

United Kingdom Continental Shelf. The submerged extension of the land territory of the UK, either to the edge of the continental margin or alternatively for a distance of up to 200 nautical miles from the coast. The UKCS can be broadly divided into five main areas of interest: Central North Sea, Northern North Sea, Southern Gas Basin, West of Britain and Atlantic Margin. See also 'NCS'.

UKOOA Matrix

Abbreviation for United Kingdom Offshore Operators' Association matrix. Most often, an officer's matrix of personnel on board the ship is sent. It shows an overview of number of people on board, their origin, rank, experience and a training/course overview of the crew on board. Different companies have their own requirements. Often there is a requirement that the crew is able to speak proper English, but for other countries, they may be even more requirements or some companies set minimum years of experience requirements per crewmember related to rank. Delivery of the matrix can be a requirement as part of vessel clearing. The terminal where loading or discharging wants to check this with the receiver's requirements. A vessel can be rejected because of people with too little experience on board or not being able to speak English. Each company has their own rules and there's not much flexibility there. It concerns company HSE regulation and that has to be respected by all parties involved with a cargo.

ULCC

Ultra Large Crude Carrier. These tankers have capacities between 320,000 and 600,000 dwt. Due to draft challenges this vessel size can only load and discharge at deep water ports. An alternative is to relate these vessels to STS operations or floating storage during contango markets. A ULCC can be considered as a dirty tanker and is mainly used for the purpose of crude oil transportation.

Ullage
The unoccupied space in a storage tank or vessel that is still available for use. If the trader wants to use that available ullage he would buy a top up in order to optimise vessel's ullage as part of a freight optimisation strategy. See also 'overage'.

ULSD
Ultra-Low Sulphur Diesel.

Ultra-Low Sulphur Distillate Fueloil
Distillate fueloil having a sulphur content of 10 ppm or lower. Ultra-low sulphur distillate fueloil that will be shipped by pipeline must satisfy the sulphur specification of the shipping pipeline if the pipeline specification is below 10 ppm. Distillate fueloil intended for pipeline shipment that fails to meet a pipeline sulphur specification that is below 10 ppm will be classified as low-sulphur distillate fueloil.

Unconventional Oil
Also known as non-conventional oil. Unconventional oil is crude produced by any means other than the conventional method of drilling and pumping it out of the ground (either on land or at sea). The two predominant sources of unconventional oil are from tar sands and oil shale. Some believe that with increased efforts and technological advances, oil derived from tar sands and oil shale could double or even quadruple the global availability of oil. So far unconventional oil production is in most cases very costly and often it also relates to very challenging grades of crudes that are produced. Those may be sold at a discount versus the benchmark.

Uncovered Position (futures)
A situation where a long positioned market player has bought more of a commodity than he has agreed to sell, or where a short positioned market player has sold more of a commodity than he has to deliver. Being outright long or short, a position at risk. This position can result from errors by giving

a wrong order, a fat finger mistake. But also wrong input to a P&L can confuse a trader. He would hedge his book based on what has been reported in the P&L. With volatile markets such situations are not wanted.

Underlift

Loading less oil than the available entitlement or loading less than contractually agreed. In crude production, a monthly availability of oil is calculated. The equity holder then knows how much he can lift in that month. If less is loaded than the available volume then the stock at the end of the month will show a positive figure. The equity holder underlifted on his entitlement. Often this is caused due to cargo size. If the availability is bigger than the standard cargo size, then underlifting cannot be avoided. After a few times underlifting the stock would be so much that the equity can load an extra cargo or overlift a bit. Underlift or overlift may be allowed in an agreement. In some circumstances, it cannot be avoided, a matter of balancing stock positions. Each equity holder of a crude field has to load a cargo. It can be that company x has not enough for a full cargo but will load anyway. This would be an overlift; too much was loaded compared with the stock position. Another equity holder has oil in stock but not enough for a cargo. That company will underlift and has to wait for next month's programme. Underlifting due to draft restrictions in a disport can lead to a deadfreight invoice.

Understated B/L

Bill of Lading on which too little volume is noted. At discharge port a big oil gain will be noticed which has a significant positive resultant effect in the buyer's P&L. The B/L figures represent the commercial invoice. If you are the seller of the oil then you give your oil away for free. To avoid that an inspector has to be used to guard the volumes. But also measurement equipment at production sites, crude oil fields and refineries, has to be calibrated. A buyer would never complain. He would buy the next cargoes as well. It may happen that the error is found after a vessel has left the berth. Then afterwards the buyer and seller will agree to re-issue the Bill of Lading, a corrected B/L.

Unfinished Oils

All oils requiring further processing, except those requiring only mechanical blending. Unfinished oils are produced by partial refining of crude oil and include naphtha and lighter oils, kerosene and light gas oils, heavy gas oils, and residuum. Straight run oil for export is produced by the simple refineries.

VGO and straight run fueloil are good examples of export unfinished oil. Unfinished oil is a good feedstock for the complex refineries. Basically blending components and oil which needs further treatment in processing units are also unfinished oils. Although blending components are often commercialised in case of over production at a refinery.

Unfractionated Streams
Mixtures of unsegregated natural gas liquid components excluding those in plant condensate. This product is extracted from natural gas.

Unloading
Removal of a shipment from a vessel. Discharging the cargo into a tank, cavern, pipeline or other vessel (STS).

Upgrading
Blending to make a quality of oil in tank a better quality at a cost in order to meet the specification of the product to be sold later as finished product. If a gasoline has an octane of 93 and the specification is minimum 95 then there is a need to add some higher octane fuel into the tank until the minimum of 95 is reached without spoiling any other specifications to be met. The high octane component is more expensive than gasoline with an octane of 95, so some blending costs are incurred in this case. Nevertheless, if the sourced unleaded 93 was bought at a low price then the potential to earn a blending margin is there. See also 'downgrading', 'giveaway' and 'blending economics'.

Upstream
All activity related to crude before it enters into the refinery. Crude marketing by the producer is an upstream activity and refined product trading is a downstream activity. Refining is mid-stream. Exploration and production departments would rather mention crude selling as a downstream activity.

Uptrend (Technical Trading)
A price pattern characterised by successive increasing highs and increasing lows. Do not forget to follow the trend when taking trading decisions. Most traders always talk bullish which might cause overtrading during an uptrend period.

USAC
Market area with price quotations available in the quotation list of price setting agencies. USAC is United States Atlantic Coast (New York Area).

USEC
Petrochemical markets abbreviation for US East Coast. Often referred to Gulf Coast, but it includes the Atlantic Coast as well.

Used Laytime
The amount of laytime that was taken by the vessel for loading and discharging on a voyage. When more time is used compared with the agreed laytime in the charter party, demurrage will be due. In most cases the time gained during loading may be used for discharging or vice versa. The charter party often describes a total time for discharging and loading. The traders split that time when selling the cargo. If the buyer uses more than the time he got then the seller would be entitled to send a demurrage invoice. He is not always obliged to share his gained laytime at loadport with his buyer at disport. Therefore as a buyer you must make sure that you add a clause in the contract stating that time gained at loadport may be used by the buyer. See also 'demurrage'.

USGC
Market area with price quotations available in the quotation list of price setting agencies. USGC is United States Gulf Coast (Houston Area).

UST
Underground Storage Tank. See 'cavern'.

Unstabilised Condensate
A hydrocarbon or mixture of hydrocarbons and non-combustible gases in the liquid state, which is extracted from reservoirs in its natural state separately or together with gaseous hydrocarbons.

USWC
Tanker and market abbreviation for US West Coast. The West Coast is very much supplied by pipelines and vessels coming through the Panama Canal. Also from the Asian and Oceania side oil could be supplied.

Uvce

Unconfined vapour cloud explosion. Explosion which may occur after release of liquid gas which forms a gas cloud in open air. Often a reason why use of a telephone at a petrol station is not allowed while filling a car. Also on refineries use of telephones or cameras with flashlight is not allowed. Also called Puvce (P=Percussive). See also 'bleve'.

V

V

A trader talking about a 'V' is talking about a VLCC.

Vacuum Distillation

A secondary refining process in which straight-run residue is distilled in a vacuum in order to separate more light hydrocarbons than through atmospheric distillation. The output of the process is vacuum gasoil and vacuum bottoms or residue which can be used as feedstock for cracking units or as boiler fuel. Under pressure the oil can be processed at higher temperatures without cracking or breaking molecules. The temperature in the vacuum unit may go up to 420°C/788°F. Through pressure in the unit the oil vaporises easier. By that the oil will not be cracked. It produces light products and VGO. The boiling point of heavy VGO at normal pressure is around 740°C/1,364°F. The unit in the refinery is also called a 'vacuum tower'.

Value-at-Risk (VaR)

A loss that will not be exceeded at some specified confidence level. Trading mandates may be based on VaR. Trading decisions are taken on outright positions and spreads. The maximum possible loss a trade can suffer based on the trading position in his book as a result of price changes in the market per day. The used VaR is calculated from the outright position and different spread positions. It is calculated in a certain percentage from the market values. It means also that at high oil prices the VaR is reached faster compared with a low oil price. In an example, if a trader has a VaR mandate of 1 million

Dollars and he has a position of 500 lots of crude oil, and the VaR calculation is based on 2% volatility on crude oil which is quoted at 100 Dollars per barrel then that trader has used his VaR mandate. 2% of 500,000 kb at 100 Dollars is used VaR of 1 million Dollars. If the crude price increases he would be out of mandate so some of the position needs to be liquidated. Would the crude price come off then the trader can take a bigger position. Another example of what VaR is: An oil company gives a mandate to a trader of VaR per day of 10 million US Dollars. Usually a confidence interval of 95% is used. In other words each day there is 5% chance of a loss larger than 10 million US Dollars per day. If a trader would lose 10 million Dollars and has been within mandate, what then?

Value Chain

All activity in a company attached to crude oil production until supply of oil products to the end consumers. This activity is under review on a daily basis in order to be optimised in the best possible way for that company. Crude production from the field is supplied to the refinery at market price. The refinery processes the crude and sells it by internal pricing to the product traders. The product trader supplies the refined oil to the marketing system which sells the fuel, diesel and gasoline to the end consumer at the petrol stations or the heating oil to the consumer's home. In this value chain a lot of market information, product information and know-how need to be exchanged. By that the value chain is a good base for all type of optimisation so competitive advantage may be found and costs can be saved. See also 'internal pricing'. Also when a company owns more than one company they must optimise their system based on the value chain. They have to do that in such a way that they extract maximum value and avoid having their own refineries compete with each other. In a big company that has to be well communicated and understood as refineries prefer to look at their own financial result. The total picture of the company is much more important.

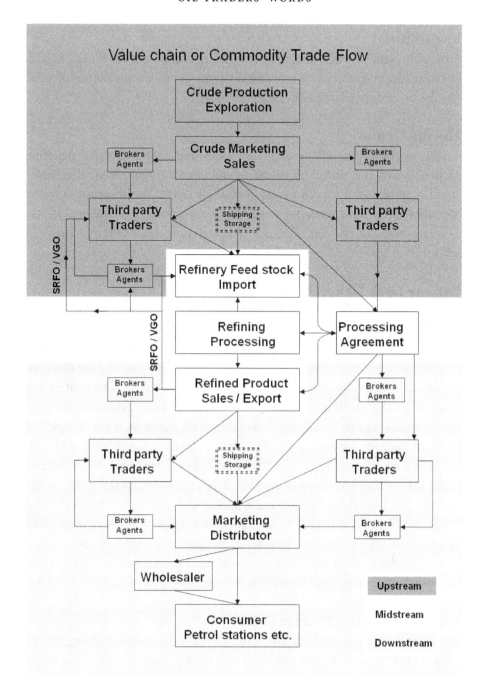

Valve

Any device for halting or regulating the flow of oil being transferred through a pipeline, pump or manifold.

Vanadium

A metal present in crude oil and after refining found again in fueloil. Fueloil has a vanadium specification for bunkers. It may cause combustion problems. The maximum specification in fueloil is 600ppm.

Vanilla Crude

Crude oil containing all product molecules and chains; butane; naphtha; jet fuel, gasoil and fueloil. A trader would say that, compared with heavy crude, a middle grade is a more vanilla quality crude. Vanilla crude is not by definition the perfect crude for a refinery as each refinery is designed to run a certain basis quality. Vanilla crude is easy to process and therefore easy to sell.

Vapour Lock Index (VLI)

Requirement related to the evaporation properties in gasoline specs. In the transitional period from summer to winter and vice versa (1 October to 15 November and 16 March to 30 April) there is an additional VLI specification in gasoline. That requirement is not valid in all countries, but for German gasoline, for example, this would be applicable. The goal is to control the emissions from gasoline in those periods. The VLI is a calculation from 2 specifications. The RVP and the percentage which is evaporated at 70°C/158°F (E70) are the two relevant specs. VLI is then calculated as follows: VLI = 10 times RVP (in kPa) + 7 times E70. The max VLI in German gasoline would be 1,150. Winter spec gasoline has an RVP of 90 kPa. A quick calculation learns that the E70 level should be around max 35.7%. (1,150 minus 900 =250 and 250 divided by 7 = roughly 35.7). If a specification goes over the limit of a VLI of 1,150 then the producer or blender of gasoline must either lower the RVP or E70, a reduction of the lightest components in gasoline such as butane and isomerate or blend in more heavy components like reformate.

Vapour Recovery System (VRS)

Procedures and equipment for the collection of hydrocarbon vapours from a vessel's tanks and the transfer to shore side recovery equipment. Main target is to reduce emissions. The process of capturing petroleum product vapours and returning them in condensed form to storage, before they escape to the atmosphere from both the logistical/distribution system and the vehicle fuelling process. During loading the vapour recovery unit is processing and liquefying the gases. When the oil has a very high RVP there will be more gasses going to the vapour recovering unit. Such a unit may have its limits and too much gas can saturate the system. In that case the loading or discharging of the oil will slow down. Such a terminal should have a better vapour recovery unit with more capacity or the buyer should know what oil he buys or sells. So some experience related to terminals and oil qualities would be of help. You can negotiate loading time, discharge time, or bid a lower price with the argument that the vapour pressure will cause problems. You may know this better than your counterparty, but no one would advise the counterparty. The one sleeping will later be surprised with extra costs. Delays due to lack of technical capacity damages the image of the terminal and may have a negative impact on the price of the commodity.

VCF

Volume Correction Factor. Relates to temperature but also a vessel's experience factor is a volume correction factor. Look at 'experience factor'.

VDU

Vacuum Distillation Unit. Where oil is distilled under pressure at temperatures up to 420°C/788°F. Through pressure in the unit the oil vaporises easier. By that the oil will not be cracked. It produces light products and VGO. The boiling point of heavy VGO at normal pressure is around 740°C/1,364°F.

VEF Load

Vessel Experience Factor at load as determined by IP/API method. See 'vessel experience factor'.

Verification

Periodic or routine performance checks that ensure that operational requirements continue to be met. Verification can be accomplished by comparing information from two or more devices sensing a given variable. An example would be a master thermometer compared to a temperature transmitter output. See also 'calibration'.

Vessel Experience Factor (VEF)

A compilation of the history of the total calculated volume (TCV) vessel measurements, adjusted for on-board quantity (OBQ) or remaining on board (ROB), compared with the TCV shore measurements. It was designed to be used primarily as a loss control tool to help assess the validity of quantities derived from shore tank measurements.

Vessel Manifest

The international carrier is obligated to make declarations of the ship's crew and contents at both the port of departure and arrival. The vessel's manifest lists various details about each shipment by B/L number. Obviously the B/L serves as the core source from which the manifest is created.

Vessel Size Categories

See 'tankers' for the naming of different oil tanker sizes.

Vetting

The general process of approving a vessel or oil terminal for use. (From old English 'to vet', to look at or review again.) Actual procedure varies from company to company. So approval or acceptance for the use of a certain vessel or oil terminal has to be checked each time between the counterparties involved in a physical deal. Trades are therefore sometimes done 'subject to approval of vessel X'. Also when long term deals are done which include activity on terminals, such as tank rental or processing deals, vetting may be required. As a company you want to know if a location is safe to store and process oil. HSE requirements related to vetting are well accepted in the market. It is important to agree on all GT&Cs related in contracts and forward those GT&Cs when selling the cargo on to the next buyer.

VGO

Vacuum GasOil, also known as catfeed. Feedstock for fluid catalytic cracker used to make cracked naphtha, a gasoline component, heating oil and other by-products.

View

The opinion of a trader about how the market moves. To create a view the trader must get information about the activities in the market. A trader receives and collects information about the activity related to his commodity in the market. He will create his market view and takes decisions accordingly. Without a view or opinion about the market a trader should have a balanced book. See also 'market view'. Knowledge about technical trading, being present in the market, receiving information from analysis teams and a good network are all good tools to create a view.

Vis-Breaking

A kind of thermal cracking which significantly lowers the viscosity of heavy crude-oil residue without affecting the boiling point range. Vis-breaking is used to reduce the pour point of waxy residues and it reduces the viscosity of residues used for blending with lighter fueloil. Middle distillates may also be produced, depending on product demand.

VISC

Viscosity. A measure of a liquid's resistance to flow. Several viscosity scales are used depending on the type of oil being measured. Measured in centistokes at 50° Celsius/122° Fahrenheit or in Engler at 80° Celsius/176° Fahrenheit.

Viscosity Meter

A device for determining the viscosity of oil. There are several methods or devices in general use. Basically, a fixed quantity of oil is allowed to pass through a fixed orifice (tube in a lab to measure the speed of liquid flow) at a specified temperature over a measured time span and then compared to a standard liquid such as a calibration oil or water.

Viscosity Spread

Spread between the value of the 180 Cst. fueloil quotations in Singapore and the 380 Cst. fueloil quotations in Singapore. The 180 Cst. swap market is a fairly liquid market in Singapore traded through brokers in both Singapore and NWE. The 380 Cst. swap is less liquid but is needed in order to hedge fueloil deliveries from Europe to Asia, as physical fueloil from Europe is most often priced on the 3.5% barge quotation which has a viscosity specification of max 380 Cst.

Viscous

Sticky oil. Oil with a very high viscosity.

VLCC

Very Large Crude Carrier. VLCCs have a capacity between 200,000 up to 320,000 dwt. (2 million barrels). Traders like to abbreviate VLCC and prefer to call it a 'V'.

Vletten (Dutch inland shipping term)

Inland shipping term for taking product temporarily as storage on board, but also meant as transporting oil from one terminal to another terminal within the ARA area ('vletreisje'). 'Vletten' is strongly connected to the ARA barge market.

VOC Emission

Volatile Organic Compounds, carbon-containing compounds which are emitted or evaporate into the atmosphere and can take part in photochemical reactions in the air. VOC emissions are highly focussed in the USA and have already been reduced in a significant manner by the use of reformulated gasoline. Nevertheless further reduction is still required. See also 'NOx'.

Voice Log

Recording of the contents of a telephone conversation onto a storage medium and retained on this medium. Traders discuss business by using a taped line. Agreements on trades are verbally discussed and confirmed and binding. The contract will be sent later. It is important that if there is a conflict between the buyer and seller related to the content of the contract, both could listen to their tape and find out if they were right or wrong. Often problems are solved quickly. If a trader commits to a deal on the mobile phone then he needs to make a recap over the taped line. See also 'recap' and 'taped line'.

Vol.

Volume. Related to litres, cubic metres, barrels or gallons. If it would be related to kilos then it would be mass. Sulphur percentage can be reported by volume or in mass. Standard volumes are calculated at 15°C or 60°F. Operationally you must be aware of the density/API of the product and the actual temperature. Warm product has more volume. The traders talk a lot about the storage capacity they have and it would not be the first time that 20,000 m³ does not fit in 20,000 m³ tank. The assumption is often that contractual volume at 15°C/60°F just fits in the tank. But oops the trader/operator forgot that the fueloil has a temperature of 60°C/140°F. The actual volume is more than what is written as standard in the contract.

Volatile

A volatile substance is one that is capable of being evaporated or changed to a vapour at a relatively low temperature. Volatile substances can also be partially removed by air stripping. Gasoline is a volatile product, a gaseous product.

Volatile Crude Oil
Crude oil having a high concentration of components boiling below ambient temperature. See also 'Gas to C4'.

Volatile Organic Compounds (VOCs)
A large family of carbon-containing compounds that are emitted or evaporate into the atmosphere and can take part in photochemical reactions in the air.

Volatility
The grade of fluctuation of market prices going up and down including speed of the fluctuation. The higher the volatility the higher the risk in the trading books, the faster the fluctuation the more difficult and risky it is to hedge a position at planned level. Markets may have moved within seconds after buying a physical cargo. When crude was 147 USD in 2008 the volatility of crude was around 7-8 Dollars per day; in such a case even the smallest mistake in a P&L would have huge consequences in the results. Due to high volatility in the oil market, most paper traders are seated behind their many screens with life prices and graphs.

Volume
The amount of space occupied by a fluid at certain conditions of temperature and pressure.

Volume Types

• **Gross Standard Volume (GSV)**
The total volume of all petroleum liquids and sediment and water, excluding free water, corrected by the appropriate volume correction factor for the observed temperature and API gravity, relative density, or density to a standard temperature such as 60°F or 15°C and also corrected by the applicable pressure correction factor and metre factor.

• **Indicated Volume**
The change in meter reading that occurs during a receipt or delivery.

- **Net Standard Volume (NSV)**
  The total volume of all petroleum liquids, excluding sediment and water and free water, corrected by the appropriate volume correction factor for the observed temperature and API Gravity, relative density, or density to a standard temperature such as 60°F or 15°C and also corrected by the applicable pressure correction factor and metre factor.

- **On Board Quantity (OBQ)**
  The material remaining in vessel tanks, void spaces, and/or pipelines prior to loading. On-board quantity includes water, oil, slops, oil residue, oil/water emulsions, sludge, and sediment.

- **Remaining On Board (ROB)**
  The material remaining in vessel tanks, void spaces, and/or pipelines after discharge. Remaining on board quantity includes water, oil, slops, oil residue, oil/water emulsions, sludge, and sediment. After discharging ROB observation is important and looked at in case losses after discharging are obtained.

- **Total Calculated Volume (TCV)**
  The total volume of all petroleum liquids and sediment and water, corrected by the appropriate volume correction factor for the observed temperature and API gravity, relative density, or density to a standard temperature such as 60°F or 15°C and also corrected by the applicable pressure factor and metre factor, and all free water measured at observed temperature and pressure (gross standard volume plus free water).

- **Total Observed Volume (TOV)**
  The total measured volume of all petroleum liquids, sediment and water, and free water at observed temperature and pressure.

Voyage Loss

The loss of oil which is obtained after discharging. It is obtained as the differential between the Bill of Lading figures and the received quantities at disport. When you obtain a loss which exceeds normal standards you may wonder if the Bill of Lading at loadport was not overstated. Inspection and loss control would have been a good investment. Check out 'loss control'. Insurances cover losses over 0.5% for cargoes from vessels and losses over 0.3%

for cargoes from barges. These percentages are standard averages; however, it is not the rule. That is up to the insurance companies. A loss on a cargo between 0.1% and 0.49% can cause a significant financial loss. These losses must be sorted out. The use of inspection at load and discharge is important. A loss up to 0.1% is generally accepted as operational loss.

Voyage order

Instruction to the vessel. Where to go, what quantity to load, who is the receiver, releasing inspectors on board in load and disport, agent appointments and where to send sailing information such as eta in load and disport. After loading, there may be a need to make a deadfreight statement. The buyer's operator issues document instructions to the seller. The seller will send those instructions amended with own added requirements to his/her shipping operator. That shipping operator makes the final voyage order by adding more instructions such as laden speed and ballast speed; finally that order goes straight to the master of the vessel and eventually to the appointed agent in loadport or disport. See also 'laden speed' and 'ballast speed'.

VR Fraction

Vacuum Residue fraction. Residue from the vacuum unit in the refinery.

VRU

Vapour Recovery Unit. A VRU captures vapours from empty transport trucks that are pushed out the truck tank during the loading process. Some units actually recover the vapours, convert them to liquid state through various means and return the product to a tank within the terminal tank farm. Other units called vapour combustors burn the vapours in a flare. The gas burned in the VRU may also be used to generate electricity. The use of a VRU may also be required when loading low flash oil cargoes like crude, naphtha and gasoline. It is better for the environment to have emissions reduced as much as possible. The VRU converts the gases back to liquids which will return back to the tank. That saves the terminal from losses. Emissions cause a bad smell in the air coming from mercaptans. As the VRU captures the gases the loading of a vessel could be done at higher pumping rate without the release of a bad smell in the air. A VRU is good for the environment, it reduces oil losses and operations can go faster, especially for those cargoes to be loaded close to populated places.

VTB

Vacuum Tower Bottoms. The fueloil or residue that is left over in the vacuum distillation unit. This fuel oil is also called 'short residue'. VTB can be exported from a refinery, but is also blended with residue from the atmospheric distillation. Then that is called 'long residue'.

VTS

Vessel Traffic Service. It is the pilot station.

W

W.f.cast

Weather forecast. You may see it on shipping communication.

WAF

West AFrican market. Most crude from WAF is sweet crude and great to process at most refineries. Local trading in WAF is still a challenge as most countries in WAF have a low score on the corruption index. IDD approval in WAF becomes a challenge. West Africa is a big source for crude oil arbitrage trading. Crude oil from West Africa is basically supplied to Asia, Europe and USA. Platts and Argus print various quotations for crude oil in the West African market (WAF). The West African market and its activity strongly affect VLCC rates. When arbs are wide open, the price of a VLCC will go up, which may affect the fueloil arb from Europe to Asia. So demand of crude oil from Asia being sourced from WAF affects the freight rates for VLCCs. Fueloil traders do have an eye on that shipping activity and discuss it a lot with their shipping department. As when freight prices move up it is better have a VLCC on subs when playing the fueloil arbitrage business to Singapore. The East/West spread is pretty much following those freight rates. Africa is an important continent to keep an eye on. Its oil business is developing and growing. It is not about crude oil only. Also oil products will find their way to the African ports.

Waiting Game

When the market is a buyers' market prices are under pressure. Buyers can pick and choose the business they like. Some buyers may speculate on it and delay the decision to purchase as long as possible. The chance is high that some producers or traders are long oil and are desperately looking for outlet. The buyer with best patience and feeling for timing might be able to get a bargain when buying a distressed cargo. Too long a wait can have the opposite effect. In the seller's market it works exactly the opposite way. Traders are prepared to take some risk. That decision depends on the quality of their cargo tracking activity. Which company would still have a cargo unsold and is that cargo becoming distressed or not? Getting the best price is a matter of winning the trading game.

Waiver

A waiver is about getting allowance to supply an oil cargo with a quality that might slightly differ from the standard quality requirements. Basically allowance to supply off-spec oil. This waiver may be granted because the counterparty can handle the parameter which is off-spec in his system. In some cases also governments may give a waiver in case the supply of oil into a certain region may come into problems and no supply would disrupt common standards too much. There are many reasons to give a waiver to be off-spec. Some waivers are at a cost, some waivers are based on deviation from own internal rules in a company. It is important that all communication around getting and giving waivers is clear. If I get a waiver then I would confirm that on paper. Allowance for being off-spec is just a reason to have it well registered. That will avoid potential problems which may arise in future, when suddenly people ask questions and start complaining. Waivers are also given based on testing methods. Specs are good but sometimes a deviation from a testing method may be requested.

Wash Trade/Wash Out

A purchase and a sale between the same buyer and seller with exactly the same loading and delivery conditions. The price and pricing may differ. Most important is that, because of this situation, a 'mirrored deal', no logistic activity is needed. Therefore the buyer and the seller will deem the B/L quantity and B/L date and make cash settlement according to the contract.

Waste Oil Demulsifiers

The label 'waste oil' covers a variety of industrial 'water-in-oil' emulsions. Waste oil (or Slop-oil) can be used motor oils (crankcase oils), tank-bottoms at refineries or other storage facilities, contaminated fueloils, waste from chemical factories, etc., etc. These are all stable mixtures (emulsions) of oil and water, often also containing other impurities like sediments and insoluble salts.

Waterborne

Trading activity and production activity related to transport over sea. Brent is waterborne and WTI is landlocked. Waterborne is the opposite of 'landlocked'.

Wax

A mixture of long chain hydrocarbons that crystallise at different temperatures as the overall fluid temperature falls. A solid or semi-solid material derived from petroleum distillates or residues by such treatments as chilling, precipitating with a solvent, or de-oiling. Rich in paraffin like a candle, e.g. Paraffinic crude oil. Sticky oil, the opposite of aromatic oil. See also 'de-waxing'.

Wax/Sediment (Sludge)

That element of the material in a ship or tank which is essentially not free-flowing. It consists of hydrocarbon waxes and may contain water/oil emulsions and sediments.

Waxy Paraffinic Crude oil

A crude oil, which by function of its total waxes content, requires heating to prevent sludge disposition during transportations and discharge. Without heating remainders will stick on board as a result of clingage. Financial losses would be the consequence as a result of out-turn losses. See also 'de-waxing'.

Weather Derivative

Derivative where the payoff depends on the weather. Electricity traders might look at those.

Weight

Cargo measured in metric tons. Weight divided by density is volume. Weight is not linked to a standard temperature; that counts for volume only.

Wellhead Price

A commodity price that has not been adjusted for transportation costs, i.e. the implicit or explicit price of a unit of hydrocarbons at the wellhead. To calculate the oil price ex seaport terminal, there is a lot to be added to the wellhead price such as taxes and cost of transport from the wellhead to the loadport. Even money exchange rates may be taken into account. The wellhead price in Russia is a price in Russian Rubles. It is easier to calculate the other way around. The price-quoting agent, such as Platts and Argus, reports the market prices for crude and the differentials versus Brent. Urals crude oil is a good example. There are price quotations in the market. From that price, all transportation costs and fees can be deducted to get to the wellhead price. Not only logistics costs are deducted from the FOB price, but also the export tax. FOB prices include export tax. The country where the oil is produced needs to be paid for the oil that is produced.

West Texas Intermediate (WTI)

A blend of crudes widely used as a price marker or benchmark for the international oil industry. It is one of the most actively traded U.S. crudes and the primary deliverable grade under the New York Mercantile Exchange light, sweet crude oil futures contract. WTI currently has an average quality of 40 API. Prices for WTI are quoted at Cushing, Oklahoma. WTI is the benchmark price in the USA, like Brent in Europe.

Wet Barrel

Industry term to specify actual physical barrels, often in a very prompt timeframe. Contrasts with paper bbl, where title is not backed up with actual physical material. Barrels are called wet when they can be commercialised and made ready for supplies. When a producer shows his production programme and nominates the cargoes, then the wet barrel is created.

Whacked

A trader gets whacked on his trade. He loses some money as a result of a swift movement in the market. Resulting in a sharp trade that goes against the trader.

White Oil

Highly refined straight mineral oil, essentially colourless, odourless, and tasteless. White oil has a high degree of chemical stability.

Window (Platts)

Time frame set by Platts in which different energy commodities can be offered or bid on. Quality per product is standardised and delivery dates and/or or loading dates are to be offered/bid in a fixed day range (5 days) between a fixed number of days after the window day itself. Often the loading days have to be 10 to 25 days after the actual window date. E.g. Window date 1 Sept, then bid/offer days to be a 5 days window between 11 and 26 Sept. The window in UK is traded from 15:45pm till 16:30pm. Bid/Offer to be posted before 15:45pm London time else the posted offer or bid will not be acknowledged by Platts. In that case the trader cannot be an active price setter during the window. Nevertheless all market participants can show interest in the bids or offers in the window and book a window deal. The outcome, the last trade done in that window will be the basis for the Platts quotation of that particular trading day. During the window the offers start high and would come down during the last 30 minutes. That results in many buyers waiting as long as possible before taking out the offer. With cargoes trading during the MOC that can be tricky as there might not be a next cargo available. Too long waiting would be a risk when you really want that cargo. It works a bit like an auction where offered prices start high and then go lower to find the first company hitting the 'button'. Most trades in cargoes are done during the last 5 minutes of this session. Bidding in the window starts at a low level and will then increase during the window session. Barges trades are more liquid in the window. Several barges will be bought and sold during the MOC session, with also most activity in the last 5 minutes. A trader flaking on a Platts window deal is risking getting boxed. Therefore look at 'boxed' as well. Bid and offers are most often sent through the use of instant messaging systems. Supplies, pricing and timing are to be performed according to the Platts standard terms.

Window

Related to a short time period, e.g. Loading window, time leg when a berth is available. The window when a vessel can arrive. A window is a time leg, in oil logistics often a 3 day or 5 day window. Such as 'Platt's window' or 'lay-can'.

Window Dressing

Selling the oil and buying the same oil back later. In storage at the year-end the title of the oil (ownership) exchanges from the company holding the oil to a buyer and then title of the oil will again exchange between the same buyer and seller after the New Year has started. Working capital at reporting moment (year-end) is at lower level and it can make a company book look better with the stakeholders. The facilitator collects a small profit. The commercial invoice here is settled like in a 'wash out' deal. It is better to plan ahead and not buy too much oil when getting nearer to the year end. December is therefore often a slow month in trading.

Wind Power
Power or energy derived from the wind (by windmills, sails, etc.).

Winter Diesel
During the winter months, on road diesel fuels may be blended with other diesel fuels or chemical additives to produce a winter diesel that will not begin to solidify or gel due to cold temperatures. See also 'cloud point' and 'CFPP'.

Winter Peak
The period in the year when temperatures go down and demand for heating oil increases. As a result prices for heating oil would go up. Crude slates in refineries are processed in order to maximise distillate production. Heating oil would be in heavy demand in Germany. The traders hope each year for a cold winter which would boost demand. Gasoil cargoes are discharged in Rotterdam and by breaking bulk the barges supply the heating oil in smaller lots to Germany.

Winter Spec
Gasoline and diesel have to perform during the whole year. Therefore the cold properties in wintertime are different compared with summertime, e.g. Gasoline in summer has a RVP of 60/70 and in winter 90/100. In diesel summer spec and winter spec differs based on cold properties such as cloud point and CFPP. See also 'cold properties'.

Wire Agency
Agency or reporter calling traders to get information about the market, opinions etc. These agencies are not making price quotation reports. They make the stories in their reports and often the stories appear on the screen. Therefore, be careful with what you say; your story can be reported. Of course there are also reporting agencies which are both writing the stories and reporting the quotations of the day according to their own findings and rules

of assessment. It is okay for traders to talk to the reporters. The reporters also give information about activities they heard about; they should be part of the traders' network, although that is often very limited. Wire reporters are good sources to talk to. The information which is given by a trader is most often the market view, the gossip and maybe a bit of their own activity. A trader would never tell something which would be bad for his own trade. Traders like to talk their book. See also 'talking the book'.

Witnessing Inspection
One inspector is looking over the shoulder of another inspector in the laboratory, looking to it that all analyses are done as per correct requirements or standards. An expeditor is looking and following the activity of the inspector outdoor and is reporting this to the company from which he got the order. It is just meant as extra control in order to ensure that no mistakes are made. Witnessing inspection is often done with insurance cases. It is certainly not a daily activity. An inspector does not like to have the competitor watching in his kitchen. Both inspectors will issue their own report with findings and results.

Work Capacity
Net capacity of the tank. This is the capacity of the tank which can be used to store oil. Just be aware that at some storage places also a heel needs to be deducted to get a real capacity to work with. See also 'max capacity' and 'heel'. Maximum safe fill capacity and the quantity below which pump suction is ineffective (bottoms). The ullage of an empty tank. The shell capacity is the total size of the tank. Storage companies let the customer pay for the shell capacity, while the customer can only utilise the ullage of the tank. It is in most cases the standard practice in oil business.

Working Days
Working days of a country in which a contract is executed. It is most often related to nomination procedures for overtime payment as on some occasions a terminal is only open during working days. Activity in weekends or official party days must be nominated upfront. UK has bank holidays and other countries also have their national day. Therefore a working day depends on the description in the contract. Can be a Russian contract, an English contract or Dutch. So read your contract and watch the international calendars.

Working Storage Capacity
The difference in volume between the maximum safe fill capacity and the quantity below which pump suction is ineffective (bottoms).

Worldscale
The shipping market uses worldscale rates to determine the costs for a total freight. Worldscale is the market index and needs to be multiplied with a flat rate to find the total freight cost from port A to port B. See also 'flat rate'. Flat rates are set once per year and are heavily affected by the bunker prices. Worldscale rates are reported by Platts and Argus just like daily oil price quotations. These are worldscales quotations for fixed routes, fixed vessel sizes and type of oil, clean or dirty. A worldscale of 100 is based on a normal market. When below 100 then the market is weak and above 100 is showing a strong market.

Writing an Option
Selling an option.

WSNP
Weather Safe Navigation Permit. Allowance to sail a certain route based on weather conditions.

Wt.
Weight, relates to kilos or mass. Litres, barrels, gallons relate to volume.

WTI/West Texas Intermediate
Benchmark crude oil with a standard quality which is traded in the North American crude oil market (physical and paper). Its API gravity is 39.6 and it contains roughly 0.25 percent of sulphur, a sweet light crude oil. Qualities coming from other places in the North American market can be of better quality and are priced on WTI plus a premium or other qualities can be worse than WTI and will be traded at the WTI price minus a discount. Brent with API 37.5 and sulphur 0.37 is a European waterborne cargo market. USA WTI is a mid-continent pipeline market at Cushing, landlocked.

WTS
West Texas Sour.

X -

X-Grade
Pipeline terminology for No. 2 fueloil.

Yahoo
Instant message system used in the oil market to communicate and discuss. A real trade is always done over the phone. Yahoo is nice for small talk. It is better to use a phone – as a trader you would get much more information that what you would get through Yahoo. Young traders love to use Yahoo as it is so easy to get introduced for the first time. The use of Yahoo has become part of traders' network and it is therefore important to participate with that.

Year End Stock
Oil is an expensive commodity and having those on title, in stock or in transport, at year end will result in pressure on return on capital employed (ROCE) figures. Most oil companies try to be low on stock at year end in order to report a good result on ROCE. As a result of that in December prices, read differential versus the benchmark (Brent), in the oil market are under pressure and the physical market is weak and many companies are not willing to have title on product. Some deals are done on a DAP (old DES) basis with delivery after New Year and some deals are done with payment due date to be in January of the New Year. Due to those rules companies may get stuck with distressed cargoes. Trading companies with less attention to year-end stocks get a good opportunity here to find a cheap cargo. See also 'window dressing'.

Year to Date YTD
The period beginning January 1st of the current year up until today's date. YTD result gets lots of attention in any business. Basically the total result or performance of the running year so far.

Y-Grade
Pipeline terminology for No. 1 fueloil. The feedstocks that are sent to a fractionator in order to extract gas liquids.

Yield
The quality and content of the crude in terms of products. When crude is refined a certain percentage of oil products will come out of the refinery. This given in percentage is the yield of a certain type of crude. The yield is used to calculate the technical value of different grades of crude. See also 'assay'.

3/5 Days Payment Term
Payment term in the product market. When a cargo of petroleum products is sold the payment terms are defined as follows: Payment 5 days after Bill of Lading or 3 days after tendering of notice of readiness, whichever date comes first will apply, is final payment day. So for a short voyage of 1 day the payment has to be done earlier than for cargoes with a voyage longer than 2 days. Arbitrage cargoes may get paid on basis of arrival dates or even after discharging, e.g. NOR pricing and payment. Related to that it is then better to keep title on the oil during transport. I would recommend a DAP delivery.

30 Days Payment Term
Standard payment term for crude oil cargoes. Payment is to be done 30 days after the Bill of Lading date. 30 days payment terms will finance the refiners as they need time to process the crude oil. The products which come available to the market and will be sold with a 3/5 day payment term. By that the invoice of the crude has to be paid on roughly the same day that the refinery receives the money for the products. The refinery minimises the financing costs for oil processing. Deviation from standard terms can be related to accelerated and deferred payment. In that case a financing fee will become part of the price for the cargo. See also 'accelerated payment' and 'deferred payment'.

15-Day Brent
The 15-Day Brent crude oil market is so-called because a seller must give a

buyer a minimum 15 days' notice of the intended loading dates for a cargo of Brent Blend North Sea crude oil in any particular month traded. 15-Day Brent is traded in discrete months. At the point where the buyer, who may be at the end of a long trading chain, is informed of the loading dates, the cargo becomes a so-called dated Brent cargo.

100 LL
Low-lead aviation gasoline designation with minimum 100 octane.

3LC: FO/FO/FO
Three last cargoes: fueloil, fueloil, fueloil. When accepting a vessel it is wise to know what the three last cargoes have been. The rest of oil in pipelines or other systems on board a vessel could contaminate the cargo on board. You do not want chemicals in refinery feedstock and you are not happy when the rest of high RVP oil makes a diesel off spec on flash point. Of course there are cases when balances of oil on board are welcome, but only when it has a value. Either quality of the new cargo would improve or the cargo is discharged with some extra volume, outturn profit. As an operator, you have to be a bit lucky with that. It works best if you control the logistics on a couple of vessels. In the vessel questionnaire, the last three cargoes are also mentioned. Just make sure that the Q88 you get is not older than 3 to 5 days; check your company and vetting department rules for this.

The Oil Trader's Word(s) of Wisdom

When being in the oil market, talking a lot with other traders, I hear many expressions. Some expressions were made up by the traders themselves and some phrases the traders probably picked up in books or magazines. So I have collected a bit of this oil traders' wisdom. Also these expressions have some meaning, but most traders smile at these expressions. It is, in the trading world, often seen as common knowledge and those using the words of wisdom try to show they are smart – and many of them are smart. Luckily most traders use these rules to determine how traders act or maybe should act with good trading discipline. It is obviously clear that 'trader's wisdom' does involve a sense of humour as well. Trading is hard working, but fun as well.

The trend is your friend.
When the market has the tendency to go up or down during a longer period, then think twice before you take an opposite position.

If you spend 99% of your efforts minimising your losses, you will make money.
A mistake in trading is easily made, one moment without the right focus and your money is gone. Trading is risky, learn from mistakes or even better avoid mistakes.

Rule number 1: Make money and then rule number 2: Follow rule number 1.
This is what a trader is hired for.

Don't be long and wrong.
Do not have a wrong position. When you are long then also do not go to a long lasting meeting without having control of the market. That can turn out to go badly wrong.

Buy low, sell high.
Simple advice on how to make money.

Buy high and sell higher.
Same as 'buy low and sell high', but here it shows that market levels over the last few years have gone up and are still in an uptrend. By that today's purchase is high priced but according to the trend tomorrow's sale is even higher priced.

Cut losses, let profits run.
Be disciplined and act at stop loss situation, but do not take profit too fast when the market goes in your direction. Go for loss from peak! Do not become a net loser.

Sell in May and stay away.
Maybe most known in the stock market. Counts also for oil paper market. Physical oil trading never stops. Summertime is gasoline season. Traders may go on holidays and pull back from their activity. Fewer participants means less liquidity in the market.

If you cannot control your cost, then don't trade.
Oil trading is an activity with lots of money involved. Without control on costs, positions etc., there is no point in participating in the market, so stay out! Be well organised with all the roles related to the trading activity. Then return to trade.

Once you're black, you never go back.
This is what fueloil traders say to new colleagues in the fueloil business, especially when the new trader traded 'clean oil' before he moved to the fueloil business. According to fueloil traders the 'dirty market' is the nicest market to be in.

Money talks, bullshit walks.
A trader can talk about whom he wants to trade with and whom he does not want to trade with, but at the end of the day a trader would always sell to the buyer bidding the best price. Decisions are based on cashing in money and not on popular talk.

It is not my bread and butter.
It is not my responsibility and not my task, let others do this. I am not a specialist in that so I am not interested in the subject. Such an attitude is not always a wise way to work for traders. For a trader is expected to know everything, surely, when issues have an effect on the P&L. The trader better shows interest and learns for next time.

Crap in, crap out.
If the input of information to any system, analyses, refinery LP model or P&L is not accurate, then the reports coming out will be of no use, which can have negative consequences. Excellent and accurate input results in professional output. A great basis for a good trading platform.

The trader is right or the market is wrong.
When a good result is made then the trader was right. When the trader lost on his position then the market was wrong. Or…?

The market is as dead as a Dodo.
No action in the market, another boring day in the office.

Patience is like eating an elephant.
Some business will come slowly. It takes a lot of effort to get to a final result. Take it step by step (one bite at a time). Especially in business development.

Time is money.
There is a lot of money to make based on market structure, the forward market. Also entering a market based on the right timing is very important, find the momentum. See also 'fat pitch'.

Buy what you don't need and sell what you don't have.
The way to create a position. Go physical long or take a short position. By that you participate actively in the oil market. Do not forget to make money.

Knowledge is power.
The more market information a trader has the faster and better he can make his decisions and possibly by that he can try to control the market and beat the competition. Economy of scale helps the level of knowledge as well.

If you never steal or never lie, you have to work until you die.
Steal like at baseball. Steal a base, be smart. And lie is to be seen as bluffing. What is bluffing and what is lying can be very different per culture, but whatever one calls it: "Being smart and a little bluff are often the ingredients for a good trade."

If Moses does not come to the mountain, then the mountain has to come to Moses.
Business does not come automatically. So take the initiative to get business done.

I am a student of the market and my job is to learn.
In a trading job you never stop learning. Lots of traders say they have done it, seen it and they have been there. The willingness to pick up new wisdom would be low due to an arrogant attitude, "who are you, to tell me!?" So the one thinking of himself as being a 'student' will keep developing himself to the next level. In a trading job one never stops learning, as the world and market keep changing. Always stay ambitious.

The market is everywhere.
The trader saying that he has no clue what is happening in the market. The price can go up and go down. The trader is looking for advice from others. In this case the trader's book should be balanced. No position at risk, the trader needs to talk in the market and reads his analyses reports. Once he has a view he will take a position. Then he will tell the market that he is bullish or bearish.

Big swinging dick.
A trader who buys and sells big cargoes on a global basis (arbitrage) and gets lots of attention from the market for it, especially when he is seen as a successful trader.

Never fall in love with a position.

Be brave enough to cut losses. Do not think that the market will come back. Also do not forget to take profit (at loss from peak). Trading discipline is the most difficult part in trading. No one likes to take losses, even when it is just to cut a small losing position.

No pain no gain.

Without risk and stress, no money can be made. Money does not come for free.

Don't get married with your position.

Same as 'never fall in love with a position'.

Pissing next to the pot.

Missing a good and potential profitable trade or just losing a tender by a couple of cents. Next time aim better and be a bit more aggressive when bidding.

No guts, no glory.

If you have a market view then take a position accordingly. Those not being able to make a decision and preferring the talk over taking the position will never become a winner in this business.

The market is never wrong.
A trader takes positions based on the market view. Not all positions are money makers.

Do not be a net loser.
Based on trading discipline. Taking a loss is difficult and often even more money is lost before one has liquidated a position. At the same time the same trader is happy to take a profit, but cashes in too early because he did not let the profit run. If a trader does not cut a loss in time and cashes in his profits too early, then in the long run he will be a net loser. The few losses are cumulatively bigger than the many small profits he made.

Plan your trade and trade your plan.
Develop your trading strategy and get support from your trading manager or even convince the trading manager that your strategy should be executed. Do not go on your own in the market and take a position. You as a trader are part of a team. Do not become a lonesome rider. Share your results, happiness. Share your losses, the pain.

When the Med. sneezes, the North is getting a cold.
When something happens in the European Med. oil market then the North West European market can be hit. E.g. Price in the Med. goes down, the North West European market may get more oil imports until the arb closes. Alternatively, vice versa a high Med Price for Oil opens the Arb from Europe until NWE price gets higher. The way the MED/NWE arbitrage works. Action – reaction. Rumours on one side may affect the other side. A nervous relationship between the Med. and NWE.

Knowledge is power
The more experience, the more quality knowledge, the more GT&C knowledge, the more market knowledge, the stronger you are in a negotiation. Sometimes a matter of being prepared for the next deal. People who want to know are curious and ambitious. The right trader attitude especially when the trader is also a good convincer and decision taker. You will always beat the competition.

Work attracts work
When you start new trading activity it may go slow in the beginning and it

may be tough to keep on going. However, if it makes money and you keep on doing the activity, more orders, deals, ideas and possibilities may follow. All I want to say is: "Do not be afraid to start up something new." Your work will be noticed and more market players may become interested in what you have to offer; take initiatives. Do not be quiet in the market, show your possibilities, market your activity.

Crude is king

A bit arrogant maybe, but in most companies crude rules. It is best to work in crude. The place with the biggest cargoes and most cashflow. Every product price relates to crude oil prices. Crude deserves most attention in a company. Besides that, most projects are related to upstream activity. Therefore 'crude is king'.

Cash is king

When making a decision then it is related to money. What are the costs, what is the profit? Not all decisions may be best for a company or to follow the agreed strategy. Bottom line is to make profit and keep cost low. Bonuses are mainly based on financial results. So often decisions by traders are related to the income into the P&L. Like 'money talks, bullshit walks'.

Don't be shy, else you die.

Take initiative and be a decision taker. If not, the competition would take your business away. Be seen in the market. Without a good network it is difficult to create business. You must have self-confidence when you are trading. If you miss that you will never be happy in your job, it will give stress.

A new rule today is an old rule tomorrow.

Think out of the box. A lot of business standards are established because people often look at the way that a certain business was done last time, the past. Be different from others and find niches. Markets are changing and prices are moving up to the new structural high levels. That requires that you must change with the market. Therefore initiative has to be taken to propose change of rules and procedures in companies. If other companies adopt new standards faster than you then you will lag behind and miss the train. You might miss creating the best trading opportunities because others are faster. Change of rules might involve a change in risk positioning; keep it in mind. Proposals for changes have to come from the work floor. That is where strategies are executed and where traders and operators obtain changes in the market at first.

Never sell a quiet market.
A dead market does not give any information on whether prices might go up or down. Why take a position then?

It is better to be out of the market.
Traders come up with this wisdom when they were too late to take a market position. Basically they are wishing they were in the market. They have to wait for the next opportunity.

Prices move in trends.
Prices move up or down in certain periods of time. Short periods of tightness in product availability and vice versa.

History repeats itself.
Certain market patterns can be seen again and again. A pattern is not necessarily bounded at same price level per event.

A trend in motion is more likely to continue than to reverse.
Based on 'the trend is your friend' and 'history repeats itself'.

Human psychology tends not to change.
People respond on certain market situations each time the same way. Especially when it concerns technical trading. Therefore history repeats itself.

The key to understanding the future lies in a study of the past.
Learn from the past and utilise that experience.

More is learned from one's errors than from one's successes.
Successes are always celebrated and no one will complain or criticise the trade in order to point out that even better results could have been achieved if certain decisions were taken in a better way. The trading errors get more focus and will be more often evaluated. As the trader does not want to lose money twice in the same way.

The markets are not random.
Markets are based on human behaviour. There are many patterns that can lead to profits.

**I don't think he'll be very active on
the market this afternoon.**
He's just thrown up on the potted plant.

He should be back from lunch any time now.
Any second now he's going to crash through the door in an alcoholic stupor.

I'll call you back....
...in two minutes = this afternoon.

**...once we've reviewed our strategy = when I uncover
your phone number on the back of this scrap of paper.**
...once we've decided which way the market's going = when hell freezes over.

**Technicals suggest the price should fall but
supply fundamentals indicate a rise.**
I have no idea where the market is going.

I am bullish / bearish.
I am long / short.

I am balanced.
I am not going to tell you what my activity or position is.

Talking the book.
When a trader talks to a wire agent, he will always talk bullish or bearish according to his position in his trading book. Talk price up or down is the big wish.

The Dutch have a lot of gas in the bottom.
Dutch way of speaking English when talking about their natural gas resources.

No one ever went broke taking profits.
Maybe most often mentioned phrase in trading (futures and stocks). After losing a couple of times on a trade in a row, the confidence level of that trader is not that good anymore. As soon as he makes a little money on his next trade he would cash it in and says he's happy as he took profit. He thinks he is not a loser any more. But as he cut losses too late and let profits not run this trader becomes basically a net loser.

**Better to be out wishing you were in than
to be in wishing you were out.**
A trader being too scared to trade. A bit running behind the market.

Enter long positions on the strength of price support.
Some technical trading advice, not fundamental.

Exit long positions on the weakness of no price support.
Looks to me the fundamental reason not to be long, better go short.

Buy on the rumour.
As long as news is not reported or official, the price is not affected yet.

Sell on the news.
Information value of the news is already adopted in the price.

Scared money loses.
Don't be afraid just because it's you. The market doesn't know or care about you.

Overtrade and lose.
Trouble sleeping? You are overtrading.

Figures don't lie but liars figure.
Remember the banks during the recession in 2009.

Luck is with the better trader.
The poorer trader has bad luck.

Bulls and bears can make money, but not pigs.

The bulls and the bears have clear opinion about the market and are able to make money in a controlled and good risk managed way. But concerning pigs, greed and fear are the enemies of success.

Enter at extreme positions.

Focus and find the momentum to benefit.

Exit at reasonable positions.

Upside and downside are even (50/50). Get out and look for a new opportunity to re-enter the market.

Beware, the market is a whore, it will take your money and you will be sorry.

Trading is not that easy; there are probably more losers than winners.

Trading is a zero sum game. Your loss is their gain.

Since there are more losers than winners, trading can be very profitable, if you're good.

Eat or be eaten.

Stay sharp to make money. If you are not sharp others will take advantage of your weakness.

Kill or be killed.

Stay sharp in trading. If you are not sharp others will take advantage of your weakness.

A future and a commodity are not always the same thing.

Compare oil futures prices with fundamental value of oil. Can be pretty technical driven.

The market indices have correctly predicted nine of the last four recessions.

Always have your own market view and trade accordingly.

If you are going to panic, panic early.

Minimise the damage in your P&L. Try to avoid late response when losing money because you fell in love with your position.

Never meet a margin call.

If you get one, it will cost you. And if you meet many it costs you a lot.

The first loss is the best.

Lesson learned, consider what steps to take in the future.

Price advances weaken the market.

Rising prices will push business activity away. Small companies may suffer from financing challenges such as credit. But also bigger companies will find out that giving open credit becomes limited when a price per oil cargo gets expensive. Cost of capital for storage in stock is increasing as well. Business gets difficult and activity might slow down.

Price declines strengthen the market.

Easier for many companies to start a business. Financing oil cargoes is relatively cheap, credit is easier to get. Activity will increase.

Money follows earnings.

Investment willingness follows the potential to make money in the targeted market.

After a sharp fall money returns to its rightful owners.

Speculators are out of the market and the real value of a commodity appears, until speculators come in again.

Nothing has a straight line up or down.

Even with an uptrend the market will have its ups and downs, volatility within the trend range. In the long term the trend will continue.

Sell down to the sleeping point.

When you have been caught in a trade not favoured by current market conditions but still interesting to be maintained for the future, you undo your positions until a point where you can assume the risk.

A bullish market is born amid pessimism, grows up under scepticism, matures with optimism and dies with euphoria.

Keep this in mind and do not take a position too late. Try to be upfront and beat the market.

In times of crisis, always blame the one who isn't in the room.

Be aware that there are not many friends in the business, this is a money game.

If some business is worth doing, it's worth doing for money.

Results are what traders are measured on, so take risk and take decisions in order to get to the target.

Have the best hand, the best draw, or get out.

Get the best position. Let profit grow; if you have a losing position then liquidate that position, cut loss. A matter of discipline.

Don't get mad, get even.

Stay in control. Cut your losses, accept those losses and with the next trade do better and make money.

Buy when there is blood on the streets.

Take advantage of big fundamental changes by taking the right decision. Libyan war 2011 or hurricane season in the Gulf. Not always friendly to take advantage of disasters, but here markets would make the biggest moves up or down.

There's no free lunch on Wall Street.

You cannot make money without risking it first.

Don't fight the tape.

Be clear and accurate in your trading orders. Understand what you are doing. Deal done, is deal done.

The market is always with us.

Short and mid-term market conditions favour the market position we have.

Currency trading is about self-government.

If you can manage your own actions, you can trade currency successfully.

The truth is that most people do not have the self-control to be currency traders.

It is a learned skill that comes after much trial and error.

There is nothing destructive about being wrong.

The mistake lies in 'staying' wrong.

We're relaxed about our position.

We're 12 cargoes long.

We could look at selling, but the price would be fairly high.

We're still 12 cargoes long and the market is falling.

I see more buyers than sellers so we may step in.

We're now thirteen cargoes long, the market's gone into free-fall and the only buyer is an unregistered Lithuanian furniture wholesaler.

If I were to sell, I'd want to conclude something this afternoon.

The Lithuanian has gone to lunch and my boss is back in the morning.

With hindsight we could have got an extra Dollar or so by selling earlier, but we didn't do too badly overall.

Another week like this and I'll be working for the Lithuanian.

Conversion Calculations

In trading different sizes in volumes are discussed. American standards are often mixed with European standards. And some price indications are, like freight, based on different formulas. As a trader you have to be aware of those and you must be able to calculate these values. Therefore I have made a small list of the most common conversion possibilities related to oil business. These calculations are to be used by most people who have an oil related job.

Barrels to litres
1 Oil Barrel = 158.987295 litres.

CBM to litres
1 CBM = 1,000 litres.

CBM to barrels
1 CBM = 6.289811 barrels.

Gallons to barrels
42 gallons = 1 barrel.

Barrels to gallons
1 Barrel = 42 gallons.

Gallon to litres
1 gallon = 3.875412 litres.

Metric tons to CBM
Metric ton divided by density = CBM.

CBM to metric tons
CBM times density = Metric tons.

CBM/tons to density
Metric tons divided by CBM = Density.

Ton to barrel (By factor calculation)
API gravity plus 131.5 = outcome **X** and then 141.5 divided by **X** = density 15°C.

1,000 kilos divided by density = Litres

Litres divided by 159 = Factor ton to barrel

Tons times factor per barrel = Number of barrels of a cargo.

Ton to barrel factor and API to density

API	Density	Ton factor	API	Density	Ton factor
25	0,9042	7,0	40	0,8251	7,6
26	0,8984	7,0	41	0,8203	7,7
27	0,8927	7,0	42	0,8156	7,7
28	0,8871	7,1	43	0,8109	7,8
29	0,8816	7,1	44	0,8063	7,8
30	0,8762	7,2	45	0,8017	7,8
31	0,8708	7,2	46	0,7972	7,9
32	0,8654	7,3	47	0,7927	7,9
33	0,8602	7,3	48	0,7883	8,0
34	0,8550	7,4	49	0,7839	8,0
35	0,8498	7,4	50	0,7796	8,1
36	0,8448	7,4	51	0,7753	8,1
37	0,8398	7,5	52	0,7711	8,2
38	0,8348	7,5	53	0,7669	8,2
39	0,8299	7,6	54	0,7628	8,2

Foot to centimetre
1 foot = 30.48 centimetres.

Centimetres to foot
1 metre = 3.28084 feet.

Density de-escalation
Value commodity times standard density divided by real density.

Cracks from USA gallons
Price per gallon times 42 minus WTI = Product crack.

Crack factor calculation
1,000 divided by actual density = litres. Litres divided by 159 = Crack factor. The Dollar value of the commodity per ton divided by the crack factor is the price per barrel of the commodity. Crude price minus the value per barrel is the crack.

Crack propane
Value propane per ton divided by 12.41 = Price bbl minus crude price = propane crack.

Crack butane
Value butane per ton divided by 10.8 = Price bbl minus crude price = butane crack.

Crack naphtha
Value naphtha per ton divided by 8.9 = Price bbl minus crude price = naphtha crack.

Crack gasoline
Value gasoline per ton divided by 8.33 = Price bbl minus crude price = gasoline crack.

Crack jet A1
Value jet A1 per ton divided by 8 = Price bbl minus crude price = jet A1 crack.

Crack gasoil
Value gasoil per ton divided by 7.45 = Price bbl minus crude price = gasoil crack.

Crack fueloil
Value fueloil per ton divided by 6.35 = Price bbl minus crude price = fueloil crack.

Crack straight run fueloil
Value SRFO per ton divided by 6.77 = Price bbl minus crude price = SRFO crack.

Bar to kPa
1 Bar is 100 kilopascals (kPa).

Bar to psi
1 Bar is 14.503774 Psi (Pounds-force/sq. inch).

Psi to bar
1 psi is 0.068948 Bars.

Natural gas volumes in standard cubic feet (SCF)
1 cubic foot is 28.3168466 litres.

1 barrel is 5.61458 feet.

Knot
1 knot = 1.852 km per hour.

1 knot = 1.150779 mile per hour.

1 knot = 1 nautical mile per hour.

Nautical mile to metres
1 Nautical mile is 1,852 metres.

Centimetres to inch
1 centimetre = 0.393701 inch.

1 inch = 2.54 centimetres.

Long ton
1 long ton = 1,016.046909 kilograms.

Long Ton Air = Metric Ton in Air x 0.984206

Short ton
1 short ton = 907.18474 kilograms.

API gravity
Degrees (°) API gravity = (141.5/density at 15 deg. C) - 131.5.

API to density
If you have API and you need density   141.5 / (API +/+ 131.5) = DENSITY

Density to API
If you have density and you need API   141.5 / DENSITY -/- 131.5 = API

Gross tons
Is total weight including BS&W but excluding free water.

Net tons
Gross tons minus BS&W.

BS&W
Gross tons minus net tons.

Engler to visco (approx. numbers from a conversion lineal)
12 Engler = 450 Cst. Visco at 50°C.

14 Engler = 550 Cst. Visco at 50°C.

16 Engler = 650 Cst. Visco at 50°C.

Visco to Engler
380 Cst. visco at 50° Celsius is roughly 10 Engler.

Celsius to Fahrenheit

°F = 9/5 x °C + 32, where °C is the temperature in degrees Celsius.

Fahrenheit to Celsius

°C= (°F -/- 32) / 1.8 where °F is the temperature in degrees Fahrenheit.

Freight WSC

WSC times flat rate times agreed cargo size (tons) divided by 100= total freight price (lumpsum).

· E.g. WSC 80 x 9.30 flat rate x 100,000 tons cargo size divided by 100
· Lumpsum 744,000 USD

Total freight divided by cargo in tons = freight per ton = 0.744 USD per ton.

Total freight divided by cargo in barrels = freight per barrel.

Not to be forgotten is to add harbour dues, port costs, fair way dues, ice dues, insurance etc. Sometimes harbour dues or port cost are included in Worldscale and sometimes not. It can differ from port to port. Information is available in the Worldscale book.

Crude Oil Voyage Loss Calculations

- **GSV** = Gross standard volume
- **NSV** = Net standard volume
- **TCV** = Total calculated volume
- **OBQ** = On board quantity
- **ROB** = Remaining on board
- **VEF** = Vessel experience factor
- **GSV** = TCV minus free water
- **NSV** = GSV minus sediment and water

NSV Loss %

$$\frac{\text{Outturn NSV - BOL NSV}}{\text{BOL NSV}} \times 100\%$$

TCV Loss %

$$\frac{\text{Outturn TCV - BOL TCV}}{\text{BOL TCV}} \times 100\%$$

Load Difference %

$$\frac{\text{Vessel TCV after loading - BOL TCV}}{\text{BOL TCV}} \times 100\%$$

Ship Loss %

$$\frac{\text{Vessel TCV before disch. - vessel TCV after load}}{\text{Vessel TCV after Load}} \times 100\%$$

Discharge Difference %

$$\frac{\text{Outturn TCV - vessel TCV before discharge TCV} \times 100\%}{\text{Outturn}}$$

OBQ - ROB Difference %

$$\frac{\text{Vessel OBQ TCV - vessel ROB TCV} \times 100\%}{\text{Vessel TCV after loading}}$$

Water Loss %

$$\frac{\text{BOL water - outturn water} \times 100\%}{\text{BOL TCV}}$$

Load Water %

$$\frac{\text{BOL water volume} \times 100\%}{\text{BOL NSV}}$$

OBQ %

$$\frac{\text{Vessel OBQ TCV} \times 100\%}{\text{BOL TCV}}$$

ROB %

$$\frac{\text{Vessel ROB TCV} \times 100\%}{\text{Outturn TCV}}$$

Barrels NSV Loss %

$$\frac{\text{Total outturn NSV - total BOL NSV} \times 100\%}{\text{Total BOL NSV}}$$

Load Loss % *(VEF and OBQ corrected load difference)*

$$\frac{[(\text{Vessel TCV after loading - OBQ TCV})/\text{VEF}] - \text{BOL TCV} \times 100\%}{\text{BOL TCV}}$$

Discharge Loss % *(VEF and ROB corrected discharge difference)*

$$\frac{\text{Outturn TCV} - [(\text{vessel TCV before discharge - ROB TCV})/\text{VEF}] \times 100\%}{\text{Outturn TCV}}$$

Publishing information

To make this book I gathered all possible oil trading related words that I could find. Many words were picked up in the business during meetings, discussions or conferences. Other words I found when reading reports from many sources. Through LinkedIn I got many emails and I received lots of suggestions from the market. Also from some research on the internet lots of words came available.

Shipping agencies, brokers, inspectors, storage companies and other service providers supplied words and helped when asked.

Some websites such as those from OPEC, Platts, Argus, Chevron, Statoil, IEA, NATO, and various banks have been a source of information as well.

Too much to mention them all, but basically the market owns a lot of words.

A lot of words have been checked for accuracy by the use of internet and by the advice from colleagues who have done a proof-reading before the final manuscript went to the publisher to make the book as it is today.

Also my family has had to suffer as a lot of my spare time has been invested in this book. I admire their patience and understanding. Now that the book is ready and published I promise an increased level of quality family time.

My main goal for this book is to keep the descriptions easy to understand and keep the content at a reasonable quality with a touch of my interpretation and my experience.

A response like: "Ahh…that's what it means!" is what I hope for.

It is up to the market to decide if I have succeeded in this.

I hope the book will be well adopted by new and existing colleagues in the oil business.

Notes and new words

Use this space to jot down any notes or
new words that you come across